CyberMedia
Tech Support
Yellow Pages

CyberMedia
3000 Ocean Park Blvd.
Suite 2001
Santa Monica, CA 90405

Main number: (310) 581-4700
FAX number: (310) 581-4720
http://www.cybermedia.com/

CyberMedia Tech Support Yellow Pages

Information in this document is subject to change without notice.

Copyright Notice

Trademarks

Introduction

The online version of the CyberMedia Tech Support Yellow Pages can connect you instantly to the Web pages of application and hardware vendors. This book is the printed version of the online CyberMedia Tech Support Yellow Pages.

While we have made every effort to verify that the names, addresses, and phone numbers in this book are correct, this is the type of information that is subject to constant change. If you have any corrections or additions, please send them to us.

E-mail: techpubs@cybermedia.com
FAX: (310) 581-4720   Attention: Technical Publications

A T & T Paradyne
8545 126th Ave. North
P.O. Box 2826
Largo, FL 34649-2826
Main.................................(813) 530-2000
Customer Svc. ....(800) 237-0016
Tech. Support ....(800) 237-0016
Sales...(800) 243-4977
Tech. Supp. Fax ....(813) 530-2453
BBS...(813) 532-5254
WWW....................................... http://www.att.com

AA Computech
28176 Crocker Ave. #105
Valencia, CA 91355
Main.................................(805) 257-6801
Tech. Support ....(805) 257-6804
Sales...(805) 257-6805
BBS...(805) 257-6805
E-Mail....................................bob@scvnet.com
WWW.................http://www.scbnet.com/telbobs

Abaco Software
6 Trafalgar Square
Nashua, NH 03063
Main.................................(603) 883-1818
Customer Svc. ....(603) 883-1818
Tech. Support ....(603) 883-1818
Sales...(603) 883-1818
Tech. Supp. Fax ....(603) 883-2019

Ability Plus Software Ltd.
4 King Charles Terrace, Soverign Close
London E1 9HL
UK
Main.................................(447) 123-1100
E-Mail.................100433,231@compuserve.com
WWW.......http://www.gus.com/emp/asc/asc.html

ABL Electronics
10942 BeAve.rdam Rd.
Hunt Valley, MD 21030
Main.................................(800) 726-0610
Tech. Support ....(410) 584-2700
Sales...(800) 726-0610
Tech. Supp. Fax ....(401) 584-2790
BBS...(301) 560-1198

AbleSoft/SAI
1001 Millersville Rd.
P.O. 4547
Lancaster, PA 17604-4547
Main .... (717) 872-6567
Customer Svc.............................. (800) 334-2722
Tech. Support............................. (717) 872-2442
Sales....................................... (800) 334-2722
Tech. Supp. Fax.......................... (717) 871-9959
BBS... (717) 872-6179
WWW................................... http://www.sai.com

Academic Software Library
PO Box 8202, NC State University
Raleigh, NC 27695-8202
Main .... (800) 955-8275
Tech. Supp. Fax.......................... (919) 515-2682
E-Mail.......................................pass@aip.org
WWW...............................http://www.aip.org/pas

ACC Computer Peripherals
7 Whatney
Irvine, CA 92718-2608
Main .... (714) 454-2441
Customer Svc.............................. (800) 854-7600
Tech. Support............................. (714) 454-2441
Sales....................................... (800) 234-7811
Tech. Supp. Fax.......................... (714) 454-8527
BBS... (714) 470-1759

Access Computer Technologies
2225 El Camino Real
Santa Clara, CA 95050
Main .... (800) 359-6800
Tech. Support............................. (408) 247-4444
Tech. Supp. Fax.......................... (408) 247-4448
BBS... (408) 247-4448

Access Software

4750 Wyley Post Way
Building 1, Suite No 200
Salt Lake City, UT 84116

Main	(800) 800-4880
Customer Svc.	(800) 800-4880
Tech. Support	(801) 359-2900
Sales	(801) 359-2900
Tech. Supp. Fax	(801) 596-9128
BBS	(801) 359-2968
E-Mail	tech@acces.com
WWW	http://www.access.com
FTP Address	ftp.access.com

Accolade

5300 Suitevens Creek Blvd.
Sutie 500
San Jose, CA 95129

Main	(408) 296-8400
Customer Svc.	(408) 296-8400
Tech. Support	(408) 296-8400
Sales	(800) 245-7744
Tech. Supp. Fax	(408) 246-0231
BBS	(408) 296-8800
WWW	http://www.accolade.com
CompuServe	GO GAMAPUB
America Online	accolade@aol.com

Accton Technology Corp.

1962 Zanker Rd.
San Jose, CA 95112

Main	(408) 452-8080
Customer Svc.	(800) 926-9288
Tech. Support	(800) 926-9288
Sales	(408) 452-8080
Tech. Supp. Fax	(408) 452-8988
BBS	(408) 452-8828
WWW	http://www.accton.com

ACE Software

22611 Markey Court
Unit 113
Sterling, VA 20166-6903

Main	(703) 450-1980
Customer Svc.	(800) 346-9413
Tech. Support	(703) 450-2318
Sales	(800) 346-9413
Tech. Supp. Fax	(703) 450-9786
E-Mail	support@aecsoft.com
WWW	http://www.aecsoft.com
FTP Address	http://wwwcec.soft.com
America Online	mstilt7714@aol.com

Acer America

2641 Orchard Parkway
San Jose, CA 95134

Main	(408) 432-6200
Customer Svc.	(800) 637-7000
Tech. Support	(800) 445-6495
Sales	(800) 733-2237
Tech. Supp. Fax	(408) 922-2933
BBS	(408) 428-0140
WWW	http://www.acer.com/aac/index.htm
FTP Address	ftp://ftp.acer.com/
CompuServe	Go Acer
America Online	Keyword Acer

Acius

20883 Suitevens Creek Blvd.
Cupertino, CA 95014

Customer Svc.	(408) 252-4444
Tech. Support	(408) 252-4444
Tech. Supp. Fax	(408) 252-4829
WWW	http://www.aci-4d.com
FTP Address	ftp.dnai.com\pub\acius\US_Intl
CompuServe	GO ACIUS

Acma Computers, Inc.
47988 Fremont Blvd.
Fremont, CA 94538
Main	(800) 456-1818
Customer Svc.	(800) 786-8998
Tech. Support	(800) 786-8998
Sales	(800) 786-6888
Tech. Supp. Fax	(510) 623-0818
BBS	(510) 651-0629
E-Mail	sales@acma.com
WWW	http://www.acma.com

ACS Communications, Inc.
10 Victor Square
Scotts Valley, CA 95066-3575
Main	(800) 538-0742
Tech. Support	(800) 995-5500
Tech. Supp. Fax	(408) 438-7730

Actel Corp.
955 East Arques Ave.
Sunnyvale, CA 94086-4533
Main	(408) 739-1010
Customer Svc.	(408) 739-1010
Tech. Support	(800) 262-1060
Tech. Supp. Fax	(408) 739-1540
WWW	http://www.actel.com/

Activision
11601 Wislhire Blvd.
Suite No 300
West Los Angeles, CA 90025
Main	(310) 473-9200
Customer Svc.	(310) 479-5644
Tech. Support	(310) 479-5644
Sales	(800) 477-3650
Tech. Supp. Fax	(310) 479-4005
BBS	(310) 479-1335
E-Mail	support@activision.com
WWW	http://www.activision.com
CompuServe	GO GAMBPUB

Ad Lib, Inc.
220 Grande-Allee E, #850
Quebec, Quebec G1R 2J1
Canada
Main	(800) 463-2686
Tech. Support	(418) 529-9676
BBS	(418) 529-1159

Adaptec
691 S Milpitas Blvd.
Milpitas, CA 95035
Main	(408) 945-8600
Customer Svc.	(800) 959-7274
Tech. Support	(408) 934-7274
Sales	(800) 959-7274
Tech. Supp. Fax	(408) 945-6776
BBS	(408) 945-7727
WWW	http://www.adaptec.com
FTP Address	ftp.adaptec.com
CompuServe	GO ADAPTEC

Adaptive Software Inc.
125 Pacifica Suite 250
Irvine, CA 92718
Main	(714) 789-7300
WWW	http://www.adaptiv.com

ADC Kentrox
PO Box 10704
Portland, OR 97210-0704
Main	(800) 733-5511
Tech. Support	(503) 643-1681
Tech. Supp. Fax	(503) 641-3341
BBS	(503) 643-1681
WWW	http://www.kentrox.com
FTP Address	ftp.kentrox.com

ADC Telecommunications
4900 W 78th Street
Minneapolis, MN 55343
Main	(612) 938-8080
Tech. Support	(612) 946-3475
Sales	(800) 366-3891
Tech. Supp. Fax	(612) 946-3237
E-Mail	technical@adc.com
WWW	http://www.adc.com/

Addison- Wesley Publishing Co.
2725 Sand Hill Rd.
Menlo Park, CA 94025
Main..(415) 854-0300
WWW.......................................http://www.aw.com

Addtech Research, Inc.
41348 Christy St.
Fremont, CA 94538
Main..(510) 623-7583
Tech. Supp. Fax...............................(510) 623-7538
BBS..(510) 623-7538

Addtron Technology
46560 Fremont Blvd., #303
Fremont, CA 94538
Main..(415) 770-0120
BBS..(415) 770-0171

ADI Systems, Inc.
2115 Ringwood Ave.
San Jose, CA 95131
Main..(800) 228-0530
Tech. Support...................................(408) 944-0100
BBS..(408) 944-0300
WWW...........................http://www.adi-online.com

Adobe Systems, Inc.
1585 Charleston Rd.
PO Box 7900
Mountain View, CA 94039
Main..(415) 961-4400
Customer Svc....................................(415) 961-4400
Sales...(800) 833-6687
Tech. Supp. Fax...............................(415) 961-3769
BBS..(206) 623-6984
WWW................................http://www.adobe.com
FTP Address..................................ftp.adobe.com

ADP Network Services
175 Jackson Plaza
Ann Arbor, MI 48106
Main..(201) 994-5000
Customer Svc....................................(201) 739-3000
Tech. Support...................................(313) 769-6800
Sales...(201) 994-5839

Adtech Co.
1571 Whitmore Ave.
Ceres, CA 95307
Main..(800) 326-6548
Tech. Support...................................(408) 954-8038
Tech. Supp. Fax...............................(209) 541-1401
BBS..(408) 954-1647

Advanced Computer Communication
340 Storke Rd.
Santa Barbara, CA 93117
Main..(805) 685-4455
Tech. Support...................................(800) 666-7308
Tech. Supp. Fax...............................(805) 685-4465
BBS..(805) 562-8825
E-Mail..info@acc.com
WWW................................http://www.acc.com/

Advanced Computer Innovations
30 Burncoat Way
Pittsford, NY 14534-2216
Main..(716) 383-1939
Tech. Support...................................(716) 383-1939
BBS..(716) 383-8428

Advanced Concepts
4129 N Port Washington Ave.
Milwaukee, WI 53212
Main..(800) 222-6736
Tech. Support...................................(414) 963-0999
Tech. Supp. Fax...............................(414) 963-2090
BBS..(414) 963-2090

Advanced Digital Information Co
10201 Willows Rd.
Redmond, WA 98052
Main..(800) 336-1233
Tech. Support...................................(206) 881-8004
Tech. Supp. Fax................................(206) 881-2296
BBS..(206) 883-3211
E-Mail...support@adic.com
WWW................................http://www.adic.com

Advanced Gravis Comp. Technology+A63
3750 North Fraser Way
Burneby BC V5J5E9
Canada
Main...(604) 431-5020
Customer Svc. ....(604) 431-5020
Tech. Support ....(604) 431-1807
Tech. Supp. Fax ....(604) 431-5155
BBS..(604) 431-5927
E-Mail......................................tech@gravis.com
WWW...............................http://www.gravis.com

Advanced Matrix Technology
747 Calle Plano
Camarillo, CA 93012
Main...(800) 637-7878
Tech. Supp. Fax ....(805) 484-5282
BBS..(805) 484-5282

Advanced Micro Devices (AMD)
1 Amd Place
Sunnyvale, CA 94088-3453
Main...(800) 538-8450
Tech. Support ....(800) 222-9323
Sales..(408) 732-2400
Tech. Supp. Fax ....(408) 749-5299
BBS..(408) 982-6161
WWW.................................http://www.amd.com/

Advanced Microelectronics
WWW...................................http://www.aue.com/

Advanced Network Solutions
WWW................http://www.halcyon.com/routers/
        welcome.htm

Advanced RISC Machines Inc.
985 University Ave.
Suite 5
Los Gatos, CA 95030
Main...(408) 399-5199
Tech. Supp. Fax ....(408) 399-8854
E-Mail......................................support@arm.com
WWW.................................http://www.arm.com/

Advanced Software Concepts
9551, route de Saint-Laurent du Var
La Gaude 06610
France
Main .... (339) 324-7600
E-Mail............................... Applelink: ADV.SOFT
WWW........................ http://www.eden.com/~asc/

Advanced Software Technologies
2041 Rosecrans Dr, #297
El Segundo, CA 90245
Main .... (800) 633-3113
Tech. Support.............................. (213) 322-4440
BBS.. (213) 322-5522
WWW....... http://www.aescon.com/asti/index.htm

Advanced Systems Corp.
1324 Union Hill Rd.
Alpharetta, GA 30201
Main .... (800) 327-4853
Tech. Support.............................. (404) 751-0889
Tech. Supp. Fax........................... (404) 751-1884

Advanced Technologies International
361Sinclair-Frontage Rd.
Milpitas, CA 95035
Main .... (408) 942-1780
Tech. Supp. Fax........................... (408) 942-1260

Advanced Visual Systems Inc.
WWW................................... http://www.avs.com/

Advantest America
1100 Busch Pkwy
Buffalo Grove, IL 60089
Main .... (708) 634-2552
Tech. Supp. Fax........................... (708) 634-2872
BBS .... (708) 634-2010

AG Group
2540 Camino Diablo, Suite 200
Walnut Creek, CA 94596
Main..(510) 937-7900
Tech. Supp. Fax...........................(510) 937-2479
E-Mail .... info@ag.com
WWW..........................http://www.aggroup.com/
FTP Address..............................ftp.adgroup.com
CompuServe ..... 74431.2500@compuserve.com

Agile Networks
1300 Massachusetts Ave.
Boxborough, MA 01719
Main..(800) ATM-9LAN
Tech. Supp. Fax...........................(508) 263-5111
E-Mail ....info@agile.com
WWW................................http://www.agile.com/

Ahead Systems, Inc.
4114 Clipper Court
Fremont, CA 94538
Main..(510) 623-0900
Tech. Supp. Fax...........................(510) 623-0960
BBS..(510) 623-0961
E-Mail ....ahead@ix.netcom.com

Aicom Corp.
2381 Zanker Rd. Suite 160
San Jose, CA 95131
Main..(408) 577-0370
Tech. Supp. Fax...........................(408) 577-0373
BBS..(408) 577-0372

Aim Tech Corp.
20 Trafalgar Square
Nashua, NH 03063-1973
Main..(800) 289-2884
Tech. Support...............................(603) 883-0220

AIM Technology
4699 Old Ironside Dr, #400
Santa Clara, CA 95054
Main..(800) 848-8649
Tech. Support...............................(408) 748-8649
BBS..(408) 748-0161
WWW.......................................http://www.aim.com

AIS
180 Clossen Ave.
Elk Grove Village, IL 60067
Main...(800) 950-1100
Tech. Support ....(847) 593-2626
Tech. Supp. Fax ....(847) 593-2790
BBS..(847) 593-2798

Aladdin Knowledge Systems Ltd.
15 Beit Oved Street, PO Box 11141
Tel Aviv 61110
Israel
Main...(972) 353-7579
E-Mail................................. aladdin@aladdin.co.il
WWW...............................http://www.hasp.com/

Aladdin Software Security
350 5th Ave.
Suite 6614
New York, NY 10118
Main ....(800) 223-4277
Tech. Supp. Fax ....(212) 564-3377
E-Mail......................................support@hasp.com
WWW.......................................http://www.aks.com
FTP Address....................................ftp.hasp.com

Aladdin Systems
165 Westridge Dr.
Watsonville, CA 95076
Customer Svc. ....(408) 761-6200
Tech. Support ....(408) 761-6200
Sales..(408) 761-6200
Tech. Supp. Fax ....(408) 761-6206
E-Mail.................... cust.service@aladdinsys.com
WWW .... http://www.aladdinsys.com
FTP Address.......... ftp@//ftp.aladdinsys.com/pub
CompuServe..................................... 75300,1666
America Online ....aladdin@aol.com

Alcom Corp.
6262 N. Shoreline
Mountainview, CA 94043
Main ....(415) 694-7000
Tech. Supp. Fax ....(415) 694-7070
BBS..(415) 694-7081
WWW.................................. http://www.alcom.com

Aldridge Co, The
2500 City West Blvd., #575
Houston, TX 77042
Main ....(800) 548-5019
Tech. Support ....(713) 953-1940

Algorithmics
WWW .... http://www.algor.co.uk/

Alias Research, Inc.
110 Richmond St E
Toronto, ONT M5C 1P1
Canada
Main..(416) 362-9181

Alias Wavefront
WWW ....http://www.alias.com/

Alisa Systems, Inc.
221 E Walnut St, #175
Pasadena, CA 91101
Main..(818) 792-9474
Tech. Support ....(800) 992-5472
Sales...(800) 628-3274
Tech. Supp. Fax ....(818) 792-4068
BBS..(818) 683-8479
WWW ....http://www.alisa.com

All Computer Center
224 S. 5th Ave.
City of Industry, CA 91746
Main...(818) 369-4181
Tech. Support ....(818) 369-4181
Tech. Supp. Fax ....(818) 961-7462
BBS..(818) 961-7462

All Computers, Inc.
1220 Yonge St, 2nd Floor
Toronto, ONT M4T 1W1
Canada
Main..(800) 387-2744
Tech. Support ....(416) 960-0111
BBS..(416) 960-5426

Allegro New Media
16 Passaic Ave.
Unit 6
Fairfield, NJ 07004-3835
Main ....(201) 808-1992
WWW .... http://www.allegronm.com/

Allied Telesyn Interantional
950 Kifer Rd.
Sunnyvale, CA 94086
Main ....(800) 424-4282
Customer Svc..................................(800) 424-5012
Tech. Support.................................(800) 428-4835
Sales ....(800) 424-4284
Tech. Supp. Fax..............................(408) 736-0292
BBS ....(206) 483-7979
E-Mail .... ati_sales@centr.com
CompuServe ....GO ALLIED

Alpha Software
168 Middlesex Turnpike
Burlington, MA 01863
Main ....(617) 229-2924
Customer Svc...................................(617) 229-2924
Tech. Support..................................(800) 229-3460
Sales ....(800) 451-1018
Tech. Supp. Fax...............................(617) 272-4876
BBS ....(617) 229-2915
CompuServe ....GO ALPHA

Alpha Technologies
3767 Alpha Way
Bellingham, WA 98226
Main ....(360) 647-2360
Tech. Supp. Fax...........................(360) 733-8690
BBS ....(206) 671-4936

Alphatronix
4022 Stirup Creek Dr.
Suite 315
Durham, NC 27703
Main ....(919) 544-0001
BBS ....(919) 544-4079

ALPS Electric (USA), Inc.
3553 N. First St.
San Jose, CA 95134
Main...(800) 825-2577
Customer Svc.............................(800) 950-2577
Tech. Support.............................(800) 449-2577
Sales ....(800) 449-2577
WWW.....................................http://www.alps.com

ALR - Advanced Logic Research
9401 Jeronimo
Irvine, CA 92718
Main...(800) 444-4257
Customer Svc.............................(714) 458-1952
Tech. Support.............................(714) 458-1952
Sales ....(714) 458-1952
Tech. Supp. Fax..........................(714) 581-9240
BBS ....(714) 458-6834
E-Mail .... tech@alr.com
WWW.....................................http://www.alr.com

Alta Technology
9500 South, 500 West
Sandy, UT 84070-6655
Main...(801) 562-1010
Tech. Supp. Fax..........................(801) 254-2020
E-Mail ....support@altatech.com
WWW...........http://www.xmission.com/~altatech/

Altec Systems
122 Faris Industrial Pk Dr
Shreveport, LA 71106
Main...(318) 226-1702

Altec Technology Corp.
18555 E Gale Ave.
Industry, CA 91748
Main...(800) 255-9971
Tech. Support.............................(818) 912-8688
BBS ....(818) 912-8048

Altera Corp.
WWW...............................http://www.altera.com/

Altex Electronics, Inc.
11342 IH-35 N
San Antonio, TX 78233
Main ....(210) 655-8882
Tech. Support ....(512) 349-8795
Tech. Supp. Fax ....(210) 637-6234
BBS..(512) 637-3264
E-Mail..................................support@altex.com
WWW...................................http://www.altex.com

Altra
WWW................................ http://www.altra.com/

AM Communications
1900 AM Dr
Quakertown, PA 18951-9004
Main...(215) 536-1354
Tech. Supp. Fax ....(215) 536-1475

Amber Wave Systems
WWW...................... http://www.amberwave.com/

AMCC
6195 Lusk Blvd.
San Diego, CA 92121-2793
Main ....(619) 450-9333
Sales..(800) 755-2622
Tech. Supp. Fax ....(619) 450-9885
E-Mail................................ compinfo@amcc.com
WWW................................ http://www.amcc.com/

Amdek Corp. & Wise Teck
3471 N 1st St
San Jose, CA 95134
Main..(800) 792-6335
Customer Svc. ....(800) 800-9973
Tech. Support ....(408) 435-2770
Tech. Supp. Fax ....(408) 922-4480
BBS..(408) 922-5729
WWW.....................................http://www.wise.com

Ameri Data
12 Beaumont Rd.
Wallingford, CT 06492
Main..(800) 638-5625
Tech. Support ....(203) 294-5800
Tech. Supp. Fax ....(203) 269-9021
BBS..(203) 758-3858

America Online
8619 Westwood Center Dr.
Vienna, VA 22182-2285
Main..(703) 448-8700
WWW............................. http://www.blue.aol.com

Americal Group
PO BOX 16388
North Hollywood, CA 91615
Main..(800) 288-8025
Customer Svc. ....(818) 765-3040
Tech. Support ....(818) 765-3040
Sales..(818) 288-8025
Tech. Supp. Fax ....(818) 765-3887
BBS..(818) 765-3887

American Business Systems
315 Littleton Rd.
PO Box 460
Chelmsford, MA 01824
Main..(508) 250-9600
Tech. Supp. Fax ....(508) 250-8027
BBS..(508) 250-8027

American Chemical Society
1155 16th Street, NW
Washington, DC 20036
Main..(202) 872-4378
WWW...................................... http://www.acs.org

American Computer Hardware
2205 S Wright St.
Santa Ana, CA 92705-5315
Main..(714) 549-2688
Tech. Support ....(800) 447-1236
Tech. Supp. Fax ....(714) 662-0491

American Covers
102 West 12200 South
P.O. Box 987
Draper, UT 84020
Main .... (801) 553-0600
Customer Svc................................ (800) 228-8987
Tech. Support................................ (800) 228-8987
Sales .... (800) 553-0600
Tech. Supp. Fax........................... (801) 553-1212

American Fundware
1385 S. Colorado Blvd.
Suite 400
Denver, CO 80222
Main .... (303) 756-3030
Tech. Support................................ (800) 227-7575
Tech. Supp. Fax........................... (303) 756-3514
BBS.. (303) 879-6850

American Megatrends, Inc. (AMI)
6145-F Northbelt Pkwy.
Norcross, GA 30071-2906
Main .... (770) 246-8600
Customer Svc................................ (770) 246-8645
Tech. Support................................ (770) 246-8645
Sales .... (800) 828-9264
Tech. Supp. Fax........................... (770) 246-8791
BBS.. (770) 246-8782
E-Mail .... support@american.megatrends.com
WWW........................http://www.megatrends.com

American Multisystems
1830 Houret Ct.
Milties, CA 95055
Main .... (800) 888-6615
Customer Svc................................ (800) 888-6645
Tech. Support................................ (408) 922-0707
Tech. Supp. Fax........................... (408) 405-9199
BBS.. (408) 922-0652
E-Mail .... info@gold2aol.com
WWW............. http://www.dnai.com~/infogol/html

American Power Conversion

132 Fair Grounds Rd.
West Kingston, RI 02892
Main..(800) 541-8896
Customer Svc...............................(800) 800-4272
Tech. Support...............................(800) 800-4272
Sales ....(401) 789-5735
Tech. Supp. Fax...........................(401) 789-3180
E-Mail ....apctech@apcc.com
WWW...................................http://www.apcc.com
CompuServe ....GO APCSUPPORT

American Research Corp. (ARC)

1101 Monterey Pass Rd.
Monterey Pakr, CA 91754
Main..(800) 346-3272
Tech. Supp. Fax...........................(818) 284-4213
BBS...(213) 265-1973

American Ribbon Co.

2895 W. Prospect Rd.
Ft. Lauderdale, FL 33309
Main..(800) 327-1013
Tech. Support...............................(305) 733-4552
Tech. Supp. Fax...........................(959) 733-0319
BBS...(305) 733-0319

American Small Business Computers

1 American Way
Pryor, OK 74361
Main..(918) 825-4844
Customer Svc...............................(918) 825-4844
Tech. Support...............................(918) 825-4844
Sales ....(918) 825-7555
Tech. Supp. Fax...........................(918) 825-6359
BBS...(918) 825-4878
E-Mail ....support@viagraphix.com
CompuServe ....GO DESIGNCAD

Amiga Technologies GmbH (English)

WWW.......................http://www.amiga-tech.com/

Amka

15328 E. Valley Blvd.
City of Industry, CA 91746
Main..(818) 369-2121
Tech. Support ....(818) 369-2121
Tech. Supp. Fax ....(818) 961-0482
BBS...(818) 961-0482

Amkly Systems, Inc.

60 Technology Dr.
Irving, CA 92718
Main..(714) 727-0788

AMP, Inc.

PO Box 3608
Harrisburg, PA 17105-3608
Main..(800) 522-6752
Tech. Support ....(717) 564-0100
BBS...(717) 986-7575
WWW...................................http://www.amp.com/

AMT International

2393 Qume Dr.
San Jose, CA 95131
Main..(408) 432-1790
Tech. Support ....(408) 432-0552
Sales...(408) 383-9044
Tech. Supp. Fax ....(408) 383-9047
BBS...(408) 944-9801

ANA Technolgoy+A129

WWW. http://www.EmporiumOne.COM/anatech/

Analog Devices

WWW..............................http://www.analog.com/

Anawave Software, Inc.

WWW...........................http://www.anawave.com

Anco Corp.

1140 N. Palm Street
Brea, CA 92620
Main..(714) 992-9000
Tech. Supp. Fax ....(714) 992-1672

ANDATACO

WWW...........................http://www.andataco.com/

Anderson International Corp.
37 Campus Dr
Edison, NJ 08837
Main...(908) 417-0551
Tech. Support ....(908) 417-0551
BBS..(908) 417-0550

Andrew Corp.
10500 W. 153 St
Oraland Pk., IL 60462
Main...(800) 531-5167
Tech. Support ....(800) 826-3739
Tech. Supp. Fax ....(708) 399-5673
BBS..(512) 338-3199

Andrew/Emerald Technologies
18912 N Creek Pkwy, #102
Bothell, WA 98011
Main...(800) 776-6174
Tech. Support ....(800) 826-3739
Sales..(800) 328-2696
Tech. Supp. Fax ....(708) 349-5673
BBS..(206) 487-1065

Animated Voice Corp.
PO Box 819
San Marcos, CA 92079
Main...(800) 942-3699
Tech. Support ....(619) 744-8190
BBS..(619) 744-8903

Annex Telecommunications
WWW...............................http://www.annex.com/

Anritsu America, Inc.
15 Thornton Rd.
Oakland, NJ 07436
Main...(800) 255-7234
Tech. Support ....(201) 337-1111
BBS..(201) 337-1033

Ansoft Corp.
WWW...............................http://www.ansoft.com/

Answer Software
20045 Suitevens Creek Blvd.
Cupertino, CA 95014
Main ....(408) 253-7515

Antares Electronics
1 Antares Dr, #400
Nepean, ONT K2E 8C4
Canada
Main ....(800) 267-4261
Tech. Support..............................(613) 723-1174
BBS..(613) 225-7971
WWW.........................http://www.ibd.ar.com/IBD/
Antares_Microsystems.html

Antec
2859 Bayview Dr.
Fremont, CA 94538
Main ....(510) 770-1200
Customer Svc...............................(510) 770-1200
Tech. Support...............................(510) 770-1200
Sales ....(510) 770-1200
Tech. Supp. Fax...........................(510) 770-1288
E-Mail.................................antec-inc.com
WWW............................http://www.antec-inc.com

Antex Electronics Corp.
16100 S Figueroa St
Gardena, CA 90248
Main ....(800) 338-4231
Customer Svc...............................(800) 338-4231
Tech. Support...............................(310) 532-3092
Tech. Supp. Fax...........................(310) 532-8509
BBS..(310) 532-8509
WWW................................http://www.antex.com

Anthem Technology Systems
1160 Riter Park Dr.
San Jose, CA 95131
Main ....(408) 453-1200
Tech. Supp. Fax...........................(408) 441-4504

Aperture Technologies
100 Summit Lk Dr
Valhalla, NY 10595
Main...(800) 346-6828
Tech. Support................................(914) 769-7800
BBS...(914) 769-8951

Apertus Technologies
WWW............................. http://www.apertus.com/

Apex Data
4305 Cushing Pkwy
Fremont, CA 94538
Main...(510) 416-5656
Customer Svc................................(800) 841-2739
Tech. Support................................(510) 249-1605
Sales ....(800) 841-2729
Tech. Supp. Fax............................(510) 249-1600

Apex Software Corp.
WWW...............................http://www.apexsc.com/

Apex Voice Communications, Inc.
15250 Ventura Blvd.
3rd Floor
Sherman Oaks, CA 91403
Main...(800) 727-3970
Tech. Support................................(818) 379-8400
Tech. Supp. Fax............................(818) 379-8410
BBS...(818) 379-8410

Apple Atlantis Home Page
WWW..........http://www.atlantis.austin.apple.com/

Apple Austin
WWW..................... http://www.austin.apple.com/

Apple Cambridge
WWW..............http://www.cambridge.apple.com/

Apple Computer
Newton Systems Group
1 Infinite Loop
Cupertino, CA 95014
Main...(408) 996-1010
Customer Svc. ....(800) 776-2333
Tech. Support ....(800) 767-2775
BBS...(408) 996-0275
WWW.................................. http://www.apple.com

Apple Information
WWW.......................... http://www.info.apple.com/

Apple Island
WWW..................................... http://www.apple.is/

Application Techniques
10 Lomar Park Dr.
Pepperall, MA 01463
Main..(508) 433-5201
Customer Svc. ....(508) 433-8464
Tech. Support ....(508) 433-8464
Sales...(508) 433-5201
Tech. Supp. Fax ....(508) 433-8466
E-Mail...........................support@zizazz-us.com

Applied Automated Engineering
65 S Main St.
Bldg C
Pennington, NJ 08534
Main..(609) 737-6800
BBS...(609) 737-9570

Applied Business Technology
361 Broadway
New York, NY 10013
Main..(212) 219-8945
Tech. Support ....(212) 219-2448
BBS...(212) 219-3597

Applied Computer Sciences, Inc.
11807 Northcreek Pkwy S, #102
Bothell, WA 98011
Main..(800) 525-5512
Tech. Support ....(206) 486-2722
BBS...(206) 485-4776

Applied Computer Systems, Inc.
3060 Johnstown-Utica Rd.
Johnstown, OH 43031
Main....................................(800) 237-5465
Tech. Support ....(614) 892-2100

Applied Creative Technology, Inc.
2626 Lombardy Ln.
Suite 107
Dallas, TX 75225
Main....................................(800) 433-5373
Tech. Support ....(214) 358-4800
Tech. Supp. Fax ....(314) 351-6741

Applied Information Systems, Inc.
100 Europa Dr.
Chapel Hill, NC 27514
Main....................................(800) 334-5510
Tech. Support ....(919) 942-7801
Tech. Supp. Fax ....(919) 493-7563
BBS....................................(919) 493-7563
E-Mail.................................... info@ais.com
WWW....................................http://www.ais.com

Applied Innovation
651 Lakeview Plaza Blvd., #C
Columbus, OH 43085
Main....................................(800) 247-9482

Applied Medical Informatics
2681 Parley's Way
Suite 204
Salt Lake City, UT 84109-1630
Main....................................(801) 464-6200
Customer Svc. ....(801) 464-6200
Tech. Support ....(801) 464-6200
Sales....................................(801) 464-6200
Tech. Supp. Fax ....(801) 464-6201
E-Mail.................................... info@ami-med.com
WWW....................................http://www.ami-med.com

Applied Microsystems
WWW.................................. http://www.amc.com/

Applied Testing and Technology
WWW............................... http://www.aptest.com/

APT Communications
9607 Dr Perry Rd.
Iamesville, MD 21754
Main .... (800) 842-0626
Tech. Supp. Fax....................(301) 871-5255
BBS..............................(301) 874-5255
E-Mail.............................. support@aptcom.com
WWW.............................. http://www.aptcom.com

Arachnae Management, Ltd.
225 East BeAve.r Creek Rd., Pkwy Ctr., Suite 230
Richmond Hill, ON L4B 3P4
Canada
Main .... (905) 771-6161
WWW..........................http://www.arachnae.com

Arcada Software
37 Skyline Dr.
Suite No 1101
Lake Mary, FL 32746
Main .... (407) 333-7500
Customer Svc..............................(800) 327-2232
Tech. Support..............................(407) 333-7500
Sales .... (800) 327-2232
Tech. Supp. Fax...........................(407) 333-7770
BBS..............................(407) 444-9979
E-Mail.............................. support@arcada.com
WWW.............................. http://www.arcada.com
FTP Address ....ftp.arcada.com
CompuServe ....GO ARCADA

Architext Software
WWW..............................http://www.atext.com/

Ares Software Corp.
565 Pilgrim Dr.
Suite A
Foster City, CA 94404
Customer Svc.............................. (415) 578-9090
Tech. Support............................. (415) 578-9090
Sales .... (800) 783-2737
Tech. Supp. Fax........................... (415) 378-8999
BBS.............................. (415) 286-8879
CompuServe ..... 70253.3164@compuserve.com

Arista Entrprises

125 Commerce Dr.
Hauppauge, NY 11788
Main..(516) 435-0200
Customer Svc.............................(800) 274-7824
Tech. Support.............................(800) 274-7824
Sales ....(516) 435-0200
Tech. Supp. Fax...........................(516) 435-4545
CompuServe ..... 74404.3334@compuserve.com

Aristosoft

7041 Koll Center Parkway
Suite 160
Pleasanton, CA 94566
Main..(510) 426-5355
WWW............................http://www.aristosoft.com/

Arity Corp.

30 Domino Dr
Corcord, MA 01742
Main..(617) 371-1243

Arkay Technologies, Inc.

851 Commerce Ct.
Buffalo Grove, IL 60089
Main..(800) 786-2419
Customer Svc.............................(708) 541-6333
Tech. Support.............................(708) 541-6583
Tech. Supp. Fax...........................(708) 541-6881
BBS ....(603) 434-5674

Arlington Computer Products, Inc.

1970 Carboy
Mt Prospect, IL 60056
Main..(800) 548-5105
Tech. Support.............................(708) 228-1470
BBS ....(708) 228-0516

Arlington Software Corp.

WWW............................http://www.arlingsoft.com

Arnet Corp.

618 Grassmere Pk Dr, #6
Nashville, TN 37211-9918
Main..(800) 366-8844
Tech. Support.............................(615) 834-8000
BBS ....(615) 834-5399

Arrow Electronics, Inc.

1502 Crocker Ave.
Hayward, CA 94544
Main..(800) 851-8880
Tech. Support ....(800) 332-2315
Tech. Supp. Fax ....(510) 489-9393

ARSoftware Corp.

8201 Corporate Dr., Suite 1110
Landover, MD 20785-2230
Main..(301) 459-3773
WWW..............http://www.clark.net/pub/arsoftwa/

Artecon

630 S. El Camino Real
Callstad, CA 92009
Main..(619) 931-5500
Tech. Supp. Fax ....(619) 931-5527

Artel Communications Corp.

22 Kane Industrial Dr
Hudson, MA 01749
Main..(800) 225-0228
Tech. Support ....(508) 562-2100
BBS..(508) 562-6942

Artic Technologies International

55 Park St, #2
Troy, MI 48083
Main..(810) 588-7370
BBS..(313) 588-2650

Artisoft

2202 North Forbes Blvd.
Tucson, AZ 85745
Main..(800) 846-9726
Customer Svc. ....(800) 846-9726
Tech. Support ....(602) 670-7000
Sales..(800) 846-9726
Tech. Supp. Fax ....(602) 670-7101
BBS..(602) 884-8648
WWW .... http://www.artisoft.com

Asante` Technologies
821 Fox Lane
San Jose, CA 95131
Main...(408) 435-8388
Customer Svc. ....(800) 662-9686
Tech. Support ....(800) 622-7464
Sales...(800) 662-9686
Tech. Supp. Fax ....(408) 432-6018
BBS...(408) 432-1416
E-Mail...............................techpubs@asante.com
WWW ....http://www.asante.com
FTP Address.............................ftp@asante.com
CompuServe.......................................GO Asante

Asco Technology, Inc.
486 Casita Way
Los Altos, CA 94022
Main...(415) 949-0969
BBS...(415) 949-3814

Asiatek
2421 W 205th St, #D-100
Torrance, CA 90501
Main...(213) 320-4384
BBS...(213) 328-5892

AskSam Systems
PO Box 1428
Perry, FL 32347
Main...(800) 327-5726
Tech. Support ....(904) 584-6590

ASP Computer
285 North Wolfe Rd.
Sunnyvale, CA 94086
Main...(408) 746-2965
Customer Svc. ....(408) 746-2965
Tech. Support ....(408) 746-2965
Sales...(408) 746-2965
Tech. Supp. Fax ....(408) 746-2803
BBS...(408) 749-8240
WWW ....http://www.asp.net

Aspen Systems Inc.
WWW ....http://www.aspsys.com/

AST Research, Inc.
16215 Alton Pky.
Irvine, CA 92718
Main ....(714) 727-4141
Customer Svc...............................(800) 876-4278
Tech. Support...............................(800) 727-1278
Sales ....(800) 723-2278
Tech. Supp. Fax...........................(714) 727-9355
BBS...(817) 230-6850
WWW.......................................http://www.ast.com

Asuka Technologies
17145 Von Karman Ave., #110
Irvine, CA 92714
Main ....(714) 757-1212
BBS...(714) 757-1288

Asymetrix
110 110th Ave. Northeast
Suite No 700
Bellevue, WA 98004-5840
Main ....(206) 462-0501
Customer Svc...............................(800) 448-6543
Tech. Support...............................(206) 637-1600
Sales ....(800) 448-6543
Tech. Supp. Fax...........................(206) 455-3071
BBS...(206) 451-1173
E-Mail.........................techsupp@asymetrix.com
WWW..........................http://www.asymetrix.com

AT&T Global Information Solution
WWW.................................http://www.attgis.com/

AT&T Multimedia Software Solutions
2701 Maidlan Center Parkway
Maidlan, FL 32751
Main ....(407) 662-7235
WWW.......................................http://www.att.com

Atari
1196 Borregas
Sunnyvale, CA 94088
Main ....(408) 745-2000

ATI Technologies
33 Commerce Valley Dr. East
Thorn Hill, ONT I3T7N6
Canada
Main...(905) 882-2600
Customer Svc................................(905) 882-2600
Tech. Support................................(905) 882-2626
Sales ....(905) 882-2600
Tech. Supp. Fax...........................(905) 882-2620
BBS ....(905) 764-9404
WWW..............................http://www.atitech.com
FTP Address.......................................ftp.atitech.ca
CompuServe 74740,667

Attachmate Inc.
3617 131st Ave. Southeast
Bellevue, WA 98006
Main...(206) 644-4010
Tech. Support................................(800) 688-3270
Sales ....(206) 426-6283
Tech. Supp. Fax...........................(206) 747-9924
BBS ....(206) 649-6660
E-Mail ....support@attachmate.com
WWW..........................http://www.attachmate.com
FTP Address....gopher://gopher.attachmate.com/
CompuServe .... GO ATTACHMATE

Attachmates
1129 San Antonio Rd.
PO Box 51860
Palo Alto, CA 94303
Main...(800) 872-8649
Tech. Support................................(415) 962-7100
BBS ....(415) 969-5547

Attain
48 Grove Street
Summerville, MA 02145
Main...(617) 776-1110
Customer Svc................................(617) 776-1110
Tech. Support................................(617) 776-2711
Sales ....(800) 925-5615
Tech. Supp. Fax...........................(617) 776-1626
E-Mail ....support@attain.com
WWW..................................http://www.attain.com

Attest Systems, Inc.
WWW.........http://www.attest-gasp.com/~attestsy

Aureal Semiconductor
4245 Technology Dr.
Fremont, CA 94538
Main...(510) 770-8600
Customer Svc................................(800) 638-2807
Tech. Support................................(503) 882-1177
BBS ....(510) 770-0968

AUSCAN Software Ltd.
WWW.. http://www.interlog.com/~rjp/auscan.html

Auspex Systems
5200 Grate America
Santa Clara, CA 95054
Main...(408) 492-0900
Tech. Support................................(800) 328-7739
Tech. Supp. Fax...........................(408) 986-2020
BBS ....(408) 492-0909
WWW..............................http://www.auspex.com/

Austin Computer Systems
10300 Metric Blvd.
Austin, TX 78758
Main...(800) 752-1577
Customer Svc................................(800) 752-1577
Tech. Support................................(800) 752-4171
BBS ....(512) 454-1357
WWW.......................http://www.austindirect.com

Austin-Hayne Corp.
3 Lagoon Dr., Suite 340
Redwood City, CA 94065
Main...(415) 610-6800

Autodesk
111 McInnis Parkway
San Rafael, CA 94903
Main...(415) 507-5000
Customer Svc................................(800) 228-3601
Sales...(800) 435-7771
Tech. Supp. Fax...........................(415) 507-5100
BBS ....(415) 507-5921
WWW.............................http://www.autodesk.com
FTP Address..............................ftp.autodesk.com
CompuServe.......................................GO ACAD

Automap, Inc.
1309 114th Ave. SE, Suite 110
Bellevue, WA 98004-6999
Main...(206) 455-3552

Automata
WWW.........................http://www.automata.com/

Automated Programming Tech., Inc.
30100 Telegraph Rd., #402
Bingham Farms, MI 48025-9939
Main...(810) 540-9877
Tech. Supp. Fax ....(810) 540-0403
E-Mail...............................support@aptnet.com
WWW...............................http://www.aptnet.com

Automation Group, The
340 Townsend St, #432
San Francisco, CA 94107
Main...(415) 777-9167
Tech. Supp. Fax ....(415) 777-9168

AutoSig Systems
PO Box 16505
Irving, TX 75016
Main...(800) 843-9235
Customer Svc. ....(800) 843-9235
Tech. Support ....(214) 258-8083
Sales...(800) 843-9235
Tech. Supp. Fax ....(214) 258-1412
BBS...(214) 258-1412

AVA Instrumentation
WWW.............http://www.aimnet.com/~avasales/

Avalan Technology
PO BOX 6888
Holliston, MA 01746
Main...(800) 441-2281
Tech. Support ....(508) 429-6482
BBS...(508) 429-3179

Avanti Technology
13492 Research Blvd. Suite 120
Austin, TX 78750
Main...(512) 335-1168
Customer Svc. ....(512) 335-1168

Avantos Performance Systems
5900 Hollis St.
Suite No A
Emeryville, CA 94608
Main .... (510) 654-4600
Customer Svc..............................(510) 654-4600
Tech. Support...............................(510) 654-4727
Sales .... (800) AVA-NTOS
Tech. Supp. Fax...........................(510) 654-1276
BBS .... (510) 654-1521
E-Mail............................... avantos@aol.com
WWW.........................http://www.avantos.com
CompuServe .... GO AVANTOS
America Online................. avantos@aol.com

Avery International
20955 Pathfinder Rd.
Diamond Bar, CA 91765-4000
Main .... (800) 252-8379
Customer Svc..............................(800) 252-8379
Tech. Support...............................(214) 389-3699
Sales .... (800) 252-8379
Tech. Supp. Fax...........................(800) 862-8379
WWW................. http://www.averydennison.com
CompuServe ....GO AVERY

Avnet Inc.
WWW..................................http://www.avnet.com/

Axil Computer Inc.
WWW.....................................http://www.axil.com/

Axis Communications
WWW...http://www.axis.se/

Aydin Controls, Inc.
414 Commerce Dr
Ft Washington, PA 19034
Main .... (800) 366-8889
Tech. Support...............................(215) 542-7800

Azron, Inc.
WWW.................................http://www.azron.com/

AZTech
WWW................................http://www.aztech.com/

Azure Technologies
63 South St.
Hopkinton, MA 01748
Main...(800) 233-3800
Tech. Support...............................(508) 435-3800
Tech. Supp. Fax...........................(508) 435-0448
BBS...(508) 435-0448
WWW..................................http://www.azure.com

B & B Electronics Manufacturing
707 Dayton Rd.
PO BOX 1040
Ottawa, IL 61350-9973
Main...(815) 434-0846
Tech. Supp. Fax...........................(815) 434-7094
WWW..................................http://www.bb/elec.com

Baler Software / Techtools
3-I Taggart Dr.
Nashua, NH 03060
Main...(603) 888-8400
Customer Svc...............................(800) 501-2677
Tech. Support...............................(603) 888-8400
Sales ....(603) 888-8400
Tech. Supp. Fax...........................(603) 888-8413
BBS...(603) 888-8411
E-Mail.....................................support@techtools.com
WWW..................................http://www.techtools.com
CompuServe ....GO TECHTOOLS

BancTec Technologies
WWW........... http://www.bti-ok.com/bti/index.html

Bandy
201 International Rd.
Garland, TX 75042
Main...(214) 272-5455
Tech. Support...............................(214) 272-5455
Tech. Supp. Fax...........................(214) 272-5613
BBS...(214) 272-5613

Banner Blue Software
39500 Suitevenson Place
Suite 204
Fremont, CA 94539
Main...(510) 794-6850
Customer Svc...............................(510) 794-6850
Tech. Support ....(510) 794-6850
Tech. Supp. Fax ....(510) 794-9152
CompuServe.......................................71333,3713

Bannister Lake Software
WWW............http://www.hookup.net/ads/bls.html

Banyan Systems, Inc.
120 Flanders Rd.
Westborough, MA 01581
Main...(800) 828-2404
Customer Svc...............................(800) 222-6926
Tech. Support ....(508) 898-1000
Tech. Supp. Fax ....(508) 898-1755
BBS...(508) 898-1810
WWW.................................http://www.banyan.com
CompuServe............................GO BAN FORUM

Banyan Systems, Inc.
WWW.................................http://www.banyan.com/

Barr Systems
4131 NW 28th Ln
Gainesville, FL 32606-7015
Main...(800) 227-7797
Customer Svc...............................(800) 227-7797
Tech. Support ....(352) 371-3050
Tech. Supp. Fax ....(352) 491-3141
BBS...(352) 371-3018
E-Mail.....................................sales@barrsys.com
WWW.............................http://www.barrsys.com

Baseline Software
PO Box 1219
Sausalito, CA 94966
Main...(800) 829-9955
Tech. Support ....(415) 332-7763
Tech. Supp. Fax ....(415) 332-8032
BBS...(415) 332-8039
E-Mail.................................info@baselinesoft.com
WWWhttp://www.baselinesoft.com/people/infosec

BASF
9 Oak Park Dr.
Beford, MA 01730-1471
Main.................................(617) 271-4000
Customer Svc. ....(800) 356-9006
Tech. Support ....(800) 225-3326
Sales.................................(800) 356-9006
Tech. Supp. Fax ....(617) 275-3069
WWW................................ http://www.basf.com

Basic Needs
118 State Place
Suite No 202
Escondido, CA 92029
Main.................................(619) 738-7020
Customer Svc. ....(800) 633-3703
Tech. Support ....(800) 633-3703
Sales.................................(619) 738-7020
Tech. Supp. Fax ....(619) 738-0515

Bawamba Software, Inc.
150 East Olive Ave., #203
Burbank, CA 91502
Main.................................(818) 843-1627
Tech. Support ....(818) 843-5557
Tech. Supp. Fax ....(818) 843-8364
E-Mail.............................. support@sirenplay.com
WWW............. http://www.well.com/user/dramatic

Bay Networks
WWW....................http://www.baynetworks.com/

Bay Technical Associates
200 N 2nd St, PO Box 387
Bay St Louis, MS 39520
Main.................................(800) 523-2702
Customer Svc. ....(800) 523-2702
Tech. Support ....(601) 467-8231
Sales.................................(800) 523-2702
Tech. Supp. Fax ....(601) 467-4551
BBS.................................(601) 467-4551
WWW............................. http://www.toll.mmb.com

BBN Software Products
150 Cambridge Pk Dr
Cambridge, MA 02140
Main ....(800) 251-1717
Tech. Support.............................(617) 873-5000
Tech. Supp. Fax..........................(617) 491-1496

BDT Products
17152 Armstrong Ave.
Irvine, CA 92714
Main ....(714) 660-1386
Tech. Support.............................(714) 263-6376

BE Software
WWW................................http://www.besoft.com/

Bear River Associates, Inc.
2560 Ninth Street
Berkeley, CA 94710
Main ....(510) 644-9400
Tech. Support.............................(510) 644-9788
E-Mail.....................................info@bearriver.com
WWW............................ http://www.bearriver.com

Bear Rock Technologies, Inc.
4140 Mother Lode Dr., Suite 100
Shingle Springs, CA 95682
Main ....(916) 672-0244
WWW............................ http://www.bearrock.com

Belkin Components
1303 Walnut Parkway
Compton, CA 90220
Main ....(310) 898-1100
Customer Svc.............................(310) 898-1100
Tech. Support.............................(310) 898-1100
Sales ....(310) 898-1100
Tech. Supp. Fax..........................(213) 898-1111
BBS ....(213) 898-1111

Bell Atlantic Corp.
1500 Maccorkla Ave.
Charleston, WV 25314
Main ....(800) 522-6617
Tech. Support.............................(703) 974-3000

Bell Atlantic Thinx Software
1725 Duke St.
Morgantown, VV 26505
Main...(800) 688-4469

Bell Microproducts
WWW..............................http://www.bellmicro.com/

Bentley Systems
WWW................................http://www.bentley.com/

Berg Electronics
WWW............................ http://www.bergelect.com/

Berkeley Software Design, Inc.
WWW....................................http://www.bsdi.com/

Berkeley Speech Technologies
2246 6th St
Berkeley, CA 94710
Main...(510) 841-5083
E-Mail..general@bst.com

Berkeley Systems Design
2095 Rose Street
Berkeley, CA 94709
Main...(510) 540-5535
Customer Svc................................(510) 540-5535
Tech. Support...............................(510) 540-5535
Sales ....(510) 540-5535
Tech. Supp. Fax............................(510) 540-5630
E-Mail .... tech@berksys.com
WWW.............................http://www.berksys.com

Best Computer Supplies, Inc.
690 Kresge Ln. #101
Sparks, NV 89431
Main...(800) 544-3472
Customer Svc................................(800) 544-3472
Tech. Supp. Fax............................(800) 829-4881
BBS ....(408) 727-9225

Best Data Products
21800 Nordoff
Chatsworth, CA 91311
Main..(818) 773-9600
Customer Svc. ....(818) 773-9600
Tech. Support ....(818) 773-9600
Sales..(818) 773-9600
Tech. Supp. Fax ....(818) 773-9619
BBS...(818) 773-3943
E-Mail.................................. admin@bestdata.com
WWW .... http://www.bestdata.com
CompuServe...... 74431.3250@compuserve.com
America Online .... bestdata@aol.com

Best Power Technology
N9246 Highway 80
Necedah, WI 54646
Main..(608) 565-7200
Customer Svc. ....(800) 356-5737
Tech. Support ....(800) 356-5737
Sales..(800) 356-5794
Tech. Supp. Fax ....(608) 565-2221
BBS...(608) 565-7424

Bethesda Softworks
1370 Piceard Dr.
Suite 120
Rockville, MD 20850-4304
Main..(301) 926-8300
Customer Svc. ....(301) 926-8300
Tech. Support ....(301) 963-2002
Sales..(800) 677-0700
Tech. Supp. Fax ....(301) 926-8010
BBS...(301) 990-7552
E-Mail.............................. support@bethsoft.com
WWW .... http://www.bethsoft.com

Better Business Systems
7949 Woodly Ave.
Van Nuys, CA 91406
Main..(800) 829-9991
Customer Svc. ....(818) 376-1558
Tech. Support ....(818) 407-5111
BBS...(818) 376-1581

BG Micro
PO Box 280298
Dallas, TX 75228
Main....................................(214) 271-5546
Customer Svc. ....(214) 271-5546
Tech. Support ....(214) 271-9834
Tech. Supp. Fax ....(214) 271-2462
BBS..................................(214) 271-2462

BGI technology Corp.
455 W 115th Ave. Unit 1
Northglemm, CO 80234
Main....................................(303) 451-5005
Tech. Supp. Fax ....(303) 451-5227

Bible Research Systems
2013 Wells Branch Pkwy, #304
Austin, TX 78728
Main....................................(800) 423-1228
Customer Svc. ....(800) 423-1228
Tech. Support ....(512) 251-7541
Tech. Supp. Fax ....(512) 251-4401
CompuServe......72203.2004@compuserve.com

Big Top Productions
548 Fourth Street
San Francisco, CA 94107
Main....................................(415) 978-5363
WWW..............................http://www.bigtop.com

Biscom
85 Rangeway Rd.
Billerica, MA 01821
Main....................................(800) 477-2472
Tech. Support ....(508) 670-5521
BBS..................................(508) 671-0075

Bitstream
215 First Street
Cambridge, MA 02142
Main....................................(617) 497-6222
Customer Svc. ....(800) 223-3176
Tech. Support ....(617) 497-7514
Sales..................................(800) 522-3668
Tech. Supp. Fax ....(617) 828-0784
E-Mail..............................sales@bitstream.com
WWW..............................http://www.bitstream.com

Bitwise Designs, Inc.
Building 50 Water Dam
Industrial Park, NY 12308
Main ....(800) 367-5906
Tech. Support............................(518) 274-0755
BBS....................................(518) 356-9749

BIX - Byte Information Exchange
1 Phoenix Mill Ln
Peterborough, NH 03458
Main ....(603) 924-9281
Customer Svc...........................(800) 232-2983
Tech. Support............................(603) 924-7681
Tech. Supp. Fax..........................(603) 924-2603
E-Mail................................editors@bix.com
WWW....................................http://www.bix.com

Black Box
Mayview Rd. at Park Dr.
PO Box 12800
Pittsburgh, PA 15241
Main ....(412) 746-5500

Blaise Computing, Inc.
2560 9th St, #316
Berkeley, CA 94710
Main ....(800) 333-8087
Tech. Support............................(415) 540-5441
BBS....................................(415) 540-1938

Blast Inc.
PO Box 808
Pittsboro, NC. 27312
Main ....(800) 242-5278
Tech. Support............................(504) 923-0888
Tech. Supp. Fax..........................(919) 542-0161
BBS....................................(504) 926-2155

Blossom Software Corp.
1 Kendall Square, Bldg. 600
PO Box 9171
Cambridge, MA 02139
Main ....(617) 738-1516
E-Mail..............................support@blossom.com

Blue Lance Software, Inc.
1700 W Loop S, #1100
PO Box 430546
Houston, TX 77027
Main..................................(713) 680-1187
Tech. Supp. Fax..........................(713) 622-1370
BBS ....(713) 622-1370

Blue Ocean Software
15310 Amerly Dr.
Tampa, FL 33647
Main..................................(813) 977-4553
Tech. Supp. Fax..........................(813) 979-4447
BBS ....(813) 979-4447
WWW...................http://www.blueocean.com
CompuServe ....GO NOVUSER

Blue Sky Software Corp.
7777 Fay Ave.
La Hoya, CA 92037
Main..................................(619) 551-2485
Tech. Support............................(619) 551-5680
Tech. Supp. Fax..........................(619) 551-2486
E-Mail ....info@bluesky.com
WWW..............................http://www.bluesky.com

Blue Star Marketing
2312 Central Ave. NE
Minneapolis, MN 55418
Main..................................(800) 950-8884
Tech. Support............................(612) 788-3711
BBS ....(612) 788-3442

Bluebird Systems
5900 La Place Ct
Carlsbad, CA 92008
Main..................................(800) 346-8232
Tech. Support............................(619) 438-2220

Blyth Software, Inc.
1065 E Hillsdale Blvd., #300
Foster City, CA 94404
Main..................................(800) 346-6647
Tech. Support............................(415) 571-0222
Sales ....(800) 346-6647

Boca Research
1377 Clint Moore Rd.
Boca Rotan, FL 33487-2722
Main.................................(407) 997-6227
Customer Svc. ....(407) 997-6227
Tech. Support ....(407) 241-8088
Sales...................................(407) 997-6227
Tech. Supp. Fax ....(407) 994-5848
BBS.....................................(407) 241-1601
E-Mail..........................techsup@boca.org
WWW...........................http://www.boca.org
FTP Address...........http://www.boca.org/support/
          ftpmain.htm
CompuServe.......................... GO BOCA

Booklink Technology, Inc.
WWW...........................http://www.booklink.com/

Books That Work
2300 Geng Rd., Building 3
Suite 100
Palo Alto, CA 94303-0930
Main.................................(415) 843-4400
WWW...............................http://www.btw.com

Border Network Technologies, Inc.
WWW.............................. http://www.border.com/

Borland International
100 Borland Way
Scotts Valley, CA 95066
Main.................................(408) 431-1000
Customer Svc. ....(408) 461-9000
Tech. Support ....(800) 841-8180
Sales...................................(408) 461-9000
Tech. Supp. Fax ....(510) 657-0816
BBS.....................................(408) 431-5096
E-Mail...............customer-support@borland.com
WWW...............................http://www.borland.com
FTP Address....ftp://ftp.borland.com/pub/techinfo/
CompuServe...............................GO BORLAND

Boss Technology
6050 McDonough Dr.
Norcross, GA 30093
Main.................................(800) 628-1787
BBS.................................(404) 368-2077

Bourbaki, Inc.
615 W Hays
Boise, ID 83701
Tech. Support ....(208) 342-5849
BBS..(208) 342-5823

Bravo Communications, Inc.
1310 Tully Rd., #107
San Jose, CA 95122
Main..(800) 366-0297
Tech. Support ....(408) 297-8700
Tech. Supp. Fax ....(408) 297-8701

Bristol Technology, Inc.
WWW................................http://www.bristol.com/

Broadband Networks
2820 E College Ave., #B
State College, PA 16801
Main..(814) 237-4073
Tech. Supp. Fax ....(814) 234-2841
BBS..(814) 234-2841

Broderbund
500 Redwood Blvd.
P.O. Box 6121
Novato, CA 94948-6121
Main..(415) 382-4400
Customer Svc. ....(415) 382-4700
Tech. Support ....(415) 382-4700
Sales...(415) 382-4700
Tech. Supp. Fax ....(415) 382-4419
BBS..(415) 883-5889
WWW.......................http://www.broderbund.com
CompuServe.. GO BB
America Online ....broderbund@aol.com

Brooktrout Technology, Inc.
144 Gould St.
Suite 200
Needham Malls, MA 02192
Main..(617) 449-4100
Tech. Supp. Fax ....(617) 449-9009
BBS..(617) 449-9009

Brother International Corp.
200 Cottontail Lane
Somerset, NJ 08875
Main .... (908) 356-8880
BBS .... (201) 469-4415
WWWhttp://www.brother.co.jp/E-printer/index.html

Bruker Analytische Meßtechnik
WWW...............http://www.bruker.de/Bruker.html

Bryant Software
WWW................................http://www.bryant.com/

BSDI
WWW................................... http://www.bsdi.com/

BSI
9440 Telstar Ave., #4
El Monte, CA 91731
Main .... (800) 872-4547
Customer Svc............................. (800) 872-4547
Tech. Support............................. (818) 442-7038
BBS .... (818) 442-4527
E-Mail.....................................bsi@earthlink.com

BTG Inc.
WWW....................................http://www.btg.com

Buffalo Products, Inc.
2805 19th St SE
Salem, OR 97302-1520
Main .... (800) 345-2356
Tech. Support............................. (503) 585-3414
Tech. Supp. Fax........................... (503) 585-4505
BBS .... (503) 585-4505
E-Mail.....................................sales@buffing.com
WWW..............................http://www.busfimp.com

Building Block Software
49 Waltham St
Lexington, MA 02173
Main .... (617) 628-5217
Tech. Support............................. (617) 860-9091
Tech. Supp. Fax........................... (617) 860-9066
CompuServe ....70471.734@compuserve.com

Bull
WWW.................................... http://www.bull.com/

Bull HN Information Systems
Technology Pk
Billerica, MA 01821
Tech. Support................................(508) 294-6000

Bulldog Computers
851 Commerse Ct.
Buffalo Grove, IL 60089
Main...(800) 438-6039
Tech. Support...............................(404) 860-6905
Tech. Supp. Fax............................(708) 541-6988
BBS...(404) 860-7358

Bureau of Electronic Publishing
141 New Rd.
Parsippany, NJ 07054
Main...(201) 808-2700
Customer Svc...............................(201) 808-2700
Tech. Support................................(201) 808-2700
Sales ....(800) 828-4766
Tech. Supp. Fax...........................(201) 808-2676
BBS...(201) 080-2676
E-Mail ....info@www.bep.com
WWW..http://www.bep.com
CompuServe .... GO CDVEN
America Online.................... thebureau@aol.com

Bus-Tech, Inc.
129 Middlesex Turnpike
Burlington, MA 01803
Main...(617) 272-8200

Business Forecast Systems, Inc.
68 Leonard St
Belmont, MA 02176
Main...(617) 484-5050
Tech. Supp. Fax...........................(617) 484-9219
CompuServe ..... 76773.1634@compuserve.com

BusTek Corp.
4151 Burton Dr
Santa Clara, CA 95054
Main...(408) 492-9090
Tech. Support ....(408) 654-0760
Tech. Supp. Fax ....(408) 492-1542
BBS...(408) 492-1542
WWW..............................http://www.buslogic.com

BVM Limited
WWW............. http://www.bvmltd.co.uk/welcome/

Byte/Wide Software
PO Box 1778
DeLand, FL 32721
Main...(904) 738-4923
Tech. Supp. Fax ....(904) 736-7635
BBS...(904) 736-7635
WWW............. http://www.toc.con.com4/bytewide

Bytex Corp.
4 Tecknoalge Dr.
West Borough, MA 01581-1760
Main...(800) 232-9839
Tech. Support ....(508) 480-0840
BBS...(508) 481-5111

C Gate Technology
19925 Suiterem Creek Blvd. 150
Cupertino, CA 95014
Main...(408) 342-4500
Tech. Support ....(800) 961-0501
Tech. Supp. Fax ....(408) 342-4600

C Itoh Electronics, Inc.
19300 S Hamilton Ave.
PO Box 9116
Torrance, CA 90508
Main...(213) 327-9100

C X R
2040 Fortune Dr.
San Jose, CA 95131
Main...(800) 537-5762
Customer Svc. ....(408) 435-8520
Tech. Supp. Fax ....(408) 435-5556
BBS...(408) 435-1276

C-Cor Electronics
60 Decibel Rd.
State College, PA 16801
Main..(800) 233-2267
Tech. Support ....(814) 238-2461
Tech. Supp. Fax ....(814) 238-4065

C-Lab/DigiDesign
1360 Willow Rd., #101
Menlo Park, CA 94025
Main..(415) 327-8811
Customer Svc. ....(415) 842-6699
Tech. Support ....(415) 842-6699
Sales..(800) 333-2137
Tech. Supp. Fax ....(415) 327-0777

C-Tech Electronics
2515 McCabe Way
PO Box 19763
Irvine, CA 92713-9673
Main..(800) 347-4017
BBS..(714) 757-4533

CablExpress
500 E Brighton Ave.
Syracuse, NY 13210
Main..(315) 476-3000
BBS..(315) 476-3034

Caci Products
3333 N. Torrey Pines Ct.
La Jolla, CA 92037
Main..(619) 457-9681
Tech. Support ....(619) 455-6300
Tech. Supp. Fax ....(619) 457-1184
BBS..(619) 457-1184
WWW..............................http://www.paciasl.com

CAD & Graphics Computers
1175 Chess Dr.
Suite C
Foster City, CA 94404
Main..(800) 288-1611
Tech. Supp. Fax ....(415) 378-6414
BBS..(415) 647-0240

Cadco
2405 S Shiloh Rd.
Garland, TX 75041
Main .... (800) 877-2288
Tech. Support................................(214) 271-3651
Tech. Supp. Fax...........................(214) 271-3654
BBS..(214) 271-3654

Cadkey, Inc.
4 Griffin Rd. N
Windsor, CT 06095-1511
Main .... (203) 298-8888
BBS..(203) 298-6401

Cadre Technologies
222 Richmond St
Providence, RI 02903
Main .... (800) 547-4445
Tech. Support................................(401) 351-5950
Tech. Supp. Fax...........................(401) 455-6800

Caere Corp.
100 Cooper Court
Los Gatos, CA 95030
Main .... (408) 395-7000
Customer Svc................................(800) 654-1187
Tech. Support................................(408) 395-8319
Sales ....(800) 535-7226
Tech. Supp. Fax...........................(408) 395-1994
BBS..(408) 395-1631
E-Mail....................................support@caere.com
WWW................................http://www.caere.com/
CompuServe ....GO CAERE

CalComp
2411 West La Palma
Anheim, CA 92801
Main .... (714) 821-2000
Customer Svc................................(800) 541-7877
Tech. Support................................(800) 225-2667
Sales ....(714) 821-2000
Tech. Supp. Fax...........................(714) 821-2760
BBS..(714) 236-3045
WWW................................http://www.calcomp.com

California Software Products
525 N Cabrillo Park Dr
Santa Ana, CA 92701
Main...(714) 973-0440
Tech. Supp. Fax...........................(714) 558-9341
BBS ....(714) 558-9341
CompuServe ..... 74644.3140@compuserve.com

Cam Software
750 N 200 W, #208
Westpark Bldg
Provo, UT 84601
Main...(801) 373-4080
BBS ....(801) 373-4008

Cambridge Scientific
WWW..............................http://www.camsci.com/

Cambrix Publishing
9304 Deering Ave.
Chatsworth, CA 91311
Main...(818) 992-8484
Customer Svc.................................(818) 992-8484
Tech. Support.................................(818) 992-8484
Sales ....(818) 992-8484
Tech. Supp. Fax...........................(818) 993-6201
E-Mail ....cambrix@aol.com
WWW..........................http://www.movieweb.com

Campbell Services
21700 Northwestern Highway
10th Floor
Southfield, MI 48075
Main...(810) 559-5955
Customer Svc.................................(810) 559-5955
Tech. Support.................................(810) 559-5955
Sales ....(810) 559-5955
Tech. Supp. Fax...........................(810) 559-1034

Canadian Software Distributors
Box 199
Munster, ONT K0A 3P0
Canada

Canai
59 Iber Rd.
Stittsvile, ONT K2S 1E7
Canada
Main...(613) 831-8300
BBS...(613) 831-3283

Canary Communications
1851 Zanker Rd.
San Jose, CA 95112-4610
Main...(408) 453-9201
Tech. Supp. Fax ....(408) 453-0940
BBS...(408) 453-0940

Candlelight Software
2375 E Tropicana Ave., #320
Las Vegas, NV 89119
Main...(702) 456-6365

Canoga-Perkins
21012 Lassen St
Chatsworth, CA 91311
Main...(818) 718-6300
Customer Svc. ....(800) 360-6642
Tech. Support ....(818) 718-6300
Sales...(818) 718-6300
Tech. Supp. Fax ....(818) 718-6312
BBS...(818) 718-6312

Canon Computer Systems
2995 Red Hill Ave.
Costa Mesa, CA 92626-5048
Main...(714) 438-3000
Customer Svc. ....(714) 438-3391
Tech. Support ....(800) 423-2366
Sales...(800) 423-2366
Tech. Supp. Fax ....(800) 922-9068
BBS...(804) 420-2000
WWW.......................http://www.usa.cannon.com

Canon USA - Printer Division
1 Canon Plaza
Lake Success, NY 11042
Main..(800) 221-3333
Customer Svc. ....(800) 221-3333
Tech. Support ....(516) 488-6700
Sales..(800) 221-3333
BBS..(516) 354-5805

Canstar
3900 Victoria Park Ave.
North York, ONT M2H 3H7
Canada
Main..(905) 946-7600

Capital Equipment Corp.
900 Middlesex Turnpike
Billerica, MA 01821
Main..(800) 234-4232
Customer Svc. ....(800) 234-4232
Tech. Support ....(508) 663-2002
Sales..(800) 234-4232
Tech. Supp. Fax ....(505) 663-2626
WWW..............................http://www.cec488.com

Capstone
501 Brickell Key Dr.
Suite 600
Miami, FL 33131
Main..(305) 373-7700
Customer Svc. ....(305) 373-3770
Tech. Support ....(305) 373-3770
Sales..(800) 468-7226
Tech. Supp. Fax ....(305) 577-9488
BBS..(305) 374-6872
E-Mail.. intracor@gate.net
WWW..................... http://www.gate.net/~intracor

Card Shop, The
7335 E Acoma Dr, #203
Scottsdale, AZ 85260
Main..(800) 346-0055
Tech. Support ....(800) 255-2328
BBS..(602) 948-8458

Cardinal Technologies
1827 Freedom Rd.
Lancaster, PA 17601
Main ....(717) 293-3000
Customer Svc...............................(717) 293-3049
Tech. Support...............................(717) 293-3124
Sales ....(717) 293-3049
Tech. Supp. Fax..........................(717) 293-3043
BBS..(717) 293-3074
E-Mail.................................techs@cardtech.com

Carlisle Computer
959 Hill Rd.
Las Cruces, NM 88005
Main ....(505) 642-1919
Tech. Support...............................(505) 526-7770
BBS..(505) 524-7356

Carnegie Group
WWW............. http://www.cgi.com/CGI/index.html

Casady & Green
22734 Portola Dr.
Salinas, CA 93908-1119
Main ....(408) 484-9228
Customer Svc...............................(408) 484-9228
Tech. Support...............................(408) 484-9228
Sales ....(800) 359-4920
Tech. Supp. Fax..........................(408) 484-9218
E-Mail .... tech@casadyg.com
WWW.............................http://www.casadyg.com
CompuServe 71333,616
America Online.........................Casady@aol.com

Casat Technology
10 Northern Blvd.
Amherst, NH 03031
Main ....(603) 880-1833
BBS..(603) 881-9888

Castelle
3255-3 Scott Blvd.
Santa Clara, CA 95054
Main.................................(408) 496-0474
Customer Svc............................(408) 496-0474
Tech. Support......................(408) 496-0474
Tech. Supp. Fax.......................(408) 492-1338
BBS ....(408) 496-1807
CompuServe ....GO CASTELLE

Cawthon Software Group
24224 Michigan Ave.
Dearborn, MI 48124-1897
Main.................................(313) 565-4000
Tech. Support......................(313) 565-4000
Tech. Supp. Fax.......................(313) 565-4001
WWW..........................http://www.chipchat.com

Cayman Systems
100 Maple Street
Stoneham, MA 02180
Main.................................(617) 279-1101
Customer Svc............................(617) 279-1101
Tech. Support......................(617) 279-1101
Sales ....(800) 473-4776
Tech. Supp. Fax.......................(617) 438-5560
BBS ....(617) 494-9270
E-Mail.............................. support@cayman.com
WWW........................... http://www.cayman.com
FTP Address.............................ftp.cayman.com

cc: Mail / Lotus Development
55 Cambridge Parkway
Cambridge, MA 02142
Main.................................(617) 577-8500
Customer Svc............................(800) 343-5414
Tech. Support......................(800) 448-2500
Sales ....(800) 343-5414
Tech. Supp. Fax.......................(617) 693-7811
BBS ....(415) 691-0401
WWW.................................http://www.lotus.com
FTP Address.......... ftp://ftp.support.lotus.com/pub
CompuServe ....GO LOTUS

CD Connection
5805 State Bridge Rd.
Duluth, GA 30155
Main.................................(770) 446-1332
Tech. Supp. Fax...........................(770) 446-9164
BBS.......................................(404) 446-9164

CD Publishing, Inc.
345 Madison Ave.
Suite 317
New York, NY 10115

CD Technologies
762 San Aleso Ave.
Sunnyvale, CA 94086
Main.................................(408) 752-8500
Customer Svc............................(408) 752-8500
Tech. Support......................(408) 752-8500
Sales.................................(408) 752-8500
Tech. Supp. Fax..........................(408) 752-8501

CDE Technology
WWW...... http://www.ipac.net/cde/cdehome.html

CE Software
1801 Industrial Circle
West Des Moines, IA 50265
Main.................................(515) 221-1801
Customer Svc. ....(515) 224-1995
Tech. Support ....(515) 221-1803
Sales.................................(800) 523-7638
Tech. Supp. Fax ....(515) 221-1806
BBS.......................................(800) 579-9732
E-Mail............................ ce_support@cesoft.com
WWW .... http://www.cesoft.com
FTP Address.................................ftp.cesoft.com
CompuServe.............................. GO MACAVEN
America Online ....cesoftware@aol.com

Central Computer Products
387 Zachary Ave. #103
Moorepark, CA 93021
Main.................................(800) 456-4123
Tech. Support ....(805) 532-9171
Tech. Supp. Fax ....(805) 532-9174
BBS..(805) 524-4026

Central Data
WWW.................................http://www.cd.com/

Central Point Software
175 West Broadway
Eugene, OR 97401
Customer Svc. ....(800) 441-7234
Sales...(800) 278-6657
Tech. Supp. Fax ....(800) 554-4403
BBS...(503) 984-5366
WWW...........................http://www.symantec.com
CompuServe.............................GO SYMANTEC
America Online ....central@aol.com

Century Software
5284 South 320 West
Suite No "C" 134
Salt Lake City, UT 84107
Main..(801) 268-3088
Customer Svc. ....(801) 268-3088
Tech. Support ....(801) 268-3088
Sales...(801) 268-3088
Tech. Supp. Fax ....(801) 268-2772
BBS...(801) 266-0330
E-Mail...................................tech@censoft.com
WWW.............................http://www.censoft.com
FTP Address.............................ftp@censoft.com
CompuServe...............................GO CENTURY

Century Software
711 Second Street
Boca Raton, FL 33486

Cerveau
1213Saint Catherine St E
Montreal, Quebec H2L 2H1
Canada
Main..(514) 525-7776

Cettlan Corp.
PO Box 397
Irvine, CA 92650
Main..(714) 559-4016
BBS...(714) 262-0708

CGI Systems, Inc.
1 Blue Hill Plaza
Pearl River, NY 10965
Main .... (800) 722-1866
Tech. Support.............................(914) 735-5030
Tech. Supp. Fax.........................(914) 735-2231
BBS..(914) 735-2231

CH Products
970 Park Center Dr.
Vista, CA 92083
Main .... (619) 598-2518
Customer Svc................................ (800) 624-5804
Tech. Support.............................(619) 598-2518
Sales .... (800) 624-5804
Tech. Supp. Fax.........................(619) 598-2524
BBS .... (619) 598-3224
E-Mail...............................tech@chproducts.com
WWW.......................http://www.chproducts.com
FTP Address ......http://www.chproducts.com/CH/
chdown.html

Channel Computing, Inc.
63 Main St
Newmarket, NH 03857
Main .... (800) 289-0053
Tech. Support.............................(603) 659-2832
BBS .... (603) 659-7590

Charles River Analytics
55 Wheeler Street
Cambridge, MA 02138
Main .... (617) 491-3474
E-Mail.......................................sesame@cra.com
WWW....................http://www.opensesame.com/

Chase Research, Inc.
545 Marriott Dr, #100
Nashville, TN 37210
Main .... (615) 872-0770
Tech. Support.............................(615) 872-0770
Tech. Supp. Fax.........................(615) 872-0771
BBS .... (615) 872-0771
E-Mail.................................support@chaser.com
WWW................................http://www.chaser.com

CheckMark Software

724 Whalers Way
Builidng "H"
Fot Collins, CO 80525
Main..............................(970) 225-0522
Customer Svc...............................(800) 444-9922
Tech. Support..............................(970) 225-0387
Sales ....(800) 444-9922
Tech. Supp. Fax..........................(970) 225-0611
E-Mail .... CheckMark@fortnet.com
WWW........................ http://www.checkmark.com

Cheetah Computer Systems, Inc.

3928 S. Broadway
Tyler, TX 75701
Main..............................(800) 243-3824
Customer Svc...............................(800) 243-3824
Tech. Support..............................(214) 757-3001

Cheyenne Software

3 Expressway Plaza
Roslyn Heights, NY 11577
Main..............................(516) 484-5110
Customer Svc...............................(516) 484-5110
Tech. Support..............................(800) 243-9832
Sales ....(800) 243-9462
Tech. Supp. Fax..........................(516) 465-5115
BBS ....(516) 465-3900
E-Mail ....EMAIL done by product only
WWW........................... http://www.cheyenne.com
FTP Address............................ftp.cheyenne.com
CompuServe .... GO CHEYENNE

Chi/Cor Information Management

300 S Wacker Dr
Chicago, IL 60606
Main..............................(800) 448-8777
Tech. Support..............................(312) 322-0150
BBS ....(312) 322-0161

Chicago Computer Works

PO Box 14691
Chicago, IL 60614-6911
Main..............................(312) 280-9378

Children's Software Co.

WWW.............. http://www.childsoft.com/childsoft

Children's Software Revue

WWW http://www.microweb.com/pepsite/Revue/
revue

Chinon America

165 Hawaii Ave.
Torrence, Ca 90503
Main..............................(310) 533-0274
Customer Svc. ....(800) 441-0222
Tech. Support ....(800) 441-0222
Sales..(310) 533-0274
Tech. Supp. Fax ....(310) 533-1727
BBS..(310) 320-4161

Chipcom Corp.

118 Turnpike Rd.
Southborough, MA 01772
Main..............................(800) 228-9930
Tech. Support ....(508) 460-8900
BBS..(508) 460-8950

Chipcom Corp.

WWW........................... http://www.chipcom.com/

Chips & Technologies, Inc.

3050 Zanker Rd.
San Jose, CA 95134
Main..............................(408) 434-0600

Chuo Electronics Co.

WWW.................................. http://www.cec.co.jp/

Cincinnati Microwave

WWW............................... http://www.cnmw.com/

Ciprico, Inc.

2800 Campus Dr. Suite #60
Plymouth, MN 55441
Main..............................(800) 727-4669
Tech. Support ....(612) 551-4000
BBS..(612) 559-4002

Circo Computer Systems
8513 E Garvey Ave., #A
Rosemead, CA 91770
Main.................................(800) 678-1688
Tech. Support ....(818) 571-4948
BBS..(818) 571-8821

Circuit Technology
WWWhttp://www.halcyon.com/sverne/home.html

Cisco Systems, Inc.
170 West Tasman Dr.
San Jose, CA 95134
Main.................................(408) 526-4000
Tech. Support ....(415) 326-1941
BBS..(415) 326-1989
WWW................................http://www.cisco.com/

Citadel Systems
2950 N. Loop W. Suite #1080
Houston, TX 77092
Main.................................(800) 962-0701
BBS..(713) 292-0617

Citel America
7403 Miami Lakes Dr
Miami Lakes, FL 33014
Main.................................(800) 874-3323
Tech. Support ....(305) 558-1133
BBS..(305) 556-9640

Citizen America
2450 Broadway
Suite No 600
Santa Monica, CA 90404-3060
Main.................................(310) 453-0614
Customer Svc. ....(310) 453-0614
Tech. Support ....(310) 453-0614
Sales..(815) 455-4050
Tech. Supp. Fax ....(310) 453-2814
BBS..(310) 453-7564

Citrix Systems, Inc.
210 University Dr, #700
Coral Springs, FL 33071
Main .... (800) 437-7503
Tech. Support.............................. (305) 755-0559
BBS.. (954) 346-9004
WWW....................................http://www.citrix.com/

Clarion Software/Top Speed Software
150 East Sample Rd.
Pompano, FL 33064
Main .... (305) 785-4555
Customer Svc............................... (305) 785-4555
Tech. Support.............................. (305) 785-4556
Sales .... (800) 354-5444
Tech. Supp. Fax............................. (305) 946-1650
BBS.. (305) 781-3578
WWW........................... http://www.topspeed.com
CompuServe ....GO TOPSPEED

Claris
5201 Patrick Henry Dr.
Santa Clara, CA 95054-1171
Main .... (408) 987-7000
Customer Svc............................... (408) 727-8227
Tech. Support.............................. (408) 725-9004
Sales .... (800) 325-2747
Tech. Supp. Fax............................. (408) 987-7447
BBS.. (408) 987-7421
WWW.............................. http://www.claris.com
FTP Address ....ftp.claris.com
CompuServe .... GO CLARIS
America Online.............................claris@aol.com

Clark Development Co
3950 S. 700 E. Suite #303
Murray, UT 84157
Main .... (800) 356-1686
Tech. Support.............................. (801) 261-1686

Clear software, Inc.
199 Wells Ave.
Newton, MA 02159
Main .... (800) 338-1759
Tech. Support.............................. (617) 965-5019
Tech. Supp. Fax............................. (617) 965-5310
BBS.. (617) 232-9788

Clearpoint Research
25 Birch St. Suite #B-41
Milford, MA 01757
Main.....................................(800) 253-2778
Tech. Support.......................(508) 435-2000
BBS ....(508) 435-7530

Cleo Communications
4203 Galleria Dr.
Loves Park, IL 61111
Main.....................................(800) 233-2536
Tech. Support.......................(313) 662-2002
Tech. Supp. Fax..................(815) 654-8294
BBS ....(313) 662-1965

Cliffs Notes
4851 South 16th Street
Lincoln, NE 68512
Main.....................................(402) 423-5050
Customer Svc.......................(800) 228-4078
Tech. Support.......................(402) 421-8324
Sales ....(800) 228-4078
Tech. Supp. Fax..................(800) 826-6831
E-Mail .... techsupport@cliffs.com
CompuServe 71344,3404
America Online......................... clifftsts@aol.com

CMS
382 N Lemon Ave.
Walnut, CA 91789
Main.....................................(714) 594-5051

CNet Technology, Inc.
2199 Zanker Rd.
San Jose, CA 95131
Main.....................................(408) 954-8000
Customer Svc.......................(408) 954-8800
Tech. Support.......................(408) 954-8800
Sales ....(408) 954-8800
Tech. Supp. Fax..................(408) 954-8866
BBS ....(408) 954-8866
E-Mail ....support@cnet.com

Coastcom
1151 Harbor Bay Pkwy
Alameda, CA 94512
Main.....................................(800) 433-3433
Tech. Support ....(800) 385-4689
Tech. Supp. Fax ....(415) 523-6150

Coda
6210 Bury Dr.
Eden Pairie, MN 55346
Main.....................................(800) 843-2066
Tech. Supp. Fax ....(612) 937-9760
E-Mail.................................. codatech@aol.com

Codenoll Technology
1086 N Broadway
Yonkers, NY 10701
Main.....................................(914) 965-6300
Tech. Supp. Fax ....(914) 965-9811
BBS.....................................(914) 965-9811

Codex/Motorola Corp.
20 Cabot Blvd.
Mansfield, MA 02048
Main.....................................(800) 426-1212
Tech. Support ....(508) 261-4000
BBS.....................................(508) 337-8004

Cogent Data Technologies
640 Mullis St.
Friday Harbor, WA 98250
Main.....................................(360) 378-2929
Tech. Supp. Fax ....(360) 378-2882
BBS.....................................(206) 378-2882

Cognitech
500 Sugar Mill Rd. Suite #240-A
Atlanta, GA 30350
Main.....................................(770) 518-4577
Customer Svc. ....(770) 518-3285
Tech. Support ....(770) 518-5010
Sales...................................(800) 947-5075
Tech. Supp. Fax ....(770) 518-9137
BBS.....................................(770) 518-7617

Cognitive Technology Corp.orati
9 El Camenio Dr.
Corte Medera, CA 94925
Main...(415) 925-2323
Tech. Supp. Fax ....(415) 461-4010
BBS...(415) 925-0733
E-Mail...ctc@well.com
WWW ....http://www.well.com/user/ctc
CompuServe......76600.1623@compuserve.com

Coker Electronics
1430 Lexington Ave.
San Mateo, CA 94402
Main...(415) 573-5515

Collins Printed Circuits
WWWhttp://www.rockwell.com/rockwell/bus_units/
cca/cpc/

Colorado Memory Systems
A Division of Hewlett-Packard
800 S. Taft Ave.
Loveland, CO 80537
Main...(970) 635-1500
Customer Svc. ....(970) 635-1500
Tech. Support ....(970) 635-1500
Sales..(970) 635-1500
BBS...(970) 635-0650
FTP Addressftp.hp.com/pub/information_storage/
hp-colorado

Colorgraphic Communications Co
5980 Peachtree Rd.
Atlanta, GA 30341
Main...(770) 455-3921
Tech. Supp. Fax ....(770) 458-0616

Columbia Data Products
1070-B Riner Dr.
Altamonte Springs, FL 32714
Main...(407) 869-6700
Tech. Support ....(407) 869-6700
Tech. Supp. Fax ....(407) 862-4725
BBS...(407) 862-4725

Columbia University Kermit Pro
WWW ....http://www.columbia.edu/kermit

Comcab
PO BOX 44027
Pittsburg, PA 15205
Main ....(614) 828-2468
Tech. Supp. Fax...........................(412) 922-7523

ComData
7900 N Nagle Ave.
Morton Grove, IL 60053
Main ....(800) 255-2570
Tech. Support...............................(708) 470-9600

Comdisco
555 N. Matilda Ave.
Sunnydale, CA 94086
Main ....(415) 574-5800
Tech. Supp. Fax...........................(408) 523-4601
BBS...(415) 358-3601

Command Software Systems
1061 E Indiantown Rd., #2500
Jupiter, FL 33477
Main ....(800) 423-9147
Tech. Support...............................(407) 575-3200
Tech. Supp. Fax...........................(407) 575-3026
BBS...(407) 575-3026

Command Technology Corp. (CTC)
1040 Marina Village Pkwy.
Alameda, CA 94501-1041
Main ....(800) 648-6700
Tech. Support...............................(510) 521-5900
Tech. Supp. Fax...........................(510) 521-0369
BBS...(510) 521-0369

Common Ground Software
WWW ....http://www.commonground.com/

Commvision
510 logue Ave.
Mountainview, CA 94043
Main ....(800) 832-6526
Tech. Support...............................(408) 923-0301
BBS...(408) 923-0427
WWW ....http://www.commvision.com

Compaq
20555 State Highway 249
Houston, TX 77070-2698
Main.................................(713) 370-0670
Customer Svc.............................(800) 345-1518
Tech. Support...............................(800) 345-1518
Sales ....(800) 652-6672
Tech. Supp. Fax.........................(713) 514-1743
BBS ....(713) 518-1418
E-Mail ....Support@Compaq.Com
WWW.......................http://www.es.compaq.com

Compatible Systems Corp.
PO Drawer 17220
Boulder, CO 80308
Main.................................(800) 356-0283
Tech. Support..............................(303) 444-9532
Tech. Supp. Fax..........................(303) 444-9595
BBS ....(303) 444-9595
WWW.......................http://www.compatible.com/

Compex, Inc.
4051 E La Palma, #C
Anaheim, CA 92807
Main.................................(714) 630-7302
Tech. Support..............................(714) 630-5451
Tech. Supp. Fax..........................(714) 630-6521
BBS ....(714) 630-6521

Complementary Solutions, Inc.
4470 Chamblee-Dunwoody Rd.
Atlanta, GA 30338
Main...............................(770) 454-8033

Compression Labs, Inc.
2860 Junction Ave.
San Jose, CA 95134
Main.................................(800) 225-5254
Tech. Support..............................(800) 767-2254
BBS ....(408) 922-5429

Compton's New Media
2320 Camino Vida Roble
Carlsbad, CA 92009
Main..............................(800) 862-2206
Customer Svc. ....(800) 862-2206
Tech. Support ....(716) 871-7318
Sales..............................(800) 261-6109
Tech. Supp. Fax ....(716) 871-7591
E-Mail...........................support@comptons.com
WWW.........................http://www.comptons.com
FTP Addresshttp://www.comptons.com/patch.html
CompuServe.............................GO COMPTONS

CompuAdd Corp.
12303 Technology Blvd.
Austin, TX 78727
Main.................................(800) 627-1967
BBS.................................(512) 335-6236

CompuData Translators, Inc.
8816 A. Rescida Blvd.
Northridge, CA 91324
Main.................................(818) 700-9090
Tech. Support ....(213) 387-4477
Tech. Supp. Fax ....(818) 700-1500
BBS.................................(213) 387-1619

Compulink Management Center
370 South Crenshaw Blvd.
Torrance, CA 90503
Main.................................(310) 212-5465
Customer Svc. ....(310) 212-5465
Tech. Support ....(310) 212-5465
Sales.................................(310) 212-5465
Tech. Supp. Fax ....(310) 212-5064
BBS.................................(310) 212-5850
WWW.........http://www.imaging@ix.netcom.com
CompuServe.............................GO COMPULINK

CompuMart International
537-1/2 Venice Way
Venice, CA 90291
Main.................................(310) 823-0826

CompUSA, Inc.
15167 Business Ave.
Dallas, TX 75244
Main..............................(800) 932-2667
Tech. Support...............(214) 702-0055
Tech. Supp. Fax ....(214) 888-5743
BBS.................................(214) 702-0300

CompuServe Information Service
5000 Arlington Centre Blvd.
PO Box 2
Columbus, OH 43220
Main..............................(800) 848-8199

CompuServe, Inc.
5000 Arlington Centre Blvd.
Columbus, OH 43220
Main..............................(614) 538-4600
WWW......................http://www.compuserve.com

ComputAbility Consumer Electro
PO Box 17882
Milwaukee, WI 53217
Main..............................(800) 558-0003
Tech. Support...............(414) 357-8181
BBS.................................(414) 357-7814

Computational Logic
WWW.....................................http://www.cli.com/

CompuTeach
16541 Redmond Way
Suite 137-C
Redmond, WA 98052
Main..............................(206) 885-0517
Customer Svc. ....(206) 885-0517
Tech. Support...............(206) 885-0517
Sales.............................(800) 448-3224
Tech. Supp. Fax ....(206) 883-9169

Computer & Control Solutions
1510 Stone Ridge Dr
Stone Mountain, GA 30083
Main..............................(800) 782-3525
Tech. Support...............(404) 491-1046
Tech. Supp. Fax ....(770) 493-7033
BBS.................................(404) 493-7033

Computer Aided Business Soluti
607-19th St. Suite #200
Golden, CO 80401
Main ....(303) 279-1868
Tech. Supp. Fax...........(303) 279-5305
BBS................................(303) 279-5305

Computer Aided Management
1318 Redwood Way, #210
Petaluma, CA 94954
Tech. Support................(415) 454-7101
BBS................................(707) 795-0441

Computer Associates
1 Computer Associates Plaza
Islandaia, NY 11788-7000
Main ....(516) 342-5224
Customer Svc...............(800) 773-5445
Tech. Support................(516) 342-5466
Sales ....(800) 225-5224
Tech. Supp. Fax............(516) 342-5734
WWW...................................http://www.cai.com
FTP Address ....http://www.cai.com/cafixes.htm
CompuServe ....GO CAI

Computer Discount Warehouse
1020 E. Lake Cook Rd.
Buffalo Grove, IL 60089
Main ....(800) 233-4426
Tech. Support...............(708) 498-1426
Tech. Supp. Fax............(708) 465-6800
BBS................................(708) 291-1737

Computer Dynamics Sales
7640 Telham Rd.
Greenville, SC 29615
Main ....(803) 877-8700
Tech. Supp. Fax...........(864) 675-0106
BBS................................(803) 879-2030

Computer Friends
14250 NW Science Pk Dr
Portland, OR 97229
Main ....(800) 547-3303
Tech. Support...............(506) 626-2291
Tech. Supp. Fax...........(503) 643-5379
BBS................................(503) 643-5379

Computer Industries
PO Box 176, 1025 Blueberry Ln
Liberty, MO 64068
Main..(816) 792-2400

Computer Innovations, Inc.
980 Shrewsbury Ave.
Tinton Falls, NJ 07724-3003
Main..(800) 922-0169
Tech. Support...................................(908) 542-5920
BBS...(908) 542-6121

Computer Language Research
1555 Valwood Pkwy
Carrollton, TX 75006-6828
Main..(800) 367-6373
Tech. Support...................................(800) 934-7728

Computer Logics
75 International Blvd.
Toranto, ONTM9W 6L9
Canada
Main..(800) 829-2810
Tech. Support...................................(416) 674-1111
BBS...(416) 674-1130

Computer Mail Order (CMO)
2400 Reach Rd.
Williamsport, PA 17701
Tech. Support...................................(800) 221-4283
Tech. Supp. Fax..............................(717) 327-9252
BBS...(717) 327-1217

Computer Network Technology
6655 Wedgewood Rd.
Maple Grove, MN 55369
Main..(612) 420-4466

Computer Parts Express
WWW...................http://www.netzone.com/~mac/
        parts_express.html

Computer Peripherals, Inc.
7 Wahtney
Irvine, CA 92718
Main..(800) 854-7600
Tech. Support ....(805) 499-5751
Tech. Supp. Fax ....(714) 454-8527
BBS..(805) 498-8306

Computer Power, Inc.
124 W Main St
High Bridge, NJ 08829
Tech. Support ....(908) 638-8000
Tech. Supp. Fax ....(908) 638-4931
BBS..(908) 638-4931

Computer Products Corp.
1431 S Cherryvail Rd.
Boulder, CO 80303
Main..(800) 338-4273
Tech. Support ....(800) 338-4273
Tech. Supp. Fax ....(303) 442-0501
BBS..(303) 442-7985

Computer Products Plus
16580 Harbor Blvd.
Fountain Valley, CA 92708
Main..(800) 274-4277
Tech. Support ....(714) 418-1400
Tech. Supp. Fax ....(714) 839-6282

Computer Products, Inc.
2900 Gateway Dr
Pompano Beach, FL 33069-4378
Main..(305) 974-5500
BBS..(305) 979-7371

Computer Reset
PO Box 461782
Garland, TX 75046
Main..(214) 276-8072
Tech. Support ....(214) 276-8072
Tech. Supp. Fax ....(214) 272-7920
BBS..(214) 272-7920

Computer Solutions, NW

PO Box 446
Benzonia, MI 49616
Main..(616) 325-2540
Tech. Support ....(616) 325-2540
BBS..(616) 325-2505

Computer Station Corp.

6611 Bissonnet, #112
Houston, TX 77074
Main..(713) 777-3464
Tech. Support ....(713) 777-3464
Tech. Supp. Fax ....(713) 777-3431
BBS..(713) 777-3431

Computer Support

15926 Midway Rd.
Dallas, TX 75244-2123
Main..(214) 661-8960
Customer Svc. ....(214) 661-8960
Tech. Support ....(214) 661-8960
Sales..(214) 661-8960
Tech. Supp. Fax ....(214) 661-5429
BBS..(214) 404-8652
CompuServe...................................... 71370,3273

Computer System Advisers

300 Tice Blvd.
Woodcliff Lake, NJ 07675
Main..(201) 391-6500
Tech. Supp. Fax ....(201) 391-2210

Computer System Products, Inc.

14305 21st Ave. N
Minneapolis, MN 55447
Main..(800) 422-2537
Tech. Support ....(612) 476-6866
Tech. Supp. Fax ....(612) 475-8457

Computer Tyme

411 N Sherman, #300
Springfield, MO 65802
Main..(800) 548-5353
Tech. Support ....(417) 866-1222
Tech. Supp. Fax ....(417) 866-1665

Computerized Processes Unlimited

WWW.....................................http://www.cpu.com

ComputersFirst

27 W 20th St
New York, NY 10003
Main ....(800) 875-7580

Computertime Network

10340 Cote De Liesse
Montreal, Quebec H8T 1A3
Canada
Tech. Support................................(514) 633-9900
Tech. Supp. Fax...........................(514) 633-9886
BBS..(514) 633-9886

Computone Corp.

1100 Northmeadow Pky. Suite 150
Roswell, GA 30076
Main ....(770) 475-2725
Customer Svc...............................(800) 241-3946
Tech. Support................................(770) 475-2725
Sales ....(800) 241-3946
Tech. Supp. Fax...........................(770) 664-1110
BBS ....(770) 343-9737
E-Mail ....support@computone.com
WWW......................http://www.computone.com
FTP Address ....ftp.computone.com

CompuTrend

1306-1308 John Reed Ct
City of Industry, CA 91745
Main ....(818) 333-5121
Tech. Support................................(818) 333-5176
Tech. Supp. Fax...........................(818) 369-6803
BBS ....(818) 369-6803
WWW.........................http://www.premio.pc.com

Compuware Frontiers

12 W 31st St
New York, NY 10001
Main ....(212) 279-6060
Tech. Supp. Fax...........................(212) 268-0885
BBS ....(212) 268-0885

Compuworld
1443 N Highland Ave.
Hollywood, CA 90028
Main...(213) 461-0779
Tech. Support..............................(213) 461-0825
BBS ....(213) 461-4858

Comshare
3001 S State St, PO Box 1588
Ann Arbor, MI 48106
Main...(800) 922-7979
Tech. Support..............................(313) 994-4800

Comtech Publishing, Ltd.
Box 12340
Reno, NV 89510
Main...(800) 456-7005
Tech. Support..............................(702) 825-9000
Tech. Supp. Fax...........................(702) 825-1818
BBS ....(702) 825-1818
WWW.............. http://www.accutek.com/comtech

Comtrade
1215 Bixie Dr.
City of Industry, CA 91745
Main...(800) 969-2123
Tech. Support..............................(818) 964-6688
Tech. Supp. Fax...........................(818) 369-1479
BBS ....(818) 964-2492

Comtrol
WWW........... .... http://www.comtrol.com/

Comtrol Corp.
2675 Patton Rd.
PO Box 64750
St Paul, MN 55113
Main...(800) 926-6876
Tech. Support..............................(612) 631-7654
Tech. Supp. Fax...........................(612) 631-8117
WWW.............................. http://www.comtrol.com

Concentric Data Systems, Inc.
110 Turnpike Rd.
Westboro, MA 01581
Main...(800) 325-9035
Tech. Support ....(508) 366-1122
BBS...(508) 366-2954

Concept Development Systems, Inc.
PO Drawer 1988
Kennesaw, GA 30144-9917
Main...(770) 424-6240
BBS...(404) 424-8995

Concept Software
WWW.................. http://www.holonet.net/consoft/

Concord Communications, Inc.
33 W. Boston Post Rd.
Marlboro, MA 01752
Main...(508) 460-4646
Tech. Supp. Fax ....(508) 481-9772
BBS...(508) 481-9772

Connect Software
11130 Northeast 33rd Place
Suite 250
Bellevue, WA 98004
Main...(206) 827-6467
Customer Svc. ....(800) 234-9497
Tech. Support ....(206) 803-3039
Sales...(800) 234-9497
Tech. Supp. Fax ....(206) 822-9095
BBS...(612) 944-9290
E-Mail.........................support@connectsoft.com
WWW......................http://www.connectsoft.com
FTP Address..........................ftp.connectsoft.com
CompuServe.................................... 71333,2244

Connect Tech, Inc.
20-340 Woodlawn Rd. W
Guelph, Ontario, Canada N1H 7K6
Main...(519) 836-1291
BBS...(519) 836-4878

Connectix
2655 Campus Dr.
San Mateo, CA 94403
Main.................................(415) 571-5100
Customer Svc. ....(800) 950-5880
Tech. Support ....(800) 950-5880
Sales.................................(800) 950-5880
Tech. Supp. Fax ....(415) 571-5195
E-Mail............................ support@connectix.com
WWW.......................... http://www.connectix.com
FTP Address. http://www.pcworld.com/connectix/
    techsupp.html
CompuServe............................... GO MACAVEN
America Online .... connectix@aol.com

Connector
1372 N McDowell Blvd.
Petaluma, CA 94954
Main.................................(800) 282-2535
Tech. Support ....(415) 341-1376
BBS.................................(707) 763-6291

Conner Peripherals
MS 4309, 3081 Zanker Rd.
San Jose, CA 95134-2128
Main.................................(408) 456-3019
Customer Svc. ....(800) 851-4200
Tech. Support ....(800) 426-6637
Sales.................................(800) 626-6637
BBS.................................(408) 456-4415
WWW..............................http://www.conner.com

Connexperts
2626 Lombardy Ln Suite #107
Dallas, TX 75220
Main.................................(800) 433-5373
Tech. Support ....(214) 739-4200
Tech. Supp. Fax ....(214) 351-6741
BBS.................................(214) 396-3925

Connors Communications
873 Broadway, Suite 201
New York, NY 10003-1209
Main.................................(212) 995-2200
WWW..............................http://www.connors.com

Conrac Corp.
1724 S Mountain Ave.
Duarte, CA 91010
Main .... (818) 303-0095
Tech. Supp. Fax.......................... (818) 303-5484
BBS................................. (818) 303-5485

Consan
7676 Executive Dr.
Eden Prairie, MN 55344
Main .... (800) 229-3475
Tech. Support.......................... (612) 949-0053
Tech. Supp. Fax.......................... (612) 949-0453
BBS................................. (612) 949-0453

Consultex
2140 S Dupont Dr
Anaheim, CA 92806
Main .... (800) 243-3338
Tech. Support.......................... (714) 634-8448
Tech. Supp. Fax.......................... (714) 634-2193
BBS................................. (714) 634-2193

Consumer Technology Northwest
Tview, Inc
7853 Southwest Cirrus Drive
Beaverton, OR 97008
Main .... (503) 643-1662
Customer Svc.......................... (800) 356-3983
Tech. Support.......................... (503) 643-1662
Sales .... (503) 643-1662
Tech. Supp. Fax.......................... (503) 671-9066
E-Mail.................................dougw@tview.com
WWW.................................. http://www.tview.com
FTP Address .... ftp.tview.com

Contemporary Cybernetics Group
Tera One
Yorktown, VA 23693
Main .... (804) 833-900
Tech. Supp. Fax.......................... (804) 833-9300
BBS................................. (804) 873-8836

Control Data Corp. (CDC)
8100 34th Ave. S, PO Box O
Minneapolis, MN 55440
Main..(612) 851-4131
WWW.....................................http://www.cdc.com/

Control Technology, Inc
7608 N Hudson
Oklahoma City, OK 73116
Main..(405) 840-3163
Tech. Supp. Fax............................(405) 848-0489
BBS...(405) 848-0489

Controller Power
1955 Suitephenson Hwy
Troy, MI 48083
Main..(800) 521-4792
Tech. Support................................(313) 528-3700
BBS...(313) 528-0411

CONVEX Computer Corp.
WWW...............................http://www.convex.com

Copia International, Ltd.
1964 Richton Dr
Wheaton, IL 60187
Main..(708) 682-8898
BBS...(708) 665-9841

Corbis Corp.
WWW................................http://www.corbis.com

Cordant Corp.
11400 Commerce Park Dr
Reston, VA 22091
Main..(800) 843-1132
Tech. Support................................(703) 758-7080
Tech. Supp. Fax............................(703) 758-7318
BBS...(703) 758-7320
WWWhttp://www.ideal.com/cordant/cordhome.html

Core International, Inc.
6500 E. Rogers Circle
Boca Raton, FL 33487
Main..(407) 997-6055
Tech. Support ....(407) 997-6033
Tech. Supp. Fax ....(407) 997-6202
BBS...(407) 997-6009

Core Software
26303 Oak Ridge Dr
Spring, TX 77380
Main..(713) 292-2177
BBS...(713) 298-1492

Core Technology Corp.
WWW............................http://www.ctc-core.com/

Corel Systems, Inc.
1600 Carling Ave.
Ottawa, Ontario, K1Z 8R7
Canada
Main..(613) 728-8200
Customer Svc. ....(800) 772-6735
Tech. Support ....(613) 728-1010
BBS...(613) 728-4752
WWW...................................http://www.corel.com
FTP Address.........................ftp://ftp.corel.ca/pub/

Corman Technologies
75 Bathurst Dr
Waterloo, Ontario, N2V 1N2
Canada
Main...(519) 884-4430

Cornerstone Imaging
1710 Fortune Dr.
San Jose, Ca 95131-1744
Main..(408) 435-8900
Customer Svc. ....(408) 435-8900
Tech. Support ....(408) 435-8900
Tech. Supp. Fax ....(408) 435-8998
BBS...(408) 435-8943

Cornerstone Systems
1000 W Wilshire, #310
Oklahoma City, OK 73116
Main..(405) 843-8631

Cornerstone Technology, Inc.
1990 Concourse Dr
San Jose, CA 95131
Main...(800) 562-2552
Tech. Support ....(408) 435-8900
BBS...(408) 279-5603

Corning Optical Fiber
P.O. Box 7429
Union Station
Endicott, NY 13760
Main...(800) 525-2524
Tech. Supp. Fax ....(800) 834-3504
E-Mail......................................fiber@corning.com
WWW............... http://www.usa.net/corning-fiber/

Corollary, Inc.
2802 Kelvin Ave.
Irvine, CA 92714
Main...(800) 338-4020
Tech. Support ....(714) 250-4040
Tech. Supp. Fax ....(714) 250-4043
BBS...(714) 250-4043

Corporate Microsystems, Inc. (CMI)
Box 2059 Mt Support Rd.
Lebanon, NJ 03766
Main...(412) 494-2500
BBS...(603) 448-4836

Corvus Systems, Inc.
160 Great Oaks Blvd.
San Jose, CA 95119-1347
Main...(800) 426-7887
Tech. Support ....(408) 281-4100
BBS...(408) 578-4102

CoStar
599 West Putnam Ave.
Greenwich, CT 06830-6092
Main ....(203) 661-9700
Customer Svc...................................(800) 426-7827
Tech. Support...................................(203) 661-9700
Sales ....(800) 426-7827
Tech. Supp. Fax................................(203) 661-1540
BBS...(203) 661-6292
E-Mail...................................support@costar.com
WWW................................http://www.costar.com
CompuServe 75300,2225
America Online... CoStar

Cougar Mountain Software
7180 Potomac Dr. Suite D
Boise, ID 83707
Main ....(800) 388-3038
Tech. Support...................................(800) 707-9912
Tech. Supp. Fax................................(208) 375-4460
BBS...(208) 343-0267

Courseware Technologies, Inc.
4500 150th Ave.
Redmond, WA 98052
Main ....(800) 736-1936
Tech. Supp. Fax................................(206) 883-4910
BBS...(619) 452-8711

CPU
1120 Kaibab
Flagstaff, AZ 86001
Main ....(602) 779-3341
Tech. Supp. Fax................................(602) 779-5998
BBS...(602) 779-5998

Cracchiolo & Feder, Inc.
4400 E Broadway, #312
Tucson, AZ 85711
Main ....(602) 327-1357
Tech. Supp. Fax................................(520) 321-7456
BBS...(602) 321-7450

Cranston Software
PO Box 2679
Mineapolis, MN 55402-0679
Main ....(800) 321-4270

Cray Research
WWW....................................http://www.cray.com/

Creative Labs
1901 McCarthy Blvd.
Milpitas, CA 95035
Main..(408) 428-6600
Customer Svc..............................(800) 998-5227
Tech. Support...............................(405) 742-6655
Sales ....(800) 998-1000
Tech. Supp. Fax............................(405) 742-6633
BBS ....(405) 742-6660
WWW.......................................http://www.creat.com
FTP Address.................................ftp.creat.com
CompuServe ....GO BLASTER

Creative Multimedia
225 Southwest Broadway
Suite No 600
Portland, OR 97205
Main..(503) 241-4351
Customer Svc..............................(503) 241-4351
Tech. Support...............................(503) 241-1530
Sales ....(800) 262-7668
Tech. Supp. Fax............................(503) 241-4370
BBS ....(503) 241-1573
E-Mail .... 71333.3143@compuserve.com
WWW.......................http://www.creativemm.com
CompuServe ....GO CREATIVE

Crescent Software, Inc.
32 Seventy Acres
West Redding, CT 06896
Main..(800) 352-2742
Tech. Support...............................(203) 438-5300
BBS ....(203) 431-4626

CrossComm Corp.
133 E Main St, PO Box 699
Marlboro, MA 01752
Main..(800) 388-1200
Tech. Support...............................(508) 481-4060
BBS ....(508) 481-4216

Crossley Group, The
PO Box 921759
Norcross, GA 30092
Main..(770) 751-3703
BBS...(404) 751-3704

Crosswise
WWW........................http://www.crosswise.com/

Crystal Point, Inc.
22232 17th Ave. S.E.
Suite 301
Bothell, WA 98021
Main..(206) 487-3656
Tech. Supp. Fax ....(206) 487-3773
BBS..(206) 487-3773

Crystal Services
1095 West Penter Street
4th Floor
Vancouver, BC, Canada V6E2M6
Main..(604) 681-3435
Customer Svc. ....(604) 681-3435
Tech. Support ....(604) 681-3435
Sales..(604) 681-3435
Tech. Supp. Fax ....(604) 681-2934
BBS..(604) 681-9516
E-Mail..................................sales@crystalinc.com
WWW. http://www.seagate.com/software/crystal/
CompuServe..................................GO REPORTS

CrystaLake Multimedia
1202 NW Irving Street
Portland, OR 97209
Main..(503) 222-2603
WWW.......... http://www.teleport.com:80/~crystal/

CSS Laboratories, Inc.
1641 McGraw Ave.
Irvine, CA 92714
Main..(800) 966-2771
Customer Svc. ....(800) 966-2771
Tech. Support ....(800) 966-2771
Sales...(714) 852-8161
Tech. Supp. Fax ....(714) 852-0410
BBS..(714) 852-0410

CTA
747 3rd Ave., 3rd Floor
New York, NY 10017
Main...(800) 252-1442
Tech. Support ....(212) 935-2280

Ctrlalt Associates
PO Box 130
Henry, MD 21541
Main...(800) 872-4768
Tech. Supp. Fax ....(301) 387-7322

CTX
20530 Earlgate St.
Walnut, CA 91789
Main...(909) 598-8094
Customer Svc. ....(800) 282-2205
Tech. Support ....(800) 888-2012
Sales..(909) 598-8094
Tech. Supp. Fax ....(909) 598-8294
BBS...(214) 242-8730

CTX South, Inc.
6624 Jimmy Carter Blvd.
Norcross, GA 30071
Main...(770) 729-8909
Customer Svc. ....(770) 724-8909
Tech. Support ....(770) 729-8909
Tech. Supp. Fax ....(770) 453-7782
BBS...(404) 729-8805

Cubix Corp.
2800 Lockheed Way
Carson City, NV 89706
Main...(800) 829-0550
Tech. Support ....(702) 883-7611
Tech. Supp. Fax ....(702) 881-001
BBS...(702) 882-2407

Curtis by Rolodex
225 Secaucus Rd.
Secaucus, NJ 07094
Main...(201) 422-0240
Customer Svc. ....(800) 727-7656
Tech. Support ....(201) 422-0254
Sales..(201) 422-0240
Tech. Supp. Fax ....(201) 422-0254

Curtis, Inc.
418 W. County Rd. D
St Paul, MN 55112
Main ....(612) 631-9512
Tech. Supp. Fax...........................(612) 631-9508
BBS...(612) 631-9508

CYANTIC Systems
24 Mabelle Ave., #3309
Etobicoke, ONT M9A 4X8
Canada
Main ....(416) 621-6161

CyberMedia
3000 Ocean Park Blvd.
Suite 2001
Santa Monica, CA 90405
Main ....(310) 581-4700
Customer Svc...............................(310) 581-4700
Tech. Support...............................(310) 581-4710
Sales ....(310) 581-4700
Tech. Supp. Fax...........................(310) 581-4720
BBS ....(310) 581-4724
E-Mail......................... support@cybermedia.com
WWW........................ http://www.cybermedia.com
FTP Address ....ftp.cybermedia.com
CompuServe .... GO CYBERMEDIA
America Online.............. keyword CYBERMEDIA

Cybernet Systems
WWW............................. http://www.cybernet.com

Cygnus Technology
WWW.............................http://www.cygnus.com/

Cykic Software
123 Camino De La Reina
Suite N200
San Diego, CA 92108
Main ....(619) 220-7970
Tech. Supp. Fax...........................(619) 220-7959

CYMA Solutions
1400 E Southern
Tempe, AZ 85282
Main......................................(800) 292-2962
Tech. Support...................(602) 831-2607
BBS ....(602) 345-5703

Cypress Research
240 East Caribbean Dr.
Sunnyvale, CA 94089
Main......................................(408) 752-2700
Customer Svc...................(408) 752-2700
Tech. Support...................(408) 752-2700
Sales ....(408) 752-2700
Tech. Supp. Fax.............(408) 752-2735

Cypress Semiconductor
WWW..............................http://www.cypress.com/

Cyrix
2703 North Central Expressway
Richardson, TX 75080
Main......................................(214) 968-8388
Customer Svc...................(800) 462-9749
Tech. Support...................(800) 462-9749
Sales ....(800) 462-9749
Tech. Supp. Fax.............(214) 968-8070
BBS ....(214) 968-8610
E-Mail ....tech_support@cyrix.com
WWW..................................http://www.cyrix.com

D & H Distributing Co.
2525 N 7th St
Harrisburg, PA 17110-5967
Main......................................(800) 877-1200
Tech. Supp. Fax...........(717) 255-7822

D-Link Systems, Inc.
3075 Ridgeway Dr, #26
Missisauga, Ontario, Canada L5L 3S9
Main......................................(416) 828-0260
BBS ....(416) 828-5669

DA Systems, Inc.
1503 E Campbell Ave.
Campbell, CA 95008
Main......................................(408) 559-7434

Da Vinci Systems/On Technology
507 Airport Blvd.
Suite No 115
Morris, NC 27560
Main ....(919) 319-7000
Customer Svc. ....(919) 319-7070
Tech. Support ....(919) 881-4320
Sales.............................(919) 319-7000
Tech. Supp. Fax ....(919) 319-7088
BBS...............................(919) 319-7075
E-Mail...................support@davinci.com
WWW...................... http://www.on.com
CompuServe..................GO DAVINCI

DacEasy
17950 Preston Rd.
Suite 800
Dallas, TX 75252
Main...............................(214) 248-0205
Customer Svc. ....(800) 322-3279
Tech. Support ....(214) 248-0205
Sales.............................(800) 322-3279
Tech. Supp. Fax ....(214) 713-6331
BBS...............................(214) 931-6617

Dalco Electronics
275 Pioneer Blvd.
Springboro, OH 45066
Main...............................(800) 445-5342
Tech. Support ....(513) 743-8042
Tech. Supp. Fax ....(513) 743-9251
BBS...............................(513) 743-9251

Dallas Semiconductor Corp.
WWW.......................... http://www.dalsemi.com/

Dantz Development
4 Orinda Way
Builidng C
Orinda, CA 94563
Main...............................(510) 253-3000
Customer Svc. ....(510) 253-3000
Tech. Support ....(510) 253-3050
Sales.............................(510) 253-3000
Tech. Supp. Fax ....(510) 253-9099
E-Mail......................tech_support@dantz.com
WWW..................... http://www.dantz.com
FTP Address..................ftp.dantz.com

Data Access Corp.
14000 SW 119th Ave.
Miami, FL 33186
Main..(800) 451-3539
Tech. Support ....(305) 238-0012
Tech. Supp. Fax ....(305) 238-0017
BBS..(305) 238-0017

Data Code, Inc.
7208 Sand Lake Rd., #202
Orlando, FL 32819
Main...(407) 351-3441
Tech. Supp. Fax ....(407) 351-5019
BBS..(407) 351-5019

Data Fellows
WWW............................ http://www.datafellows.fi/

Data General Corp.
4400 Computer Dr
Westboro, MA 01580
Main...(800) 328-2436
Tech. Support ....(508) 366-8911
Tech. Supp. Fax ....(508) 366-8078
BBS..(508) 366-8078
WWW.................................... http://www.dg.com/

Data I/O
10525 Willows Rd. N.E.
Redmond, WA 98073-9746
Main..(206) 881-6444
Customer Svc. ....(800) 735-6070
Tech. Support ....(800) 247-5700
Sales...(800) 247-5700
Tech. Supp. Fax ....(206) 869-2821
BBS..(206) 882-3211
E-Mail................... techhelp@data-io.com
WWW...............................http://www.data-io.com
FTP Address.................................ftp.data-io.com

Data Interface Systems Corp.
11130 Jollyville Rd.
Suite 300
Austin, TX 78759-4895
Main .... (800) 351-4244
Tech. Support............................(512) 346-5641
Tech. Supp. Fax...........................(512) 346-4035
BBS...(512) 346-4035

Data Pro
5439 Beaumont Center Blvd., #1050
Tampa, FL 33634
Main ....(800) 237-6377
Tech. Support...............................(813) 885-9459
Tech. Supp. Fax...........................(813) 882-8143
BBS...(813) 882-8143

Data Race
11550 Interstate Highway No 10
San Antonio, TX 78230
Main ....(210) 558-1900
Customer Svc...............................(210) 558-1900
Tech. Support...............................(210) 558-1900
Sales ....(210) 558-1900
Tech. Supp. Fax...........................(210) 558-1910
BBS ....(210) 558-1933
WWW............................ http://www.datarace.com

Data Research Associates, Inc.
WWW.......................................http://www.dra.com

Data Spec
9410 Owensmouth Ave.
Chatsworth, CA 91311
Main ....(800) 431-8124
Tech. Support...............................(818) 772-9977
WWW............................http://www.dataspec.com

Data Switch
1 Waterview Dr.
Shelton, CT 06484
Main ....(800) 328-3279
Tech. Support...............................(203) 926-1801
Tech. Supp. Fax...........................(203) 924-6400
BBS ....(203) 929-3890

Data Translation, Inc.
100 Locke Dr
Marlboro, MA 01752-1192
Main..(508) 481-3700
Tech. Supp. Fax...........................(508) 481-8620
BBS ....(508) 481-8620

Data Watch
234 Ballardzale St.
Willmington, MA 01887
Main..(508) 988-9700
Tech. Supp. Fax...........................(508) 988-2040
BBS ....(919) 549-0042
WWW.........................http://www.datawatch.com

Data-Cal Corp.
531 E Elliot Rd., #145
Chandler, AZ 85225
Main..(800) 223-0123
Tech. Support...............................(800) 223-0123
Tech. Supp. Fax...........................(602) 545-8090
BBS ....(602) 545-8090

Datacom technologies, Inc.
11001 31st Pl W
Everett, WA 98204
Main..(206) 355-0590
Tech. Supp. Fax...........................(206) 290-1600
BBS ....(206) 353-9292

DataEase International, Inc.
7 Cambridge Dr
Trumbull, CT 06611
Main..(800) 243-5123
Tech. Support...............................(203) 374-8000
Tech. Supp. Fax...........................(203) 365-2397
BBS ....(203) 374-3374

Datalux Corp.
155 Avaietion Dr.
Winchester, VA 22602
Main..(800) 328-2589
Tech. Support...............................(703) 662-1500
Tech. Supp. Fax...........................(504) 662-1682
BBS ....(703) 662-1682

Datamar Systems
6969 Corte Santa Fe
San Diego, CA 92101
Main..(800) 223-9963
Tech. Support...............................(619) 452-0044
Tech. Supp. Fax...........................(619) 452-0088
BBS ....(619) 452-0088

Datapoint Corp.
8400 Datapoint Dr
San Antonio, TX 78229
Main..(800) 733-1500
Tech. Support...............................(512) 593-7900
Tech. Supp. Fax...........................(512) 593-7920
BBS ....(512) 593-7920

Dataproducts Corp.
1757 Tapo Canyon Rd.
Simi Valley, CA 93063
Main..(800) 334-3174
Tech. Support...............................(805) 578-4000
Tech. Supp. Fax...........................(805) 578-4001
BBS ....(818) 887-3816

Dataquest, A Dun & Bradstreet Co.
1290 Ridder Park Dr.
San Jose, CA 95131
Main..(408) 437-8000
WWW.........................http://www.dataquest.com

DataStorm Technologies
P.O. Box 1471
Columbia, MO 65205-1471
Main..(314) 443-3282
Customer Svc. ....(314) 443-3282
Tech. Support...............................(314) 875-0530
Sales..(314) 443-3282
Tech. Supp. Fax...........................(314) 499-1552
BBS ....(314) 875-0503
CompuServe...........................GO DATASTORM

DataTimes Corp.
14000 Quail Springs Pkwy, #450
Oklahoma City, OK 73134
Main..(800) 642-2525
Tech. Support...............................(405) 751-6400
Tech. Supp. Fax...........................(405) 755-8028

Dataviews
47 Pleasant St
Northampton, MA 01060
Main..(413) 586-4144
Tech. Supp. Fax...........................(413) 586-3805

Dataviz
55 Corporate Dr.
Trumbull, CT 06611
Main..(800) 733-0030
Customer Svc. ....(800) 733-0030
Tech. Support ....(203) 268-0030
Tech. Supp. Fax...........................(203) 268-4345
E-Mail...........................techsupport@dataviz.com
WWW...............................http://www.dataviz.com

DataWiz
1500 Fashion Island Blvd. #209
San Mateo, CA 94404
Main..(415) 571-1300
Tech. Supp. Fax...........................(415) 574-2336

Dauphin Technology
3100 Dundee Rd.
Suite 705
Northbrook, IL 60062
Main..(708) 559-8443
Customer Svc. ....(708) 559-8443
Tech. Support ....(708) 559-8443
Sales..(708) 559-8443
Tech. Supp. Fax...........................(708) 559-8918

David Systems, Inc. (3 Com)
701 E Evelyn Ave.
Sunnyvale, CA 94086-6527
Main..(800) 762-7848
Customer Svc. ....(800) 638-6884
Sales..(800) 638-3266
BBS..(408) 720-1092

Davidson & Associates
19840 Pioneer Ave.
Torrance, CA 90503
Main .... (310) 793-0600
Customer Svc................................ (800) 545-7677
Tech. Support................................ (800) 556-6141
Sales .... (800) 545-7677
Tech. Supp. Fax............................ (310) 214-7937
BBS .... (310) 793-9966
E-Mail...................................support@davd.com
WWW...................................http://www.davd.com
FTP Address .... ftp.davd.com

Davis & Associates, Jeff
650 Mountain Meadows
Boulder, CO 80302
Main .... (303) 444-4047

Dayna Communications
Sorenson Research Park
849 West Levoy Drive
Salt Lake City, UT 84123-2544
Main .... (801) 269-7200
Customer Svc................................ (801) 269-7200
Tech. Support................................ (801) 269-7287
Sales .... (801) 269-7200
Tech. Supp. Fax............................ (801) 269-7363
BBS .... (801) 269-7398
WWW...........................http://www.dayna.com
FTP Address .... ftp.dayna.com
CompuServe .... GO DAYNACOM

DayStar Digital
5556 Atlanta Hwy.
Flowery Branch, GA 30542
Main .... (770) 967-2077
Customer Svc................................ (800) 962-2077
Tech. Support................................ (770) 967-2077
Sales .... (800) 962-2077
Tech. Supp. Fax............................ (770) 967-3018
BBS .... (770) 967-2978
E-Mail..................................support@daystar.com
WWW............................http://www.daystar.com
FTP Address ftp://204.180.128.20/daystar/
CompuServe 75300,1544
America Online......................... daystar@aol.com

DC Drives
3716 Timber Dr.
Dickenson, TX 77539
Main...(800) 872-6007
Tech. Supp. Fax...........................(713) 534-6457
BBS..(713) 333-3024

DCD Corp.
WWW.............................http://www.dcdcorp.com/

DD&TT Enterprise
5680 Rickenbacker Rd.
Bell, CA 90201
Main...(213) 780-0099
Customer Svc...............................(213) 780-0099
Tech. Support...............................(213) 780-0099
Sales ....(213) 780-0099
Tech. Supp. Fax...........................(213) 780-0419

DDC Publishing
275 Madison Ave.
New York City, NY 10016
Main...(212) 986-7300
Customer Svc...............................(800) 528-3897
Tech. Support...............................(212) 986-7300
Sales ....(800) 528-3897
Tech. Supp. Fax...........................(212) 986-7302

DEC (Digital Equipment Corp.
111 Power Mill Rd.
Manyard, MA 01754
Main...(508) 493-5432
Customer Svc...............................(800) 354-9000
Tech. Support...............................(800) 354-9000
Sales ....(800) 344-4825
Tech. Supp. Fax...........................(508) 493-6244
BBS..(508) 496-8800
WWW............................http://www.pc.digital.com
FTP Address.............................ftp.pc.digital.com

Decision Data
50 E. Swedeford Rd.
Forzarpa, PA 19377
Main...(610) 296-6000

Dell Computer Corp.
9505 Arboretum Blvd.
Austin, TX 78759-7299
Main...(800) 426-5150
Tech. Support ....(800) 624-9896
Tech. Supp. Fax ....(512) 338-8700
BBS..(512) 338-870
WWW...................................... http://www.del.com

DeLorme Mapping
PO Box 298
Lower Main Street
Freeport, ME 04032
Main...(207) 865-1234
WWW ....http://www.delorme.com/

Delphi Internet
WWW................................. http://www.delphi.com/

Delrina Corp.
Foster House, Maxwell Rd.
Borehamwood, Herts WD6 1JH
Main...(448) 120-7316
WWW .... http://www.delrina.com

Delrina Technology
6320 San Ignacio Ave.
San Jose, CA 95119-1209
Main...(800) 268-6082
Customer Svc. ....(800) 441-7234
Tech. Support ....(416) 441-6110
BBS..(416) 441-2752
E-Mail.................................. support@delrina.com
WWW .... http://www.delrina.com
FTP Address.........................ftp://ftp.delrina.com/
CompuServe...................................GO DELRINA

DeltaPoint
22 Lower Ragsdale
Monterey, CA 93940
Main ....(408) 648-4000
Customer Svc. ....(408) 648-4000
Tech. Support ....(408) 375-4700
Sales...(800) 446-5955
Tech. Supp. Fax ....(408) 648-4048
E-Mail....................tech_support@deltapoint.com
WWW ....http://www.deltapoint.com
FTP Address.............................ftp.delapoint.com
CompuServe...........................GO DELTAPOINT
America Online ....deltapoint@aol.com

Deltec
2727 Kurtz St
San Diego, CA 92110-9980
Main...(800) 854-2658
Tech. Support ....(619) 291-4211

Deneba Software
7400 S.W. 87th Ave.
Miami, FL 33173
Main...(305) 596-5644
Customer Svc. ....(305) 596-5644
Tech. Support ....(305) 596-5644
Sales...(305) 596-5644
Tech. Supp. Fax ....(305) 273-9069

DerbyTech Computers, Inc.
700 16th Ave.
East Moline, IL 61244
Main...(800) 243-3729
Tech. Support ....(800) 243-3729
Tech. Supp. Fax ....(312) 755-7299

DeScribe, Inc.
3841 N. Freeway Blvd. #275
Sacramento, CA 95834
Main...(916) 646-1111
BBS...(916) 923-3447

Develcon
WWW ....http://www.develcon.com/

Develcon Electronics
856 51 St. E.
S. Saslatoon, SK 57K5C7
Main ....(800) 667-9333
Tech. Support..............................(306) 933-3300
BBS..(306) 931-1370

DFI, Inc.
135 Main Ave.
Sacramento, CA 95838-2041
Main ....(916) 373-1234
Tech. Supp. Fax...........................(916) 568-1233
BBS..(916) 373-0221

DiagSoft
5615 Scotts Valley Dr.
Suite 140
Scotts Valley, CA 95066
Main ....(408) 438-8247
Customer Svc..............................(408) 438-8427
Tech. Support..............................(408) 438-8247
Sales ....(408) 438-8427
Tech. Supp. Fax...........................(408) 438-7113
BBS..(408) 438-8997
WWW............................http://www.diagsoft.com

Dialog/CXR
2360 Maryland Rd.
Willow Grove, PA 19090
Main ....(800) 344-4564
Tech. Support..............................(215) 830-9400
Tech. Supp. Fax...........................(215) 830-9444
BBS..(215) 628-3935

Diamond Data Management
740 N Pilgrim Pkwy
Elm Grove, WI 53122
Main ....(414) 786-9000

Diamond Flow (Southeast), Inc.
2210 N.W. 92nd Ave.
Miami, FL 33172
Main ....(305) 477-1988
Tech. Supp. Fax...........................(305) 594-0607

Diamond Flower Inc.
135 Main Ave.
Sacramento, CA 95838-2041
Main...(916) 568-1234
Customer Svc..............................(916) 568-1708
Tech. Support..............................(916) 568-1708
Sales ....(916) 568-1708
Tech. Supp. Fax...........................(916) 568-1233
BBS ....(908) 390-4820
E-Mail ....support@dfiusa.com
WWW.................................http://www.dfiusa.com
FTP Address....................................ftp.dfiusa.com

Diamond Multimedia Systems
2880 Junction Ave.
San Jose, CA 95134-1922
Main...(408) 325-7000
Customer Svc..............................(408) 325-7100
Tech. Support..............................(408) 325-7100
Sales ....(408) 325-7100
Tech. Supp. Fax...........................(408) 325-7171
BBS ....(408) 325-7175
WWW.....................http://www.diamondmm.com
FTP Address........................ftp.diamondmm.com
CompuServe ....GO DMNDONLINE
America Online.......................diamond@aol.com

Diaquest, Inc.
1440 San Pablo Ave.
Berkeley, CA 94702
Main...(510) 526-7167
Tech. Supp. Fax...........................(510) 526-7073
BBS ....(510) 526-7073

Digi International
6400 Flying Cloud Dr.
Eden Prairie, MN 55344
Main...(612) 943-9020
Customer Svc..............................(612) 943-9020
Tech. Support..............................(612) 943-9020
Sales ....(612) 943-9020
Tech. Supp. Fax...........................(612) 943-0579
BBS ....(612) 943-0550
WWW.................................http://www.digibd.com
FTP Address..................................ftp.digibd.com

Digiboard, Inc.
6400 Flying Cloud Dr.
Eden Priarie, MN 55344
Main...(800) 344-4273
Tech. Support..............................(612) 922-8055
Tech. Supp. Fax...........................(612) 922-4287
BBS ....(612) 922-4287

Digicom Systems, Inc.
188 Topaz St.
Milpitas, CA 95035
Main...(800) 833-8900
Tech. Support..............................(408) 262-1277
Tech. Supp. Fax...........................(408) 262-0550

Digidata
8580 Dorsey Run Rd.
Jessur, MD 20794
Tech. Support..............................(301) 498-0200
Tech. Supp. Fax...........................(301) 498-0771
BBS ....(301) 498-0771

Digipro, Inc.
102 Lowry St.
Huntsville, AL 35805
Tech. Supp. Fax...........................(205) 536-2047

Digital Century
WWW.....................http://www.digitalcentury.com

Digital Corporate Research
WWW.................http://www.research.digital.com/

Digital Design
3400 Baymeadows Way
Jacksonville, FL 32256
Main...(904) 737-0908

Digital Distributing, Inc.
207 Quarker Ln
W. Warwich, RI 02893
Main...(800) 331-1090
Tech. Support..............................(401) 821-0400
Tech. Supp. Fax...........................(401) 884-0770
BBS ....(401) 884-0770

Digital Equipment

WWW.................................http://www.digital.com/

Digital Equipment Corp. (DEC)

111 Powder Mill Rd.
Maynard, MA 01754-2571
Tech. Support ....(508) 493-5111
Tech. Supp. Fax ....(508) 493-7374
BBS...(508) 493-8780
WWW..................http://www.dec.com/home.html

Digital Instrumentation Technology

127 Eastgate Dr. #20500
Los Alamos, NM 87544
Main..(505) 662-1459
Tech. Supp. Fax ....(505) 662-0897
WWW.......................................http://www.dit.com

Digital Link

217 Humboldt Ct
Sunnyvale, CA 94089
Main..(800) 441-1142
Tech. Support ....(408) 745-4200
BBS...(408) 745-6250

Digital Media Labs

2635 N. 1st St. Suite #112
San Jose, CA 95134
Main..(800) 888-5527
Tech. Support ....(408) 922-0707
Tech. Supp. Fax ....(408) 577-0548
BBS...(408) 922-0652

Digital Pathways, Inc.

201 RAve.ndale Dr
Mountain View, CA 94043
Main..(800) 344-7284
Tech. Support ....(415) 964-0707
BBS...(415) 961-7487

Digital Products, Inc.

411 WAve.rley Oaks Rd.
Waltham, MA 02154-9409
Main..(800) 243-2333
Tech. Support ....(617) 647-1234
BBS...(617) 647-4474

Digital Technology, Inc.

2300 Edwin C Moses Blvd.
Dayton, OH 45408
Tech. Support...............................(513) 443-0412
Tech. Supp. Fax...........................(513) 226-0511
BBS...(513) 226-0511

Digital Tools

WWW.............http://www.digit.com/dt/home.html

Digital Vision

270 Bridge Strreet
Dedham, MA 02026
Main ....(617) 329-5400
Customer Svc................................(617) 329-5400
Tech. Support................................(617) 329-5400
Sales ....(617) 329-5400
Tech. Supp. Fax...........................(617) 329-6286
BBS...(617) 329-8387
E-Mail................................. support@digvis.com
WWW................................ http://www.digvis.com
CompuServe ......http://www.macfaq.com/vendor/
     software/327.html
America Online.....................digvision1@aol.com

Digital Vision, Inc.

WWW......................http://www.digvis.com/digvis/

Digital's Commercial Services

WWW.. http://www.service.digital.com/home.html

DigitalAire

WWW...........................http://www.digitalaire.com

DigitalAudio Labs

WWW.......................http://www.digitalaudio.com/

Digitalk, Inc.

9841 Airport Blvd.
Los Angeles, CA 90045
Main ....(800) 922-8255

Diji International
1299 Orleans Dr.
Sunnydale, CA 94089
Main...(408) 752-2770
Tech. Supp. Fax...........................(408) 744-2793
BBS ....(415) 968-9046

Dimensions Multimedia
45 Eastman Center
Building 5
Glenview, IL 60025

Directnet Corp.
WWW...............................http://www.directnet.net

Discis Knowledge Research
90 Sherppard Ave. East
7th Floor
Toronto, Ontario, Canada M2N3A1
Main...(416) 250-6537
Customer Svc...............................(416) 250-6537
Tech. Support...............................(416) 250-6537
Sales ....(416) 250-6537
Tech. Supp. Fax...........................(416) 250-6540
BBS ....(416) 250-6784
E-Mail ....discis@goodmedia.com
WWW............. http://www.goodmedia.com/discis/
FTP Address.........ftp.goodmedia.com/pub/discis
CompuServe 75474,1415

Discovery Communications
WWW...........................http://www.discovery.com

Diskette Connection
PO Box 1674
Bethany, OK 73008
Main...(800) 654-4058
Tech. Support...............................(405) 789-0015
Tech. Supp. Fax...........................(405) 495-4598
BBS ....(405) 495-4598

Disney Computer Software
500 South Beuna Vista Street
Burbank, CA 91521-8404
Main ....(800) 228-0988
Customer Svc. ....(800) 228-0988
Tech. Support ....(800) 228-0988
Sales..(800) 228-0988
Tech. Supp. Fax ....(818) 846-0454
BBS..(818) 567-4027
E-Mail......................................disneysoft@.com
WWW .... http://www.disney.com
FTP Address.................................ftp.disney.com
CompuServe.....................................GO DISNEY
America Online ....disney@aol.com

Display Tech
WWWhttp://www.ccnet.com/~dtmi/welcome.html

Disston Ridge Software & Consulting
4915 22nd Ave. N
St Petersburg, FL 33710
Main..(800) 277-0799

Distinct Software
14082 Loma Rio Dr.
Saratoga, CA 95070
Main..(408) 366-8933
BBS..(408) 741-0795

Distributed Processing Technol
140 Candace Dr.
PO Box 1864
Maitland, FL 32751
Main..(407) 830-5522
Tech. Supp. Fax ....(407) 260-5366
BBS..(407) 260-5366
WWW .... http://www.ttt.dpc.com

Diversified Technology
112 E State St.
Ridgeland, MS 39157
Main..(800) 443-2667
Tech. Supp. Fax ....(601) 856-2888

Documagix
WWW ....http://www.documagix.com

Docunet/Docunetworks

12861 Industrial Park Blvd.
Plymouth, MN 55441
Main...(612) 550-9552
WWW..................http://www.docunetworks.com/

Dolch Computer Systems

3178 Flaurel View Ct.
Freemont, CA 94538
Main...(800) 538-7506
Tech. Supp. Fax ....(510) 490-2360
BBS...(408) 263-6305

Dolphin Computer Systems

2720 N 68th St, #S-422
Scottsdale, AZ 85257
Main...(602) 262-0759

Dow Jones & Co, Inc.

PO Box 300
Princeton, NJ 08543-0300
Main...(609) 520-4641
BBS...(609) 520-4660

Dowty Communications, Inc.

9020 Junction Dr
Annapolis Junction, MD 20701
Main...(800) 227-3134
Tech. Supp. Fax ....(301) 317-7270
BBS...(301) 317-7697

DPT

140 Candace Dr.
Maitland, FL 32751
Main...(407) 830-5522
Customer Svc. ....(407) 830-5522
Tech. Support ....(407) 830-5522
Sales...(800) 322-4378
Tech. Supp. Fax ....(407) 260-5366
BBS...(407) 830-1070
E-Mail..................................... techsupp@dpt.com
WWW...................................... http://www.dpt.com
FTP Address..ftp.dpt.com

Dragon Systems, Inc.

320 Nevada St
Newton, MA 02160
Main .... (800) 825-5897
Tech. Support.............................. (617) 965-5200
BBS... (617) 527-0372
WWW........................... http://www.oragon.s4x.com

Drover Technologies, Inc.

660 White Plains Rd.
Tarrytown, NY 10591-5134
Main .... (914) 631-4942
BBS... (914) 631-7013

DSC Communications Corp.

2940 N 1st St
San Jose, CA 95134
Main .... (800) 332-3101
BBS... (408) 954-5158

DSP Developmemt Corp.

One Kendall Square
Cambridge, MA 02139
Main .... (617) 577-1133
Tech. Supp. Fax........................... (617) 577-8211
BBS... (617) 577-8211

DSP Solutions Group

3120 Scott Blvd.
Santa Clara, CA 95054
Main .... (408) 986-4300
Customer Svc.............................. (408) 986-4300
Tech. Support.............................. (408) 986-4428
Sales .... (408) 986-4300
Tech. Supp. Fax........................... (408) 986-4323

DTK Computer

770 Epperson Dr.
City of Industry, CA 91748
Main .... (818) 810-0098
Tech. Supp. Fax........................... (818) 810-0090
BBS... (818) 810-0090

Dukane Network Integration
2900 Dukane Dr.
St Charles, IL 60174
Main...(708) 584-2300
Tech. Supp. Fax...........................(708) 584-5154
BBS..(708) 584-5154

Durand Communications Network
WWW...............................http://www.durand.com/

Duxbury Systems, Inc.
435 King St.
PO Box 1504
Littleton, MA 01460
Main...(508) 486-9766

Dycam, Inc.
9414 Eton Ave.
Chatsworth, CA 91311
Main...(818) 998-8008
Tech. Supp. Fax...........................(818) 998-7951
America Online..........................Dycam@aol.com

Dyna Computer
3081 N 1st St
San Jose, CA 95134
Main...(510) 438-0233

Dyna Micro, Inc.
48434 Milmont
Freemont, CA 94538
Main...(800) 336-3962
Tech. Supp. Fax...........................(510) 353-2020
WWW...........................http://www.addonxis.com

Dynalink Technologies, Inc.
PO Box 593
Beaconfield, Quebec H9W 5V3
Canada
Main...(514) 489-3007
Tech. Supp. Fax...........................(514) 489-3007
E-Mail.......................................peter02@ibm.com

Dynatech Communications
991 Annapolis Way
Woodbridge, VA 22191
Main...(703) 550-0011

E-Soft, Inc.
15200 E Girard Ave., #3000
Aurora, CO 80014
Main...(303) 699-6565
WWW.................................. http://www.esoft.com

Eagle Data Protection, Inc.
WWW..........................http://www.eagledata.com

Eagle Electronics
1233 E Colorado St
Glendale, CA 91205
Main...(800) 992-3191
Tech. Support ....(818) 244-3191
Tech. Supp. Fax ....(818) 244-0466

Eagle Technology, Inc. (Novell)
1160 Ridder Park Dr
San Jose, CA 95131
Main...(800) 726-5267
Tech. Support ....(408) 452-2267
Tech. Supp. Fax ....(408) 436-0348
BBS..(408) 436-0348

Eastern Language Systems
33 E. 300N Suite #4
Provo, UT 84601
Main...(801) 377-4558
Tech. Supp. Fax ....(801) 377-2200
E-Mail.. easternl@itx.com

Eastham & Associates, Inc.
11104 W. Airport Suite #102
Stafford, TX 77477
Main...(800) 543-3256
Tech. Supp. Fax ....(713) 498-6944

Eastman Kodak Co.
901 Elmgrove Rd.
Rochester, NY 14653-6305
Tech. Support ....(800) 344-0006

Easy Street Computers
21 W East St
Simi Valley, CA 83065
Main...(800) 800-3279
Tech. Support ....(800) 800-3279

EasyData Computer Products
777 E Middlefield Rd.
Mountain View, CA 94043
Main...(510) 440-3740
Tech. Support ....(415) 968-3400
BBS...(415) 964-9747

Edimax
3350 Scott Blvd.
Santa Clara, CA 95054
Main...(408) 496-1105
Tech. Supp. Fax ....(408) 980-1530
WWW.......................http://www.edimax.coc.com

Edmark
6727 185th Ave. NE
Redmond, WA 98052
Main...(206) 556-8400
Customer Svc...............................(206) 556-8484
Tech. Support ....(206) 556-8480
Sales...(206) 556-8400
Tech. Supp. Fax ....(206) 556-8950
E-Mail..................................pctech@edmark.com
WWW.............................http://www.edmark.com/

EDP Systems Services, Inc.
19905 Scriber Lake Rd.
Lynnwood, WA 98036
Main...(206) 771-3796
Tech. Supp. Fax ....(206) 778-3702

EDS
WWW.................................... http://www.eds.com

Educational Assistance, Ltd.
PO Box 3021
Glen Ellyn, IL 60138
Main...(708) 690-0010
Tech. Supp. Fax ....(708) 690-0565

EDUCOM
1112 16th Street NW, Suite 6000
Washington, DC 20036
Main...(202) 872-4200
E-Mail........................... info@educom.edu
WWW.............................http://www.educom.edu

EFI Electronics
2415 South 2300 West
Salt Lake City, UT 84119
Main .... (801) 977-9009
Customer Svc............................. (800) 877-1174
Tech. Support............................. (800) 877-1174
Sales .... (801) 977-9009
Tech. Supp. Fax........................... (801) 977-0200
WWW................................... http://www.efi.com

Egypt, Inc.
2000 SE Sojourn Ave.
Irvine, CA 92718-2022

Eicon Technology Corp. (USA)
1700 Braodway, 24th Floor
New York, NY 10102-1056
Main .... (214) 239-3270
BBS... (214) 239-3304
WWW.................................. http://www.eicon.com/

Elan Computer Group, Inc.
888 Villa St, 3rd Floor
Mountain View, CA 94041
Main .... (415) 964-2200
Tech. Supp. Fax .... (415) 964-8588
BBS... (415) 964-8588
WWW.................................. http://www.elan.com/

Elan Software
17383 Sunset Blvd. Suite #101
Pacific Palisades, CA 90272
Main .... (310) 454-6800
Customer Svc.............................. (800) 654-3526
Tech. Support.............................. (310) 459-1222
Sales .... (310) 454-6800
Tech. Supp. Fax........................... (310) 459-8222
BBS... (310) 459-3443
WWW..................... http://www.goldminesw.com
FTP Address .... ftp.goldminesw.com
CompuServe .... GO GOLDMINE

Elco Computers
229 S Raymond Ave.
Alhambra, CA 91803
Main...(818) 284-4682
Tech. Support................................(818) 284-7018
Tech. Supp. Fax............................(818) 284-4871
BBS..(818) 284-4871

Electric Magic Co.
WWW..............................http://www.emagic.com/

Electronic Arts Distribution
1450 Fashion Island Blvd.
San Mateo, CA 94404
Main...(415) 571-7171
Customer Svc...............................(800) 448-8822
Tech. Support................................(415) 572-2787
Sales...(800) 448-8822
Tech. Supp. Fax............................(415) 286-5080
E-Mail..................................support1@ea.com
WWW...http://www.ea.com
FTP Address..ftp.ea.com
CompuServe.......................................76004,237
America Online.........................elecarts@aol.com

Elementrix
WWW..........................http://www.elementrix.co.il/

ELF Communications
WWW...............http://www.elf.com/elf/home.html

Elgar Corp.
9250 Brown Deer Rd.
San Diego, CA 92121
Main...(800) 733-5427
Tech. Support................................(619) 458-0250
Tech. Supp. Fax............................(619) 458-0267
BBS..(619) 458-0267

EliaShim Microcomputers, Inc.
4005 Wedgemere Dr.
Tampa, FL 33610
Main...(813) 744-5177
WWW..............................http://www.eliashim.com/

Emerald Intelligence
3915-A1 Research Park Dr
Ann Arbor, MI 48108
Main...(313) 663-8757

Emerald Systems
9717 Pacific Heights Blvd.
San Diego, CA 92121
Main...(619) 658-9720
Customer Svc...............................(619) 658-9720
Tech. Support................................(800) 767-2587
Sales...(619) 452-7974
Tech. Supp. Fax............................(619) 452-3271
BBS..(619) 673-4617

Emeritus Technologies
2750 N Clovis Ave., #126
Fresno, CA 93727
Main...(800) 228-9236
Tech. Support................................(209) 292-8888
Tech. Supp. Fax............................(209) 292-8908
BBS..(209) 292-8908

Emerson & Stern Associates, Inc.
10150 Sorrento Valley Rd., #210
San Diego, CA 92121
Main...(619) 457-2526
BBS..(619) 457-1876

Emerson Computer Power
5041 Bake Pkwy, #L
Irvine, CA 92718
Main...(800) 222-5877
Tech. Support................................(714) 380-1005
BBS..(714) 380-0456

Emulex Corp.
3535 Harbor Blvd.
PO Box 6725
Costa Mesa, CA 92628-9928
Main...(800) 442-7563
Tech. Support................................(714) 662-5600
Tech. Supp. Fax............................(714) 241-0792
BBS..(714) 241-0792
WWW..............................http://www.emulex.com

Enable Software, Inc.
313 Ushers Rd.
Ballston Lake, NY 12019
Main .... (800) 888-0684
Tech. Support .... (518) 877-8600

Encore Computer Corp.
WWW .... http://www.encore.com/

Enhance Memory Products
18730 Oxnard Street
Tarzana, CA 91356
Main .... (818) 343-3066
Customer Svc. .... (800) 343-0100
Tech. Support .... (818) 343-3066
Sales .... (818) 343-3066
Tech. Supp. Fax .... (818) 343-1436

Enhanced Systems, Inc.
6961 Peachtree Industrial Blvd.
Norcross, GA 30092
Main .... (770) 662-1503

ENSONIQ Corp.
155 Great Valley Parkway
Malvern, PA 19355-0735
Main .... (610) 647-3930
WWW .... http://www.ensoniq.com/

Envelope Manager Software
247 High St
Palo Alto, CA 94301-1041
Main .... (415) 321-2640
Tech. Supp. Fax .... (415) 321-0356
BBS .... (415) 321-0356
America Online .... dazzleplus@aol.com

Environmental Systems Research
WWW .... http://www.esri.com/

Envisions Solutions Technology
822 Mahler Rd.
Burlingame, CA 94010
Main .... (800) 321-3689
Tech. Support .... (510) 661-4311
BBS .... (415) 692-9064

EPE Technologies
1660 Scenic Ave.
Costa Mesa, CA 92626
Main .... (714) 557-1636
Tech. Supp. Fax .... (714) 457-1103
BBS .... (714) 957-1103

EPS Technologies, Inc.
10069 Dakota St.
PO Box 278
Jefferson, SD 57038
Main .... (800) 447-0921
Tech. Support .... (800) 526-4258
BBS .... (605) 966-5482

Epson America, Inc.
20770 Madrona Ave.
Torrance, CA 90503
Main .... (800) 289-7766
Customer Svc .... (800) 289-3776
Tech. Support .... (800) 922-8911
WWW .... http://www.epson.com

Equinox Sytems
1 Equinox Way
Sunrise, FL 33351
Main .... (305) 746-9000
Customer Svc .... (305) 255-3500
Tech. Support .... (305) 255-3500
Sales .... (305) 746-9000
Tech. Supp. Fax .... (954) 746-8378
BBS .... (954) 746-0282
E-Mail .... support@equinox.com
WWW .... http://www.equinox.com
FTP Address .... ftp.equinox.com

Ergo Computing, Inc.
1 Intercontinental Way
Peabody, MA 01960
Main .... (800) 633-1925
Tech. Support .... (508) 535-7510
BBS .... (508) 535-7512

Ergotron, Inc.
3450 Yankee Dr, #100
Eagan, MN 55122-1042
Main.................................(800) 888-8458
Tech. Support...................(612) 452-8135
BBS.................................(612) 452-8346

ESCOM
WWW.................................http://www.escom.nl/

eSoft, Inc.
WWW.................................http://www.esoft.com/

Esprit
2115 Ringwood Ave.
San Jose, CA 95131
Main.................................(800) 937-7748
Tech. Support...................(408) 954-9900
Tech. Supp. Fax................(408) 954-9800
BBS.................................(408) 954-9800

Essex Systems, Inc.
One Essex Green Dr
Peabody, MA 01960
Main.................................(508) 532-5511
Tech. Support...................(508) 532-5510

Everex
5020 Brandin Ct
Fremont, CA 94538
Main.................................(800) 821-0806
Tech. Supp. Fax................(510) 683-2186

Evergreen CASE Tools
15444 NE. 95th St. Suite #244
Redmond, WA 98052
Main.................................(206) 881-5149
Tech. Supp. Fax................(206) 883-7676

Evergreen Systems, Inc.
120 Landing Ct, #A
Novato, CA 94945
Main.................................(415) 897-8888
Tech. Supp. Fax................(415) 897-6158
BBS.................................(415) 897-6158
E-Mail...............................support@everson.com

Evergreen Technologies Corp.
267 W Wsplanade, #107
North Vancouver, BC, Canada V7M 1A5
Main.................................(800) 733-0934
Tech. Support...................(206) 881-5149
BBS.................................(604) 881-5149

Evolution Computing
437 S 48th St, #106
Tempe, AZ 85281
Main.................................(602) 967-8633

Ex Machina, Inc.
11 East 26th Street, 16th Floor
New York, NY 10010–1402
Main.................................(212) 843-0000
WWW...................http://www.nyweb/exmachina/

Exabyte
1685 38th St.
Boulder, CO 80301
Main.................................(303) 442-4333
Customer Svc. ....(800) 392-2983
Tech. Support...................(800) 445-7736
Sales...............................(800) 774-7172
Tech. Supp. Fax................(303) 417-7890
BBS.................................(303) 417-7100
WWW..............................http://www.exabyte.com
FTP Address.....................ftp.exabyte.com

Excelitech
300 W 3rd St
Yankton, SD 57078
Tech. Support...................(605) 665-5811
BBS.................................(605) 665-8324

Executive Software
WWW..........http://www.earthlink.net:80/execsoft/

Exide Electronics
8521 Six Forks Rd.
Raleigh, NC 27615
Main.................................(919) 872-3020

Exim Software
PO Box 5417
Clinton, NJ 08809
Main...(908) 735-7640

Experdata
10301 Toledo Ave. S
Bloomington, MN 55437
Main...(612) 831-2122
Tech. Supp. Fax ....(612) 835-0700
BBS...(612) 835-0700

Expersoft
WWW...........................http://www.expersoft.com/

Expervision
930 Thompson Pl.
Sunnyvale, CA 94086
Main...(408) 523-0900
Tech. Support ....(408) 428-9234
Tech. Supp. Fax ....(408) 523-0909
WWW........................ http://www.expervision.com

Express Systems
2101 Fourth Ave., Suite 303
Seattle, WA 98121-2314
Main...(206) 728-8300
WWW......................................http://www.express

Extended Systems, Inc.
5777 Meeker Ave.
Boise, ID 83704
Main...(208) 322-7575
Tech. Supp. Fax ....(208) 377-1906
BBS...(208) 377-1906
WWW......................... http://www.extendsys.com

EZ-Logic, Inc.
1231 Vancouver Way
Livermore, CA 94550
Main...(800) 635-6442
Tech. Support ....(415) 949-2834

Facit
540 N. Commercial St
Manchester, NH 03101-1107
Main .... (603) 647-2700
Tech. Supp. Fax............................ (603) 647-2724
BBS.. (603) 647-2724

Fairchild Data Corp.
350 N Hayden Rd.
Scottsdale, AZ 85257-4692
Main .... (800) 247-9489
Tech. Support.................................. (602) 949-1155
Tech. Supp. Fax............................ (602) 941-0023
BBS.. (602) 941-0023

Faircom Corp.
4006 W Broadway
Columbia, MS 65203
Main .... (314) 445-6833
Tech. Supp. Fax............................ (314) 445-9698
BBS.. (314) 445-9698
E-Mail... faircom@crf.net

Falco Data Products, Inc.
440 Potrero Ave.
Sunnyvale, CA 94086-4117
Tech. Support............................... (408) 745-7123

Falcon Software
One Hollis Street
Wellesley, MA 02181
Main .... (617) 235-1767
WWW. http://www.falconsoftware.com/falconweb

Farallon Computing
2470 Mariner Square Loop
Alameda, CA 94501
Customer Svc............................... (510) 814-5000
Tech. Support................................ (510) 814-5000
Sales .... (510) 814-5100
BBS.. (510) 596-9023
E-Mail............................. techsports@farallon.com
WWW...............................http://www.farallon.com
CompuServe 75410,2702
America Online...................................FARALLON

Fargo Electronics
WWW.................................. http://www.fargo.com/

FastComm Communication Corp.ora
WWW......................... http://www.fastcomm.com/

Fastcomm Communications
6860 S. Yosemite Ct Suite #101A
Englewood, CO 80112
Main... (800) 521-2496

Faulkner Information Services
114 Cooper Ctr, 7905 Browning Rd.
Pennsauken, NJ 08109-4319
Main................................... (800) 843-0460
Tech. Supp. Fax............................ (609) 662-0905
BBS .... (609) 662-0905
WWW............................ http://www.faulkner.com

Fax of America
PO Box 1032
South Bend, IN 46624
Main................................... (800) 342-3299
Tech. Support.............................. (219) 256-3020
BBS .... (219) 258-4128

FaxFacts
1963 Richton Dr
Wheaton, IL 60187
Main................................... (708) 682-8898
BBS .... (708) 665-9841

Faximum Software, Inc.
1497 Marine Dr, #3300
West Vancouver, BC V7T 1B8
Canada
Main................................... (604) 925-3600
Tech. Supp. Fax............................ (604) 926-8182
BBS .... (604) 926-8182
WWW............................ http://www.faximum.com/

FCR Software
WWW............ http://www.fcr.com/homepage.html

FEL Computing
10 Main St, PO Box 72
Williamsville, VT 05362
Main.................................(800) 639-4110
Tech. Supp. Fax ....(802) 348-7124
E-Mail... sales@fel.com

Fellowes
WWWhttp://www.slonet.org/~hwright/fellowes.html

Fenwick & West
2 Palo Alto Square, Suite 800
Palo Alto, CA 94306
Main.................................(415) 494-0600
WWWhttp://www.counsel.com/locator/fenwick/main

Fiber Optic Interconnect Techn
5224 Katrine
Donners Grove, IL 60515
Main...(708) 969-4550
Tech. Supp. Fax ....(708) 969-1352
BBS...(708) 969-1352

Fibercom
3353 Orange Ave. NE
Roanoke, VA 24012
Main.................................(800) 423-1183
Tech. Support ....(703) 342-6700
Tech. Supp. Fax ....(703) 342-5961
BBS...(703) 342-5961

Fibermux Corp.
21415 Plummer St.
Chatsworth, CA 91311
Main.................................(818) 709-6000
Tech. Supp. Fax ....(818) 709-1556
BBS...(818) 709-1556

Fibronics International, Inc.
16 Esquire Rd.
N. Billerica, MA 01862-2590
Main.................................(800) 327-9526
Tech. Support ....(508) 778-0700
Tech. Supp. Fax ....(508) 667-7262
BBS...(508) 667-7262

Ficomp

3015 Advance Ln
Colmar, PA 18915
Main..(215) 997-2600
Tech. Supp. Fax............................(215) 997-2609
BBS...(215) 997-2609

Firefox

WWW...............http://www.firefox.com/index.html

First Byte

19840 Pioneer Ave.
Torrance, CA 90503
Main..(310) 793-0610
Tech. Support...............................(310) 793-9966
Tech. Supp. Fax............................(310) 793-0601
BBS...(310) 793-0601

First Computer Systems, Inc.

6000 Live Oak Pkwy, #107
Norcross, GA 30093
Main..(800) 325-1911
Tech. Support...............................(770) 441-1911
Tech. Supp. Fax............................(770) 441-1856
BBS...(770) 441-1856

First International Computer

WWW.................................http://www.fic.com.tw/

FirstMark Technologies, Ltd.

300-16 Concourse Gate
Ottawa, ONT K2E 7S8
Canada
Tech. Support...............................(613) 723-8020
Tech. Supp. Fax............................(613) 723-8048
BBS...(613) 723-8048
E-Mail............................firstmark@ott.hookup.net

Fitnesoft, Inc.

11 East 200 North, Suite 204
Orem, UT 84057
Main..(801) 221-7777
WWW.............................http://www.fitnesoft.com

Flashpoint, Inc.

125 Cambridge Park Dr.
Cambridge, MA 02140
Main..(617) 491-9000
WWW.................................http://www.flashpt.com

FlipTrack Learning Systems

2055 Army Trail Rd. Suite #100
Edison, IL 60101
Main..(800) 222-3547

Flytech Technology (USA), Inc.

3008 Scott Blvd.
Santa Clara, CA 95054
Main..(408) 727-7373
Tech. Supp. Fax............................(408) 727-7375
BBS...(408) 727-7375

Focus Computer Center

1303 46th St
Brooklyn, NY 11219
Main..(800) 223-3411
Tech. Support...............................(718) 871-7600
Tech. Supp. Fax............................(718) 438-4263
BBS...(718) 438-4263
America Online......focuscom@gramercy.ios.com

Focus Enhancements

WWW.......................http://www.shore.net/~focus

Folio Corp.

2072 N. 300 W.
Provo, UT 84604
Main..(800) 543-6546
Tech. Support...............................(801) 375-3700
Tech. Supp. Fax............................(801) 229-6790
WWW....................................http://www.folio.com

Force

825 Park St
Christiansburg, VA 24073
Main..(703) 382-0462
Tech. Supp. Fax............................(703) 381-0392
BBS...(703) 381-0392

Foresight Resources Corp.
10725 Ambassador Dr
Kansas City, MO 64153
Main..(800) 231-8574
Tech. Support..............................(816) 891-1040
Tech. Supp. Fax..........................(816) 891-8018
BBS..(816) 891-8018

Fotec, Inc.
155 Mistic Ave.
Metford, MA 02155
Main..(800) 537-8254
Tech. Support..............................(617) 396-6155
Tech. Supp. Fax..........................(617) 241-8616
BBS..(617) 241-8616
WWW.............................http://www.std.com/fotec

4COM Computer Systems
6446 Warren Dr.
Norcross, GA 30093
Main..(404) 449-9015
Tech. Support..............................(404) 449-9015

FourGen Software, Inc.
115 NE 100 St
Seattle, WA 98125-8098
Main..(800) 333-4436
Tech. Support..............................(206) 522-0055
Tech. Supp. Fax..........................(206) 522-0053
BBS..(206) 522-0053
E-Mail......................................info@fourgen.com

Fractal Design
PO BOX 2380
Aptos, CA 95001
Main..(408) 688-5300
Customer Svc...............................(800) 297-2665
Tech. Support..............................(408) 688-8800
Sales ....(800) 297-2665
Tech. Supp. Fax..........................(408) 688-2845
E-Mail...........................win_support@fractal.com
WWW..................................http://www.fractal.com
FTP Address..................................ftp.fractal.com
CompuServe ....GO GUGRPA
America Online...........................fractal@aol.com

Frame Technology
333 West San Carlos Street
San Jose, CA 95110
Main..(408) 975-6000
Customer Svc. ....(408) 975-6000
Tech. Support ....(408) 975-6466
Tech. Supp. Fax ....(408) 975-6651
BBS...(408) 975-6729
E-Mail.............................comments@frame.com
WWW...........................http://www.frame.com
FTP Address..................................ftp.frame.com
CompuServe...............................GO DPTVEND

Franklin Computer Corp.
1 Franklin Plaza
Burnington, NJ 08016-4907
Main..(609) 261-4800
Tech. Support ....(609) 386-2500

Franklin Quest Technologies
2200 W. Parkway Blvd.
Salt Lake City, UT 84119
Main..(800) 877-1814
Tech. Support ....(801) 975-9999
Tech. Supp. Fax ....(801) 978-1133
BBS...(801) 975-9995
CompuServe......71333.3662@compuserve.com
America Online ....FranklInsupt@AOL.com

Frontier Technologies Corp.
10201 N Port Washington Rd.
Milwaukee, WI 53092
Main..(414) 241-4555
Tech. Supp. Fax ....(414) 241-7084
BBS...(414) 241-7084
WWW........................http://www.frontiertech.com

FTG Data Systems
8381 Katella Suite J
Stanton, CA 90680
Main..(800) 962-3900
Tech. Support ....(714) 995-3900
Tech. Supp. Fax ....(714) 995-3989
CompuServe......74774.1142@compuserve.com

FTP Software, Inc.
Two High Street
North Andover, MA 01845
Main..(508) 685-4000
Tech. Support ....(508) 685-3600
Sales...(800) 282-4387
Tech. Supp. Fax ....(508) 794-4488
E-Mail................................... support@ftp.com
WWW...................................... http://www.ftp.com
FTP Address...ftp.ftp.com
CompuServe...................................GO PCVENT

Fujikama USA, Inc.
865 N ellsworth Ave.
Villa Park, IL 60181
Main..(708) 832-1166

Fujikura America, Inc.
100 Galleria Pkwy NW, #1400
Atlanta, GA 30339
Main..(770) 956-7200
BBS..(770) 956-9854

Fujitsu America, Inc.
3055 Orchard Dr
San Jose, CA 95134
Main..(800) 626-4686
Tech. Support ....(408) 894-3950
BBS..(408) 432-1318

Fujitsu Computer Personal Systems
5200 Patrick Henry Dr.
Santa Clara, CA 95054
Main..(408) 982-9500
Customer Svc. ....(800) 626-4686
Tech. Support ....(408) 894-3950
BBS..(408) 944-9899
WWW................................http://www.fujitsu.com

Fulcrum Technologies, Inc.
560 Rochester St
Ottawa, Ontario, Canada K1S 5K2
Main..(613) 238-1761
WWW..............................http://www.fulcrum.com

Full Source Software
346 Costello Ct
Los Altos, CA 94024

Funk Software, Inc.
222 Third St.
Cambridge, MA 02142
Main .... (617) 497-6339
Customer Svc............................. (800) 828-4146
Tech. Support............................. (617) 497-6339
Tech. Supp. Fax.......................... (617) 547-1031
E-Mail .... support@funk.com
WWW...................................http://www.funk.com
FTP Address ....ftp://www.funk.com/pub/
CompuServe ....GO FUNK

Future Domain
2801 McGaw Ave.
Irvine, CA 92714
Main .... (714) 253-0400
Tech. Support............................. (408) 934-7274
Sales .... (408) 245-8600
BBS... (408) 945-7727
WWW........................... http://www.adaptech.com
FTP Address ....ftp.adaptech.com

Future Soft Engineering, Inc.
1201 Wickchester Ln. Suite 600
Houston, TX 77079
Main .... (713) 496-9400
Tech. Supp. Fax.......................... (713) 996-1090
BBS... (713) 588-6870
WWW.............. http://www.fse.com/fsehome.html

Futurus
3295 River Exchange Dr. Suite 450
Norcross, GA 30092
Main .... (404) 242-7797
Tech. Support.............................. (404) 825-0379
Tech. Supp. Fax.......................... (404) 242-7221

FWB Software
1555 Adams Dr.
Menlo Park, CA 94025
Main...................................(415) 325-4392
Customer Svc..............................(415) 833-4611
Tech. Support.........................(415) 833-4580
Sales ....(415) 833-4611
Tech. Supp. Fax.........................(415) 833-4662
E-Mail ....support@fwb.com
WWW..............................http://www.fwb.com
FTP Address.....................................ftp.fwb.com
CompuServe ....GO FWB
America Online..............................fwb@aol.com

G.T.M./Gazelle Studios
7434 Trade St.
San Diego, CA 92119
Main....................................(619) 693-4030
Customer Svc..............................(800) 786-3278
Tech. Support.........................(619) 536-9999
Sales ....(800) 843-9497
Tech. Supp. Fax.........................(619) 536-2345
BBS ....(801) 375-2548
WWW....................................http://www.gtm.com

Gaitronics
PO Box 31
Reading, PA 19603
Main....................................(800) 492-1212
Sales ....(800) 882-1980
Tech. Supp. Fax.........................(703) 641-3297
BBS ....(215) 374-1474

Galacticomm, Inc.
4101 SW 47th Ave., #101
Ft Lauderdale, FL 33314
Main....................................(305) 583-5990
Tech. Support.........................(305) 583-5990
Sales ....(800) 328-1128
Tech. Supp. Fax.........................(305) 583-7846
BBS ....(305) 583-7846
WWW..............................http://www.gcomm.com/

Gametek
2999 NE 191st Street, 5th Floor
Aventura, FL 33180
Main...................................(305) 935-3995
Customer Svc. ....(800) 927-4263
Tech. Support ....(800) 439-3995
Sales...................................(415) 289-0220
Tech. Supp. Fax ....(305) 932-8651
WWW............................http://www.gametek.com

Gandalf Technologies, Inc.
WWW............................... http://www.gandalf.ca/

Gates/FA Distributing
39 Hellhem Dr.
Greenville, SC 29615
Main...................................(800) 332-2222
Tech. Support ....(800) 332-2315

Gateway 2000
610 Gateway Dr.
PO Drawer 2000
North Sioux City, SD 57049
Main...................................(800) 523-2000
Tech. Support ....(605) 232-2000
BBS...................................(605) 232-2023

Gateway Communications
PO Box 1896
Cary, NC 27512
Main...................................(919) 310-3657
Customer Svc. ....(703) 329-3700
Tech. Support ....(800) 255-3967
BBS...................................(703) 960-8509
E-Mail...................................info@gateway.com
WWW............................ http://www.gateway.com

Gateway Communications, Inc.
2941 Alton Ave.
Irvine, CA 92714
Main...................................(800) 367-6555
Tech. Support ....(714) 553-1555
BBS...................................(714) 553-1616

Gazelle Systems
305 N 500 W
Provo, UT 84601
Main...............................(800) 786-3278
Tech. Support ....(800) 733-0383
Tech. Supp. Fax ....(801) 235-7099
BBS.................................(801) 377-1288

GCOM, Inc.
41 E University
Champaign, IL 61820
Main.................................(217) 352-4266
BBS.................................(217) 352-2215

GDI
20-A Pimental Court, Suite B
Novato, CA 94949
Tech. Support ....(415) 382-6600
BBS.................................(415) 382-0742

GDT Softworks
4664 Lougheed Highway, Suite #188
Burnaby, BC V5C 6B7
Canada
Main.................................(604) 291-9121
Tech. Support ....(604) 299-3379
Sales.................................(800) 663-6222
Tech. Supp. Fax ....(604) 473-3600
E-Mail.................................info@gdt.com
WWW.....................................http://www.gdt.com

GE Computer Service
6875 Jimmy Carter Blvd., #3200
Norcross, GA 30071
Main.................................(770) 246-6200

GE Information Services
401 N Washington St
Rockville, MD 20850
Main.................................(301) 340-4485

Geac Computer Corp.
WWW.................................http://www.geac.com/

GEC-Marconi Software Systems
12110 Sunset Hills Rd., #450
Reston, VA 22090
Main ....(703) 648-1551

Geller Software Laboratories,
35 Suitephen St
Montclair, NJ 07042
Main ....(201) 746-8467
BBS...(201) 746-4868

Gen Soft Development Corp.
4122 128th Ave. SE, #200
Bellevue, WA 98006
Main ....(206) 562-1157

General Technology Corp.
PO Box 20555
Cranston, RI 02920
Main ....(800) 638-0286
Tech. Support...............................(800) 638-0286

General Technology, Inc.
415 Pineda Ct
Melbourne, FL 32940
Main ....(800) 274-2733
Tech. Support...............................(407) 242-2733
Tech. Supp. Fax...........................(407) 254-1407
BBS...(407) 254-1407

General Videotex Corp.
3 Blackstone St
Cambridge, MA 02139
Main ....(800) 544-4005
Tech. Support...............................(617) 491-3393

Genesis Integrated Systems
1000 Shelard Pkwy
Minneapolis, MN 55426
Main ....(800) 325-6582

Genicom
14800 Conference Center Dr.
Suite No 400
Chantilly, VA 22021-3806
Main...(703) 802-9200
Customer Svc...............................(800) 535-4364
Tech. Support.................................(703) 949-1031
BBS ....(703) 949-1576

Genicom Corp.
1 Genicom Dr
Waynesboro, VA 22980
Main...(800) 443-6426
Tech. Support.................................(703) 949-1000
BBS ....(703) 949-1392

GEnie - General Electric Network
401 N Washington ST
Rockville, MD 20850-1785
Main...(800) 638-9636

Genoa Systems Corp.
75 E Trimble Rd.
San Jose, CA 95131
Main...(800) 423-6211
Tech. Support.................................(408) 432-9090
BBS ....(408) 434-0997
WWW.............................. http://www.gentech.com/

Genovation
WWW........................ http://www.genovation.com/

Genovation, Inc.
17741 Mitchell N
Irvine, CA 92714
Main...(714) 833-3355
Tech. Supp. Fax...........................(714) 833-0322

GenTech
205 Hallene Rd.
Warwick, RI 02886
Main...(800) 638-0286
Tech. Support.................................(401) 732-5588
BBS ....(401) 732-5518

Genus Microporgramming, Inc.
1155 Dairy Ashford
Suite 200
Houston, TX 77079
Main...(800) 227-0918
Customer Svc. ....(800) 227-0918
Tech. Support ....(713) 870-0737
Tech. Supp. Fax ....(713) 870-0288
BBS...(713) 870-0288

Geocomp Corp.
10 Craig Rd.
Acton, MA 01720
Main...(800) 822-2669
Tech. Support ....(508) 369-8304
Tech. Supp. Fax ....(508) 635-0266
BBS...(508) 369-4392

George Lucas Educational Foundation
PO Box 3494
San Rafael, CA 94912
Main...(415) 662-1600
WWW...................................... http://www.glef.org

Georgens Industries
3346 Industrial Ct
San Diego, CA 92121
Main...(619) 481-8114

Gibson Research Corp.
22991 La Cadena
Laguna Hills, CA 92653
Main...(800) 736-0637
Tech. Support ....(800) 736-0637
BBS...(714) 830-0300

Giga Trend
2234 Rutherford Rd.
Carlsbad, CA 92008
Main...(619) 931-9122
Customer Svc. ....(800) 743-4442
Tech. Support ....(619) 931-9122
Sales...(800) 743-4442
Tech. Supp. Fax ....(619) 931-9959
BBS...(619) 931-9469
E-Mail.....................emailbackup@gigatend.com
WWW...........................http://www.gigatrend.com
FTP Address.............................. ftp.gigatrend.com

Gigatek Memory Systems
1989 Palomar Oaks Way
La Costa, CA 92009
Main...(619) 438-9010

Gilbert Engineering
5310 W. Camelback
Glendale, AZ 85301
Main...(800) 528-5567
BBS...(800) 344-6358

Gizmo Technologies
PO Box 1477
Fremont, CA 94539
Main...(415) 623-7899

GK Enterprises
8634 W National Ave.
West Allis, WI 53227
Main...(800) 365-1556
Tech. Support ....(414) 546-0111
BBS...(414) 546-2371

Glenayre Technologies, Inc.
WWW.............................http://www.glenayre.com/

Global Village Communication
1090 N Chase Pkwy.
Marietta, GA 30067
Main...(800) 343-2948
Tech. Support ....(404) 984-8088
BBS...(404) 984-9956
WWW........................http://www.globalvillag.com/

Global Village Communications
1204 O'Brien Dr.
Menlo Park, CA 94025
Main .... (415) 329-0700

Globalink, Inc.
9302 Lee Hwy.
4th Floor
Fairfax, VA 22031
Main .... (800) 255-5660
BBS... (703) 273-5600

Globe Manufacturing Sales, Inc.
1159 Rt 22
Mountainside, NJ 07092
Main .... (800) 227-3258
Tech. Support.............................. (201) 232-7301
BBS... (201) 232-4729

GNWC Wire, Cable & Network Products
1401 Brook Dr.
Downers Grove, IL 60515
Main .... (800) 468-2121
Tech. Support.............................. (708) 627-1777
Tech. Supp. Fax.......................... (708) 932-4342
BBS... (708) 932-4342

Gold Disk, Inc.
5155 Spectrum Way Unit 5
Mississauga, ONT L5M 2C
Canada
Main .... (905) 602-4000
Customer Svc............................. (800) 982-9888
Tech. Support.............................. (905) 602-5292
Tech. Supp. Fax........................... (905) 602-4001
BBS... (905) 602-7534
WWW............................ http://www.golddisk.com

Gold Hill Software
PO Box 663
Goldhill, OR 97525
Main .... (800) 234-6467
Tech. Support.............................. (503) 826-6660
BBS... (503) 826-8090

Golden Bow Systems
2665 Ariane Dr.; #207
San Diego, CA 92117
Main..(800) 284-3269
Tech. Support................................(619) 298-0901
BBS..(619) 483-1924

Golden Triangle Computers
4849 Ronson Ct.
San Diego, CA 92111
Main..(800) 326-1858
Tech. Support................................(619) 279-2100

Goldstar Technologies, Inc.
3003 N 1st St.
San Jose, CA 95134
Main..(800) 777-1192
Tech. Support................................(408) 432-1331
BBS..(408) 432-6068

GolfWeb
WWW................................http://www.golfweb.com

Gould Fiber Optics Division
6730 Baymeadow Dr, D#
Glen Burnie, MD 21061
Main..(800) 544-6853
Tech. Support................................(301) 787-8300
BBS..(301) 787-2831

Grand Junction Networks
WWW....................http://www.grandjunction.com/

Graphics Unlimited, Inc.
3000 2nd St N
Minneapolis, MN 55411
Main..(612) 588-7571
Tech. Support................................(612) 520-2345
Tech. Supp. Fax..........................(612) 588-8783
BBS..(612) 588-8783
WWW...........................http://www.visi.com/tildagu

Gravis
WWW................................http://www.gravis.com/

Great Plains Software, Inc.
1701 SW 38th St.
Fargo, ND 58103
Main..(800) 456-0025
Tech. Support................................(701) 281-0550
BBS..(701) 282-4826

Greenleaf Software, Inc.
16479 Dallas Pkwy., #570
Dallas, TX 75248
Main..(800) 523-9830
Tech. Support................................(214) 248-2561
Tech. Supp. Fax..........................(214) 248-7830
BBS..(214) 248-7830

Greenview
PO Box 1586
Ann Arbor, MI 48106
Main..(313) 996-1299
BBS..(313) 996-1308

Grolier Electronic Publishing
Sherman Turnpike
Danbury, CT 06816
Main..(203) 797-3530
Customer Svc. ....(800) 285-4534
Tech. Support................................(800) 356-5590
BBS..(203) 797-6872
WWW.... http://www.grolier.com/GEP/cust_desk/
techsupt.htm

Groundhog Graphics
101 E Mahoning St.
PO Box 325
Punxsutawney, PA 15767
Main..(800) 283-2322
Tech. Support................................(814) 938-8943
BBS..(814) 938-7035

Group 1 Software, Inc.
6404 Ivy Lane
Greenbelt, MD 20770-1400
Main..(800) 368-5806

Group 1 Software, Inc.
4200 Parliament Pl.
Suite 600
Lanham, MD 20706
Main...(301) 731-2300
Customer Svc. ....(301) 731-2300
Tech. Support ....(301) 731-2300
Sales..(301) 731-2300
Tech. Supp. Fax ....(301) 731-0360

Group Technologies Corp.
1408 N. Fillmore
Suite 10
Arlington, VA 22201
Main...(703) 528-1555
Tech. Supp. Fax ....(703) 528-3296

Gruber Software, Ted
PO Box 13408
Las Vegas, NV 89112
Main...(702) 735-1980
Tech. Supp. Fax ....(702) 735-4603
WWW...........http://www.accessnv.com/fastgraph

Gryphon Software
7220 Trade Street, Suite 120
San Diego, CA 92121-2325
Main...(619) 536-8815
Tech. Supp. Fax ....(619) 536-8932
WWW...............................http://www.gryphon.com

GTE Fiber Optic Products
2333 Reach Rd.
Williamsport, PA 17701
Main...(800) 327-6782
BBS..(717) 321-6286

Gtek, Inc.
PO Box 2310
Bay St Louis, MS 39521-2310
Main...(800) 282-4835
Tech. Support ....(601) 467-8048
Tech. Supp. Fax ....(601) 467-0935
BBS..(601) 467-0935
WWW.................................... http://www.gtek.com

GUIdance Technologies
800 Vinial St
Pittsburgh, PA 15212
BBS..(412) 231-2076

Guideware Corp.
2483 Old Middlefield Way, #224
Mountain View, CA 94043
Main .... (415) 969-6851
BBS..................................... (415) 969-3862

Gupta Technologies, Inc.
1040 Marsh Rd.
Menlo Park, CA 94025
Main .... (800) 876-3267
Tech. Support............................... (415) 321-4484
BBS..................................... (415) 688-0213
WWW..................................http://www.gupta.com

GVC Technologies, Inc.
400 Commonsway
Rockaway, NJ 07866
Main .... (800) 289-4821
Tech. Support............................... (201) 586-8686
Tech. Supp. Fax........................... (201) 586-3308
BBS..................................... (201) 579-2702
WWW.............................. http://www.matcorp.com

GW Instruments
35 Medford St
Somerville, MA 02143
Main .... (617) 625-4096
Tech. Supp. Fax........................... (617) 625-1322
BBS..................................... (617) 625-1322

GW Micro
310 Racquet Dr
Ft Wayne, IN 46825
Main .... (219) 483-3625
Tech. Supp. Fax........................... (219) 482-2492
BBS..................................... (219) 484-2510

H Co Computer Products
1228 Village Way, #D
Santa Ana, CA 92705
Main...(800) 726-2477
Tech. Support...............................(714) 842-8292
BBS..(714) 542-8648

HaL Computer Systems Inc.
WWW.....................................http://www.hal.com/

Halley Systems
2730 Orchard Pkwy
San Jose, CA 95134
Main...(800) 432-2600
Tech. Support...............................(408) 432-2600
BBS..(408) 943-1601

Hamilton Laboratories
13 Old Farm Rd.
Wayland, MA 01778-3117
Main...(508) 358-5715

Handok Information Systems Corp.
10080 Buvv Rd.
Coopertion, CA 95014
Main...(408) 252-1100
Tech. Support...............................(800) 776-4472
Tech. Supp. Fax...........................(408) 252-1123

HanZon Data, Inc.
22032 23rd Dr SE
Bothell, WA 98021
Main...(800) 842-8540
Tech. Support...............................(206) 487-1717

Harmony Computers
1801 Flatbush Ave.
Brooklyn, NY 11210
Main...(800) 441-1144
Tech. Support...............................(718) 692-2828
BBS..(718) 692-4535

HarperCollins
10 East 53rd Street
21st Floor
New York, NY 10022
Main...(212) 207-7000
WWW.....................http://www.harpercollins.com

Harris Adacom
1100 Venture Ct.
Carrollton, TX 75006
Main...(214) 386-2000
Tech. Supp. Fax...........................(214) 386-2885
BBS..(214) 386-2159

Harris Computer Systems
WWW..........................http://www.csd.harris.com/

Harris Corp.
WWW...............................http://www.harris.com/

Harris Digital Telephone Systems+A865
WWW..........................http://www.dts.harris.com/

Harris Semiconductors
WWW........................http://www.semi.harris.com/

Harvard Student Agencies
53A Church Street
Harvard University
Cambridge, MA 02138-3715
Main...(617) 495-9647
WWW........................http://hcs.harvard.edu/~hsa

Hauppauge Computer Works, Inc.
91 Cabot Ct.
Hauppauge, NY 11788-3706
Main...(800) 443-6284
Tech. Support...............................(516) 434-1600
BBS..(516) 434-3198

Haven Tree Software
PO Box 470
Fineview, NY 13692
Main ....(613) 544-6035
Customer Svc. ....(613) 544-6035
Tech. Support ....(613) 544-6035
Sales..(613) 544-6035
Tech. Supp. Fax ....(613) 544-9632
BBS...(613) 544-9632
E-Mail.........................Tech-sup@haventree.com
WWW.........................http://www.haventree.com

Hawk Computers
2050 Bering Dr.
San Jose, CA 95131
Main ....(800) 969-4295
Tech. Support ....(408) 436-8999
BBS...(408) 436-9137

Hawkeye Grafix
PO Box 1400
Oldsmar, FL 34677
Main ....(813) 855-5846

Hayes Microcomputer Products
5835 Peachtree Corners East
Norcross, GA 30092
Main ....(800) 377-4377
Customer Svc. ....(404) 441-1617
Tech. Support ....(404) 441-1617
Sales..(770) 441-1617
Tech. Supp. Fax ....(770) 449-0087
BBS...(800) 874-2937
E-Mail.........................tech_support@hayes.com
WWW............................... http://www.hayes.com
FTP Address............................ftp://ftp.hayes.com
CompuServe...................................... GO HAYES

HD Computers
3325 Kifer Rd.
Santa Clara, CA 95054
Main ....(800) 347-0493
Tech. Support ....(800) 676-0164
BBS...(408) 720-1967

HDC Computer Corp.
6742 185th Ave. NE
Redmond, WA 98052
Main .... (800) 321-4606
Tech. Support................................ (206) 885-5550
BBS... (206) 881-9770

Headbone Interactive, Inc.
1520 Bellevue Ave.
Seattle, WA 98122-9952
Main .... (206) 323-0073
WWW................................... http://headbone.com/

Heartbeat Software
1776 Massachusetts Ave.
Cambridge, MA 02140
Main .... (617) 492-0111

Heartland Software, Inc.
234 S Franklin
Ames, IA 50010
Main .... (515) 292-8216
BBS... (515) 292-8216

Helios Systems
1996 Lundy Ave.
San Jose, CA 95131
Main .... (408) 432-0292
Tech. Supp. Fax............................ (408) 943-1309
BBS... (408) 943-1309

Helix Software Company, Inc.
83-65 Daniels St.
Briarwood, NY 11435
Main .... (800) 451-0551
Tech. Support................................ (718) 392-3735
BBS... (718) 262-8808
WWW................................... http://www.helix.com

Help Desk Institute
WWW................... http://www.HelpDeskInst.com/

Hercules
3839 Spinnaker Ct.
Fremont, CA 94538
Main..(510) 623-6030
Customer Svc...............................(800) 532-0600
Tech. Support...............................(800) 323-0601
Sales ....(800) 323-0601
Tech. Supp. Fax...........................(510) 623-1112
BBS ....(510) 623-7449
E-Mail ....support@hercules.com
WWW.............................http://www.hercules.com
FTP Address.............................ftp.hercules.com
CompuServe ....GO HERCULES
America Online.......................hercules@aol.com

Hermes Communications, Inc.
6678 3rd Line Rd., PO Box 509
North Gower, ONT K0A 2T
Canada
Main..(613) 489-2578

Herrard Business Computers
PO BOX 265
Harvard, IL 60033
Tech. Support...............................(815) 943-7684
Tech. Supp. Fax...........................(815) 943-7679
BBS ....(815) 943-7669

Heurikon Corp.
WWW........................... http://www.heurikon.com/

Hewlett-Packard Federal Web
WWW............................... http://www.hpfed.com/

Hewlett-Packard Workstations
WWW........... http://www.hp.com/go/workstations

Hi-Tech Advisers
PO Box 129
Ravena, NY 12143
Main..(800) 882-4310
Tech. Support...............................(518) 756-3800

Hi-Tech Marketing
3201 Corte Malpaso
Camarillo, CA 93012
Main..(805) 388-8522
BBS...(805) 388-8503

Hi-Tech USA
1562 Centre Pointe Dr.
Milpitas, CA 95035
Main..(408) 262-8688
Customer Svc. ....(408) 956-8285
Tech. Support ....(408) 262-8688
Tech. Supp. Fax ....(408) 262-8772
BBS...(408) 262-8772

Hi-Tek Kyeboard
9730 Independence Ave.
Chatsworth, CA 91311
Main..(800) 321-3536
Tech. Support ....(818) 341-3355

Hibbs Henle Nelson Corp.
1115 Foothill Blvd.
La Canada, CA 91011
Main..(818) 952-1000

High Level Design Systems
WWW....................................http://www.hlds.com/

High Res Technologies, Inc.
PO Box 76
Lewiston, NY 14092
Main..(416) 497-6493
BBS...(416) 497-1636

Hilgraeve, Inc.
111 Conant Ave., Suite A
Monroe, MI 48161
Main..(313) 243-0576
WWW............................ http://www.hilgraeve.com

Hilgrave, Inc.
111 Conant Ave., #A
Monroe, MI 48161
Main..(800) 826-2760
Tech. Support ....(313) 243-0576
Tech. Supp. Fax ....(313) 243-0646
BBS...(313) 243-0645
WWW..............................http://www.hilgrave.com

HiQuality Systems, Inc.
740 N Mary Ave.
Sunnyvale, CA 94086
Main..(408) 245-5836
Tech. Supp. Fax ....(408) 245-3108
BBS...(408) 245-3108

Hirschman, Richard GmbH & Co.
Industrial Row
PO Box 229
Riverdale, NJ 07457
Main..(201) 835-5002

Hitachi Data Systems
750 Central Expy.
Santa Clara, CA 95050-0996
Main..(408) 727-8036

Hokkins Systemation
131 E Brokaw
San Jose, CA 95112
Main..(800) 526-2328
Tech. Support ....(408) 436-8303
BBS...(408) 436-3021

Holmes Microsystems
2620 S 900 W
Salt Lake City, UT 84119
Main..(800) 648-7488
BBS...(801) 975-9726

Honeywell
WWW....................http://www.iac.honeywell.com/

Honeywell Bull, Inc.
3800 W 80th St
Minneapolis, MN 55431
Main..(612) 896-3800

Hooleon Corp.
411 S 6th St.
Cottonwood, AZ 86326
Main ....(800) 937-1337
Tech. Support..............................(520) 634-7515
Tech. Supp. Fax..........................(520) 634-4620

Horan Data Services
708 Walnut St.
Cincinnati, OH 45202
Main ....(800) 677-8885
Tech. Supp. Fax...........................(929) 342-3
WWW.......................http://www.horandata.com
FTP Address ....ftp.horandata.net

Horizons Technology, Inc.
3990 Ruffin Rd.
San Diego, CA 92123-9644
Main ....(619) 292-8320

Horstmann Software Design Corp.
1035 S. Saratoga
Sunnydale Rd. St. 5A 915129
San Jose, CA 95113
Main ....(408) 366-1222
Tech. Supp. Fax..........................(408) 366-0822

Houghton Mifflin Co.
WWW.................................http://www.hmco.com

Houston Instrument (Summagraph)
8500 Cameron Rd.
Austin, TX 78754
Customer Svc..............................(800) 444-3425
Tech. Support..............................(800) 444-3425
BBS...(512) 873-1477
E-Mail...........techsupport@summagraphics.com
WWW................http://www.summagraphics.com

HSC Software, Inc.
1661 Lincoln Blvd., #101
Santa Monica, CA 90404
Main ....(213) 392-8441

HT Electronics
55 W. Hoover Suite #9
Mesa, AZ 85206
Main...(800) 448-2031
Tech. Support.............................(602) 832-7309
Tech. Supp. Fax.........................(602) 832-0881
BBS..(602) 832-0881

Human Designed Systems
WWW....................................http://www.hlds.com/

Humanagement, Ltd.
430 King St W, #206
Toronto, Ontario, Canada M5V 1L5
Main...(905) 795-1880

Humancad
1800 Walt Whitman Rd.
Melville, NY 11747
Main..(516) 752-3568
BBS...(516) 752-3507

Hummingbird Communications Inc.
WWW.....................http://www.hummingbird.com

Hybrid Arts
8522 National Blvd.
Los Angeles, CA 90232
Main...(213) 841-0348

Hyphen Inc.orp.orated
WWW..............................http://www.hyphen.com/

Hyundai Electronics America
510 Cottonwood Dr.
Milpitas, CA 95035
Main..(408) 232-8000
Customer Svc..............................(800) 289-4986
Tech. Support.............................(800) 289-4986
BBS...(800) 955-5432

IBM
Rt. 100
Box 100
Somers, NY 10589
Main..(800) 426-3333
Customer Svc. ....(800) 772-2227
Tech. Support ....(800) 772-2227
BBS..(919) 517-0001
E-Mail.............................askibm@info.ibm.com
WWW...................................... http://www.ibm.com

IBM National Distribution Division
101 Paragon Dr.
Montvale, NJ 07645
Main..(800) 426-2468
Sales...(800) 426-3333

IBM PC
WWW.............................. http://www.pc.ibm.com/

IC Express
15140 Valley Blvd.
City of Industry, CA 91744
Main..(800) 877-8188
Tech. Support ....(818) 369-2688
BBS...(818) 369-1236

Iconovex Corp.
7448 West 78th Street
Bloomington, MN 55439
Main..(612) 943-0292
WWW........................... http://www.iconovex.com/

Icot Corp.
3801 Zanker Rd.
San Jose, CA 95150
Main..(800) 762-3270
Tech. Support ....(408) 433-3300
BBS...(408) 433-0260

Id Software
18601 LBJ Freeway #615
Mesquite, TX 75150
Main..(214) 613-3589
E-Mail.....................................info@idsoftware.com
WWW......................... http://www.idsoftware.com/

IDEAssociates, Inc.
29 Dunham Rd.
Billerica, MA 01821
Main .... (508) 663-6878

IDG Books Worldwide, Inc.
155 Bover Rd., #730
San Mateo, CA 94402
Main .... (415) 358-1250

IDS
12800 Garden Grove Blvd. E
Garden Grove, CA 92643
Main .... (714) 530-8677
Tech. Support .... (714) 530-8697
Tech. Supp. Fax .... (714) 530-0817
BBS .... (714) 530-0815

IET
1250 Bixby Dr.
Industry, CA 91745
Main .... (818) 336-1003
Tech. Support .... (818) 336-1003
Tech. Supp. Fax .... (818) 330-0052
BBS .... (818) 330-0052

IGC
1740 Technology Dr, #300
San Jose, CA 95110
Main .... (800) 458-9108
Tech. Support .... (408) 441-0366

Ikegami Electronics (USA), Inc.
37 Brook Ave.
Maywood, NJ 07607
Main .... (201) 368-9171
Tech. Supp. Fax .... (201) 569-1626

Illustra Information Technolog
WWW .... http://www.illustra.com/

Ilog
WWW .... http://www.ilog.com/ilog/home.html

Image Computer Systems
124 Wellington Heights Rd.
Avon, CT 06001
Main .... (203) 678-8771

Image Smith
1313 West Supelveda Blvd.
Torrance, CA 90501
Main .... (310) 325-5999
Customer Svc .... (800) 876-6679
Tech. Support .... (800) 876-6679
Sales .... (310) 325-5999
Tech. Supp. Fax .... (310) 539-9784

Image Systems
PO Box 19743
2515 McCabe Way
Irvine, CA 92713-9743
Main .... (800) 347-4027

Image-In, Inc.
1820 Gateway Cr. #370
San Mateo, CA 94404
Main .... (800) 345-3540
Tech. Support .... (612) 888-3633
Tech. Supp. Fax .... (415) 358-9535
BBS .... (415) 358-9795
CompuServe .... GO IMAGEIN

ImageSoft, Inc.
2 HAve.n Ave.
Port Washington, NY 11050
Tech. Support .... (516) 767-2233

Imagetech
124 Raymond St
Hasbrouck Heights, NJ 07604
Main .... (800) 462-4348
Tech. Support .... (201) 288-5592

Imagination Network
WWW .... http://www.imaginationnet.com/

Imavox Corp.
3350 Scott Blvd., Bldg 3802
Santa Clara, CA 95054
Main...(800) 969-4628
BBS ....(408) 980-8718

IMC Networks Corp.
16931 Milliken Ave.
Irvine, CA 92714
Main...(800) 624-1070
Tech. Support.................................(714) 724-1070
Tech. Supp. Fax.............................(714) 724-1020
BBS ....(714) 724-1020
WWW.....................http://www.imcnetworks.com/

Imperial Computer Group
318 S San Gabriel Blvd., #B-C
San Gabriel< CA 91776
Main...(818) 285-1256
Tech. Support.................................(818) 285-1256
BBS ....(818) 285-9488

IMSI/(Int'l. Microcomputer Software
1895 Francisco Blvd. E
San Rafael, CA 94901
Main...(415) 257-3000
Customer Svc................................(800) 833-8082
Tech. Support.................................(415) 257-3000
Sales ....(800) 833-8082
Tech. Supp. Fax.............................(415) 257-3565
BBS ....(415) 257-8468
E-Mail ....support@imsi.com
WWW..............................http://www.imsisoft.com
FTP Address.................................ftp.imsisoft.com
CompuServe ....GO IMSI
America Online...............................imsi@aol.com

In Focus Systems, Inc.
27700B S.W. Pky.
Wilsonville, OR 97070
Main...(503) 685-8888
Customer Svc................................(800) 327-7231
Tech. Support.................................(800) 294-6400
Sales ....(800) 294-6400
Tech. Supp. Fax.............................(503) 685-8887
BBS ....(503) 692-4476
WWW....................................http://www.infs.com
CompuServe ....GO INFOCUS

Independent Technology Service
4495 Runway St.
Simi Valley, CA 93063
Main...(818) 882-7747
Tech. Support ....(805) 526-1555
Tech. Supp. Fax ....(805) 526-2590
BBS...(818) 718-8748

Index Stock Photography
126 Fifth Ave., 7th Floor
New York, NY 10011
Main...(212) 929-4644
WWW.......................http://www.indexstock.com/

Individual Software
5870 Stoneridge Dr.
Pleasonton, CA 94588
Main...(510) 734-6767
Customer Svc. ....(800) 822-3522
Tech. Support ....(800) 331-3313
Sales...(800) 822-3522
Tech. Supp. Fax ....(510) 734-8337
CompuServe....................................76366,3213

Industrial Computer Source
4837 Mercury St
San Diego, CA 92111
Main...(619) 279-0084
BBS...(619) 541-1138

Infinidisc Corp.
7 Littleton Rd.
Westford, MA 01886
Main...(508) 692-0898

Info Access
2800 156th Ave. SE
Bellevue, WA 98007
Main...(800) 344-9737
Tech. Support ....(206) 747-3203
Tech. Supp. Fax ....(206) 641-9367
WWW.......................... http://www.infoaccess.com

Infoflex, Inc.
875 Mahler Rd., #200
Burlingame, CA 94010
Main...(415) 340-0220

Information Builders, Inc.
1250 Broadway
New York, NY 10117-3701
Main...(800) 444-4303
Tech. Support ....(212) 736-4433
Tech. Supp. Fax ....(407) 727-7615
WWW.....................................http://www.ibi.com/

Information Dimensions
WWW...............................http://www.idi.oclc.org/

Information Machines
20219 Chapter Dr
Woodland Hills, CA 91364
Main...(818) 884-5779

Information Resources, Inc.
200 5th Ave.
Waltham, MA 02154
Main...(617) 890-1100
Tech. Supp. Fax ....(617) 890-4660

Informix Software, Inc.
4100 Bohannon Dr
Menlo Park, CA 94025
Main...(800) 331-1763
Tech. Support ....(415) 926-6300
BBS..(415) 322-2805
WWW.............................. http://www.informix.com

Ingenius
5970 Greenwood Plaza Blvd.
Suite 210
Englewood, CO 80111
Main...(303) 267-5800
WWW........................... http://www.ingenius.com/

Ingram Micro
1600 E. St. Andrews Place
P.O. Box 25125
Santa Ana, CA 92799-5125
Main...(714) 566-1000

Inherent Technologies
WWW...........................http://www.inherent.com/

Inmos
WWW.................http://www.pact.srf.ac.uk/inmos/
welcome.html

Innovative Technology, Ltd.
PO Box 726
Elk City, OK 73648
Main .... (800) 253-4001
Tech. Support............................. (405) 243-0030
Tech. Supp. Fax.......................... (405) 243-2810
BBS.. (405) 243-2810

Inset Systems
71 Commerce Dr.
Brookfield, CT 06804-3405
Main .... (203) 740-2400
WWW........................... http://www.insetusa.com/

Insight Computers
1912 W 4th St
Tempe, AZ 85281
Main .... (800) 776-7600
Tech. Support............................. (800) 733-0883
BBS.. (602) 829-9193

Insight Development Corp.
2420 Camino Ramon
Suite 205
San Ramon, CA 94583
Main .... (800) 825-4115
Tech. Supp. Fax.......................... (510) 244-2020

Insignia Solutions
1300 Charleston Rd.
Mountain View, CA 94043
Main .... (415) 335-7100
Customer Svc.............................. (800) 848-7677
Tech. Support............................. (415) 694-7694
WWW........................... http://www.insignia.com

Inso Corp.
401 North Wabash
Suite 600
Chicago, IL 60611-3532
Main................................(312) 329-0700
Customer Svc................................(312) 329-0700
Tech. Support................................(312) 527-4357
Sales ....(800) 333-1395
Tech. Supp. Fax................................(312) 670-0820
BBS ....(312) 670-4239

Installshield Corp.
WWW................................http://www.installshield.com

Instant Board Circuits Corp.
PO BOX 1052
Fairfax, CA 94978-1052
Main................................(415) 883-1717
Tech. Supp. Fax................................(415) 457-7253

Integra
PO Box 72063
Marietta, GA 30007
Main................................(770) 973-3586

Integrand Research Corp.
8620 Roosevelt Ave.
Visalia, CA 93291
Main................................(209) 651-1203
Tech. Supp. Fax................................(209) 651-1353
BBS ....(209) 651-1353

Integrated Computer Solution, Inc.
WWW................................http://www.ics.com/

Integrated Computer Solutions, Inc.
91 N Bertrand Rd.
Mount Arlington, NJ 07856
Main................................(201) 770-2733

Integrated Computer Systems, Inc.
165 Harvard St.
Cambridge, MA 02139
Main................................(617) 547-0510

Integrated Device Technology
WWW................................http://www.idt.com/

Intel Corp.
2200 Mission College Blvd.
Santa Clara, CA 95052
Customer Svc. ....(800) 538-3373
Tech. Support ....(503) 264-7000
WWW................................http://www.intel.com

Intel PCED
5200 NE Elam Young Pkwy.
Hillsboro, OR 97124
Main................................(800) 538-3373
Tech. Support ....(800) 538-3373
BBS................................(503) 221-6953

Intel Scalable Systems Division
2200 Mission College Blvd.
Santa Clara, CA 95052-8119
WWW.. http://www.ssd.intel.com/homepage.html

Intellicom
9259 Eton Ave.
Chatsworth, CA 91311
Main................................(818) 407-3900

IntelliCorp., Inc.
1975 El Camino Real W
Mountain View, CA 94040
Main................................(415) 965-5500

Intellidraft
790 Riverside Dr, #6-N
New York, NY 10032
Main................................(212) 281-2484

IntelligenceWare, Inc.
9800 S Sepulveda Blvd., #730
Los Angeles, CA 90045
Main................................(800) 888-2996
Tech. Support ....(213) 417-8896

IntelliGenetics
WWW................................http://www.ig.com/

Interactive Development Environment
595 Market St.
10th Floor
San Francisco, CA 94105
Main..............................(415) 543-0900
Tech. Supp. Fax ....(415) 543-0145
WWW.....................................http://www.ide.com

Interactive Software Engineeri
WWW..................................http://www.eiffel.com

Interactive Systems Corp.
2401 Colorado Ave.
Santa Monica, CA 90404
Main...............................(310) 348-8649

InterActive, Inc.
204 N Main
Humboldt, SD 57035
Tech. Support ....(605) 363-5117
Tech. Supp. Fax ....(605) 363-5102
BBS...............................(605) 363-5102
WWW.....................................http://www.iact.com

Intercon Associates, Inc.
95 Allens Creek Rd. Bldg 2
Suite 200
Rochester, NY 14618
Main...............................(800) 422-3880
Tech. Support ....(716) 244-1250
Tech. Supp. Fax ....(716) 473-4387

Intercon Systems Corp.
950 Herndon PkwY, #420
Herndon, VA 22070
Main...............................(703) 709-9890
Tech. Supp. Fax ....(703) 709-5559
BBS...............................(703) 709-9896
WWW...........................http://www.intercon.com/

Interface Systems
5855 Interface Dr
Ann Arbor, MI 48103
Main...............................(313) 769-5900

Interface Technology
67 Poland St.
Bridgeport, CT 06604
Main .... (800) 523-3199
Tech. Support...........................(203) 384-0400
Tech. Supp. Fax..........................(203) 331-9719
BBS...............................(203) 335-3128

Intergraph Corp.
1 Madison Industrial Park
Huntsville, AL 35894-0001
Main .... (800) 826-3515
Tech. Support...........................(205) 730-2000
BBS...............................(205) 730-8783

Intergraph Corp.
WWW..........................http://www.intergraph.com

Interleaf, Inc.
WWW.................................. http://www.ileaf.com/

Interlink Computer Sciences
47370 Fremont Blvd.
Fremont, CA 94538
Main .... (800) 422-3711
Tech. Support...........................(415) 657-9800
BBS...............................(415) 659-6381

International Data Sciences
501 Jefferson Blvd.
Warwick, RI 02886-1317
Main .... (800) 437-3282
Tech. Support...........................(401) 737-9900
Tech. Supp. Fax..........................(401) 737-9911
BBS...............................(401) 737-9911

International Instrument, Inc.
2282 Townsgate Rd.
Westlake Village, CA 91361
Main .... (800) 543-3475
Tech. Support...........................(805) 495-7673
Tech. Supp. Fax..........................(805) 379-0701

International Microcomputer
1895 E. Francisco Blvd.
San Rafael, CA 94901
Main..(800) 833-4674
Tech. Support...............................(415) 454-7101
Tech. Supp. Fax............................(415) 257-3565
BBS..(415) 257-8468

International Software Systems
WWWhttp://www.issi.com/issi/issi-home_page.html

International Technologies & Software
655-K N Berry St
Brea, CA 92621
Main..(714) 990-1880
Tech. Supp. Fax............................(714) 990-2503
BBS..(714) 990-2503

Internet Infinity, Inc.
SiteRating
2707 Plaza Del Amo , Suite 601
Torrance, CA 90503
Main..(310) 533-4800
Customer Svc...............................(310) 533-4800
Tech. Support...............................(310) 533-4800
Tech. Supp. Fax............................(310) 533-1993
WWW.............................http://www.siterating.com

Interpex
WWW..................http://www.csn.net:80/interpex/

InterPlay Productions
17922 Fitch Ave.
Irvine, CA 92714
Main..(714) 553-6655
Customer Svc...............................(714) 553-6678
Tech. Support...............................(714) 553-6678
Tech. Supp. Fax............................(714) 252-2820
BBS..(714) 252-2822
WWW.............................http://www.interplay.com
FTP Address..............................ftp.interplay.com

InterSolv
1700 NW 167th Pl, #2110
Beaverton, OR 97006
Main..(503) 645-1150
Tech. Supp. Fax............................(503) 645-4576
WWW.............................http://www.intersolv.com

Intersolv International plc
Abbey View, Everard Close
St. Albans AL12PS
UK
Main..(441) 727-8128
WWW.............................http://www.intersolv.com/

Intersolv Product Info Line
1700 NW 167th Pl
Beaverton, OR 97006
Main..(800) 547-4000
Tech. Support...............................(503) 645-1150
BBS..(503) 645-4576

Intex Solutions, Inc.
161 Highland Ave.
Needham, MA 02194
Main..(617) 449-6222
Tech. Supp. Fax............................(614) 444-2318
BBS..(617) 444-2318

InText Systems
WWW...............................http://www.intext.com/

Intuit
PO Box 3014
Menlo Park, CA 94026
Main..(415) 944-6000
Customer Svc. ....(800) 624-8742
Tech. Support ....(800) 624-8742
WWW...............................http://www.intuit.com

Invasion Designs
PO Box 2387
Austin, TX 78767-2387

Inventory Locator Service, Inc.
3965 Mendenhall Rd.
Memphis, TN 38115
Main .... (800) 233-3414
Tech. Support .... (901) 794-4784
Tech. Supp. Fax .... (901) 794-1760
BBS .... (901) 794-1760

Invisible Software, Inc.
1165 Chess Dr, #D
Foster City, CA 94404
Main .... (415) 570-5967

Iomega Corp.
1821 W 4000 S
Roy, UT 84067
Main .... (801) 778-1000
Customer Svc. .... (800) 456-5522
Tech. Support .... (800) 456-5522
BBS .... (801) 392-9819
WWW .... http://www.iomega.com
America Online .... iomega

IONA Technologies
WWW .. http://www.iona.ie:8000/www/index.html/

IOtech, Inc.
25791 Canon Rd.
Cleveland, OH 44146
Main .... (216) 439-4091
BBS .... (216) 439-4093

ips Publishing, Inc.
12606 NE 95th Street, C-110
Vancouver, WA 98682
Main .... (206) 944-8996
WWW .... http://www.primenet.com/~examncan/

IQ Engineering
685 N Pastoria
Sunnyvale, CA 94086
Main .... (800) 765-3668

IQ Management Systems
8471 Bellmore St
Riverside, CA 92509
Main .... (714) 360-0208
BBS .... (714) 360-0209

Isaacson Software, Eric
416 E University Ave.
Bloomington, IN 47401
Main .... (812) 339-1811
Tech. Supp. Fax .... (812) 335-1611

Isicad, Inc.
1920 W Corporate Way
PO Box 61022
Anaheim, CA 92803-6122
Main .... (714) 533-8910
Tech. Supp. Fax .... (714) 533-8642
BBS .... (714) 533-8642

Island Graphics
80 East Sir Francis Drake Blvd.
Suite 2-B
Larkspur, CA 94939
Main .... (415) 464-3800
Customer Svc. .... (415) 491-1000
Sales .... (800) 598-8118
Tech. Supp. Fax .... (415) 464-3838
E-Mail .... islandgfx2@aol.com
WWW .... http://www.island.com
FTP Address .... ftp.island.com

Isogon Corp.
330 7th Ave.
New York, NY 10001
Main .... (212) 376-3200
Tech. Supp. Fax .... (212) 376-3280

Ivan Levison Direct Mail Copywriting
14 Los Cerros Dr.
Greenbrae, CA 94904
Main .... (415) 461-0675
WWW .... http://www.levison.com

IVI Publishing
7500 Flying Cloud Dr.
Suite No 400
Minneapolis, MN 55344-3739
Main..(612) 996-6000
Customer Svc..............................(612) 996-6000
Tech. Support.............................(800) 754-1484
Sales ....(800) 952-4773
Tech. Supp. Fax..........................(612) 996-6001
E-Mail ....support@ivi.com
WWW........................http://www.helthnet.ivi.com

J F H Properties
14335 NE 24th Suite 202
Bellevue, WA 98007
Main..(206) 747-0824
Tech. Supp. Fax..........................(206) 957-1219
BBS ....(206) 644-2190

J P Software, Inc.
PO Box 1470
East Arlington, MA 02174
Main..(800) 368-8777
Tech. Support.............................(617) 646-3975
Tech. Supp. Fax..........................(617) 646-0904
BBS ....(617) 646-0904
WWW.................................http://www.jpsoft.com

J&L Information Systems
9600 Topanga Cyn Blvd.
Chatsworth, CA 91311
Main..(818) 709-1778
Tech. Support.............................(818) 718-1237
BBS ....(818) 709-5899

Jade Computer Products, Inc.
4901 W Rosecrans
Box 5046
Hawthorne, CA 90251-5046
Main..(800) 421-5500
Tech. Support.............................(213) 973-7707
BBS ....(213) 675-2522

Jameco Computer Products
1355 Shoreway Rd.
Belmont, CA 94002
Main...(415) 592-8097
Tech. Support ....(415) 592-8097
Tech. Supp. Fax ....(415) 595-2664
BBS..(415) 595-2664

James River Group, Inc.
125 N 1st St
Minneapolis, MN 55401
Tech. Supp. Fax ....(612) 339-4445
BBS..(612) 339-4445

Jamestown Software
2508 Valley Forge Dr.
Madison, WI 53719
Main..(608) 271-2090
Tech. Supp. Fax ....(608) 271-8959

Janna Systems, Inc.
WWW................................. http://www.janna.com/

Japan Electronics
15138 Valley Blvd.
City of Industry, CA 91744
Main..(818) 369-5000
BBS..(818) 369-1236

JASC, Inc.
WWW....................................http://www.jasc.com/

Jasmine Multimedia Publishing
6746 Valjean Ave.
Suite 100
Van Nuys, CA 91406
Main..(818) 780-3344
Customer Svc. ....(818) 780-3344
Tech. Support ....(800) 798-7535
Sales...(818) 780-3344
Tech. Supp. Fax ....(818) 780-8705
WWW.............................. http://www.jasmine.com
FTP Address.................................ftp.jasmine.com

Jay Pee Tech Distributors
913 Bridgeport Ave.
Shelton, CT 06484
Main...................................(203) 929-0790
Tech. Supp. Fax ....(203) 929-6948
BBS...(203) 929-6948

JB Technologies
5105 Maureen Ln
Moorpark, CA 93021
Main...(805) 529-0908
Tech. Support ....(805) 529-0908

JDR Microdevices
2233 Branham Ln
San Jose, CA 95124
Main...(800) 538-5003
Tech. Support ....(800) 538-5002
Tech. Supp. Fax ....(408) 559-0250
BBS...(408) 559-0250

JDS Microprocessing
22661 Lambert St, #205
El Toro, CA 92630
Main...(800) 554-9372
Customer Svc. ....(800) 55H-YDRA
BBS...(714) 770-4826
WWW.................................. http://www.jasm.com

Jensen Tools
7815 S 46th St
Phoenix, AZ 85044
Main...(602) 968-6241
BBS...(602) 438-1690

JetForm Corp.
560 Rodchester St.
Ottowa
Main...(800) 267-9976
Customer Svc. ....(613) 594-8886
Tech. Support ....(613) 594-3026
Sales...(613) 230-4700
Tech. Supp. Fax ....(613) 751-4808
WWW...............................http://www.jetform.com

Jinco Computers
5122 Walnut Grove Ave.
San Gabriel, CA 91776
Main .... (818) 309-1108
Tech. Support..............................(818) 309-1103
Tech. Supp. Fax...........................(818) 309-1107
BBS .... (818) 309-1107
WWW.................................. http://www.jinco.com

John Wiley and Sons
605 Third Ave.
New York, NY 10158-0012
Main .... (212) 850-6000
WWW..................................http://www.wiley.com

Johnson Computer Systems
20 Dinwoodie Pl
Newport News, VA
Main .... (804) 872-9583
Tech. Support..............................(804) 872-9583
Tech. Supp. Fax...........................(804) 874-8090

Johnson-Grace Co.
WWW..................................... http://www.jgc.com

Jostens Learning Corp.
9920 Pacific Heights Blvd., Suite 100
San Diego, CA 92121
Main .... (619) 587-0087
WWW..................... http://www.jlc.com/index.html

Journey-Ware Media
550 Center Street, Suite 123
Maroga, CA 94556
Main .... (510) 254-4520
WWW...................... http://www.journeyware.com

Jovian Logic
47929 Fremont Blvd.
Fremont, CA 94538
Main .... (510) 651-4823
Customer Svc................................ (510) 651-4823
Tech. Support............................... (510) 651-4823
Tech. Supp. Fax........................... (510) 651-1343
BBS .... (510) 651-6989
CompuServe 75300,221

Joy Systems
2144 Bering Dr
San Jose, CA 95131
Main...(408) 435-0980

JP Software
PO Box 1470
East Arlington, MA 02174
Main...(617) 646-3975

JSB
WWW.....................................http://www.jsb.com/

JYACC, Inc.
116 John St
New York, NY 10038
Main...(800) 458-3313
Tech. Support.............................(212) 267-7722
Tech. Supp. Fax........................(212) 608-6753
BBS ....(212) 608-6753
WWW................................http://www.jyacc.com

K-Talk Communications, Inc.
30 W 1st Ave., #100
Columbus, OH 43201
Main...(614) 488-8873

Kadak Products, Ltd.
206-1847 W Broadway
Vancouver, British Columbia
Canada
Main...(604) 734-2796
BBS ....(604) 734-8114

Kaleida Labs
1055-B Joaquin Rd.
Mountain View, CA 94043
Main...(415) 966-0400
WWW...............................http://www.kaleida.com

Kalglo Electronics Co, Inc.
6584 Ruch Rd. E, Allen Township
Bethlehem, PA 18017
Main...(800) 524-0400
Tech. Support.............................(215) 837-0700
BBS ....(215) 837-7978

Kaplan InterActive
444 Madison Ave., Suite 803
New York, NY 10022
Main...(212) 751-1877
WWW...............................http://www.kaplan.com

Kaplan, Alan M
101 N McDowell St, #118
Charlotte, NC 28204

Kay Elemetrics
12 Maple Ave., PO Box 2025
Pine Brook, NJ 07058
Main...(800) 289-5297
Tech. Support ....(201) 227-2000
BBS...(201) 227-7760

Kea Systems, Ltd.
3738 N Fraser Way, #101
Burnaby, British Columbia
Canada
Main...(800) 663-8702
Tech. Support ....(604) 431-0727
Sales...(604) 294-9499
BBS...(604) 431-0818

Keithley Asyst
100 Corporate Woods
Rochester, NY 14623
Main...(800) 348-0033

Keithley Metrabyte
440 Myles Standish Blvd.
Taunton, MA 02780-9962
Main...(508) 880-3000

Kenosha Computer Corp.
2133 91st St
Kenosha, WI 53143
Main...(800) 255-2989
Tech. Support ....(414) 697-9595
Tech. Supp. Fax ....(414) 697-0602
BBS...(414) 697-0602

Kensington Microware, Ltd.
251 Park Ave. S
New York, NY 10010
Main................................(800) 535-4242
Tech. Support ....(212) 475-5200
BBS..(212) 475-5996

Kentrox Industries, Inc.
14375 NW Science Pk Dr
Portland, OR 97229-9886
Main................................(800) 733-5511
Tech. Support ....(503) 643-1681
Tech. Supp. Fax ....(503) 641-3321
BBS..(503) 641-3321

Key Power, Inc.
11853 E Telegraph Rd.
Santa Fe Springs, CA 90670
Main................................(213) 948-2084
Tech. Support ....(213) 948-2084
BBS..(213) 942-0536

Keypoint Technology
12130 Mora Dr
Santa Fe Springs, CA 90670
Main................................(213) 944-3041
Tech. Support ....(213) 944-3041
BBS..(213) 944-9559

Keystone Technology
WWW............................ http://www.keytech.com/

Keytronics Corp.
North 4424 Sullivan Rd.
Spokane, WA 99214
Main................................(800) 262-6006
Tech. Support ....(509) 927-5395
BBS..(509) 927-5252

Kimtron Corp.
4181 Business Ct. Dr.
Fremont, CA 94538
Main................................(800) 777-8755
Tech. Support ....(510) 623-8900
Tech. Supp. Fax ....(510) 623-8945
BBS..(408) 436-1380

King Star Computers
46560 Fremont Blvd., #305
Fremont, CA 94538
Main .... (800) 676-8333
Tech. Support..............................(415) 659-8590
BBS..(415) 659-8644

Kingston Technology
17600 Newhope St.
Fountain Valley, CA 92708
Main .... (714) 435-2600
Customer Svc..............................(714) 435-2600
Tech. Support..............................(714) 435-2639
Tech. Supp. Fax..........................(714) 437-3310
BBS..(714) 435-2636
E-Mail......................tech_support@kingston.com
WWW..............................http://www.kingston.com

Knight- Ridder Information
WWW.............................. http://www.dialog.com

Knight-Ridder Info Inc.
2440 El Camino Real
Mountain View, CA 94040-1400
Main .... (800) 334-2564
Tech. Supp. Fax..........................(415) 254-7070

Knowledge Adventure
1311 Grand Central Ave.
Glendale, CA. 91201
WWW..........................http://www.adventure.com/

Knowledge Dynamics Corp.
PO BOX 780068
San Antonio, TX 78278
Main .... (800) 331-2783
Tech. Support..............................(210) 979-9424
Tech. Supp. Fax..........................(210) 979-9004
BBS..(512) 964-3958

Knowledge Garden, Inc.
12-8 Technology Dr
Setauket, NY 11733
Main................................(516) 862-0600
Tech. Supp. Fax...........................(516) 862-0644
BBS................................(516) 246-5452
E-Mail.....................................info@kgarden.com
WWW..............................http://www.kgarden.com

Knowledge Point, Inc.
1311 Clegge St
Petaluma, CA 94954
Main................................(707) 762-0333

Knozall Systems, Inc.
375 E Elliot Rd., #10
Chandler, AZ 85225-1130
Main................................(800) 333-8698
Tech. Support.............................(602) 545-0006
Tech. Supp. Fax...........................(602) 545-0008
BBS................................(602) 545-0008
WWW...... http://www.indirect.com./www./knozail/

Koch Software Industries
PO Box 3194
Barrington, IL 60010
Tech. Support...............................(708) 304-5544
WWW.......................................http://www.thru.net

Kodak
Digital & Applied Imaging
901 Elmgrove Rd.
Rochester, NY 14653
Main................................(800) 235-6325
Customer Svc.............................(800) 344-0006
Tech. Support.............................(800) 344-0006
WWW................................http://www.kodak.com

Kolod Research, Inc.
1898 Techny Ct
Northbrook, IL 60062
Main................................(708) 291-1586

Konica Business Machines USA
500 Day Hill Rd.
Windsor, CT 06095
Main................................(800) 456-6422

Koss
4129 N. Port Washington Ave.
Milwaukee, WI 53212
Customer Svc. ....(800) 558-8305
Tech. Support ....(800) 558-8305
WWW.....................................http://www.koss.com

Kris Technologies, Inc.
260 E Grand Ave.
South San Francisco, CA 94080
Main................................(800) 282-5747
Tech. Support ....(415) 875-6729
BBS................................(415) 877-8048

Kuck & Associates
WWW.....................................http://www.kai.com/

KW Control Systems
Rt 4, Box 194, S Plank Rd.
Middletown, NY 10940
Main................................(914) 355-5000
Tech. Supp. Fax ....(914) 355-9005
BBS................................(914) 355-9005

L-Tech
9205 S Keating
Oak Lawn, IL 60453
Main................................(800) 342-5196
BBS................................(708) 342-5196

Labtec Enterprises
3801 N.E. 109th Ave.
Suite J
Vancouver, WA 98682
Main................................(360) 896-2000
Tech. Supp. Fax ....(360) 896-2020
WWW................................ http://www.labtec.com

Lan-Link Corp.
944 Goddard
St Luis, MO 63005
Main................................(314) 537-9800

Landmark Research International
703 Grand Central St.
Clearwater, FL 34616
Main................................(800) 683-6696

Lanex Corp.
7120 Columbia Gateway Dr.
Columbia, MD 21046
Main...(800) 638-5969
Tech. Support ....(301) 312-2200
BBS..(301) 312-2225

LanMaster
1401 N 14th St.
Temple, TX 76601
Main...(800) 441-6189
Tech. Support ....(817) 771-2124

LANNET Data Communications, Ltd.
7711 Center Ave., #600
Huntington Beach, CA 92647
Main...(714) 891-5580
BBS..(714) 891-7788

LANSystems, Inc.
300 Park Ave. S
New York, NY 10010
Main...(800) 458-5267
Tech. Support ....(800) 628-5267
BBS..(212) 995-8604

Lantronix
15353 Baranca Pkwy.
Irvine, CA 92718
Main...(800) 422-7022
Customer Svc. ....(714) 453-3990
Tech. Support ....(800) 422-7044
Tech. Supp. Fax ....(714) 453-3995
WWW........................... http://www.lantronix.com/

LanWorks
3218 Wharton Way
Mississauga, ONT L4X 2C
Canada
Main...(905) 238-5528
BBS..(416) 238-9407

Laptop Shop, The
7420 Fullerton Rd., #113
Springfield, VA 22153
Main ....(800) 753-7071
Tech. Support..............................(800) 753-7071
BBS..(703) 912-6918

Larse Corp.
4600 Patrick Henry Dr.
PO Box 58138
Santa Clara, CA 95054
Main ....(408) 988-6600
Tech. Supp. Fax..........................(408) 986-8690
BBS..(408) 986-8690
WWW..............................http://www.larscom.com

Laser Communications, Inc.
1848 Charter Ln, #F
Lancaster, PA 17601
Main ....(717) 394-8634
BBS..(717) 396-9831

Laser Magnetic Storage
4425 Arrows West Dr.
Colorado Springs, CO 80907
Main ....(800) 777-5674
Tech. Support..............................(719) 593-7900
BBS..(719) 599-8713

Laser Master
7092 Shady Oak Rd.
Eden Praire, MN 55344
Main ....(800) 468-1732
Tech. Support..............................(619) 941-4919
Tech. Supp. Fax..........................(612) 941-8652

LaserGo, Inc.
9369 Carroll Park Dr, #A
San Diego, CA 92121
Main ....(800) 955-3668
Tech. Support..............................(619) 450-4600

LaserMaster
6900 Shady Oak Rd.
Eden Prairie, MN 55344
Main...(800) 477-7717
Customer Svc................................(612) 944-9457
Tech. Support................................(612) 944-9331
Tech. Supp. Fax............................(612) 944-6932
E-Mail...support@lmt.com
WWW......................http://www.lasermaster.com/

Laserplex
304 S Abbott Ave.
Milpitas, CA 95035
Main...(719) 599-4242
BBS ....(408) 946-0232

Lattice, Inc.
2500 S Highland Ave.
Lombard, IL 60148
Main...(800) 444-4309
Tech. Support................................(708) 916-1600

Leading Edge
117 Flanders Rd.
Westborough, MA 01581
Tech. Support................................(508) 562-3322
BBS ....(508) 836-3274

Leading Spect
1025 Segovia Circle
Placentia, CA 92670
Main...(714) 666-2626
Tech. Supp. Fax............................(714) 666-2900

Leasemetric, Inc.
1164 Triton Dr.
Foster City, CA 94404
Main...(800) 553-2255
BBS ....(415) 341-2651

Legacy Storage Systems, Inc.
200 Butterfield Dr., #B
Ashland, MA 01721
Main...(800) 966-6442
Tech. Support................................(508) 881-6442

Legato Systems, Inc.
260 Sheridan Ave.
Palo Alto, CA 94306
WWW ....http://www.legato.com/

Lemcom Systems, Inc.
9033 N 24th Ave. Suite 7
Phoenix, AZ 85201-2847
Main...(602) 944-1543
Tech. Supp. Fax ....(602) 943-2601
BBS...(602) 943-2601

Leo Electronics
PO Box 11307
Torrance, CA
Main...(800) 421-9565
Tech. Support ....(310) 212-6133
Tech. Supp. Fax ....(310) 212-6106
BBS...(310) 212-6106
WWW ....http://www.excess.com

Letraset Graphic Design Software
40 Eisenhower Dr.
Paramus, NJ 07653
Main...(201) 845-6100

Leviton Telcom
2222 222nd Street SE
Bothell, WA 98021-4416
Main...(800) 722-2082
Tech. Support ....(206) 486-2222
BBS...(206) 483-5270

Lexmark International
740 New Circle Rd.
Lexington, KY 40511
Main...(606) 232-2000
Customer Svc. ....(800) 453-9872
Tech. Support ....(800) 453-9872
Tech. Supp. Fax ....(606) 232-5238
BBS...(606) 232-5238
E-Mail..................ftp://ftp.lexmark.com/pub/driver
WWW ....http://www.lexmark.com

LG Electronics U.S.A., Inc.
1000 Sylvan Ave.
Englewood Cliffs, NJ 07632
Main...(201) 816-2000
Customer Svc. ....(800) 777-1192
Tech. Support ....(800) 777-1192
BBS...(205) 772-4612

Libert Corp.
1050 Dearborn Dr
Columbus, OH 43229
Main...(614) 888-0246
Tech. Supp. Fax ....(614) 841-6973

Liberty
120 Saratoga Ave., #82
Santa Clara, CA 95051
Main...(408) 983-1127
Tech. Supp. Fax ....(408) 243-2885
BBS...(408) 243-2885

Lind Electronic Design
414 Cambridge St.
Minneapolis, MN 55426
Main...(800) 697-3701
Customer Svc. ....(612) 927-6303
Tech. Support ....(612) 927-6303

Lindo Systems, Inc.
1415 N Dayton Ave.
Chicago, IL 06062
Main...(800) 441-2378

Link Computer, Inc.
560 S Melrose St.
Placentia, CA 92670
Main...(714) 993-6976

Link Technologies
3471 N. First St.
San Jose, CA 95134
Main...(408) 473-1700
Customer Svc. ....(800) 448-5465
Tech. Support ....(800) 448-5465
Tech. Supp. Fax ....(510) 623-6680
BBS...(510) 623-6680

Linotype-Hell Co.
425 Oser Ave.
Hauppage, NY 11788-9890
Main ....(800) 633-1900
Tech. Support...............................(516) 434-2000

Litespeed Software
1800 19th St.
Bakersfield, CA 93301
Main ....(805) 324-4291
Tech. Supp. Fax...........................(805) 324-1437
BBS...(805) 324-1437
WWW...............................http://www.litespeed.net

Litton Poly-Scientific
1213 N Main St.
Blacksburg, VA 24060
Main ....(800) 336-5917
Tech. Support...............................(703) 953-4751
BBS...(703) 953-1841

Loadstar Distributing
14412 E Valley Blvd.
City of Industry, CA 91746
Main ....(818) 369-5833
Tech. Support...............................(818) 369-5833
BBS...(818) 369-7846

Locus Computing
9800 La Cienega Blvd.
Inglewood, CA 90301-4440
Main ....(310) 670-6500
Customer Svc...............................(310) 670-6500
Tech. Support...............................(310) 337-5995
Tech. Supp. Fax...........................(310) 670-2980
BBS...(310) 670-2980
WWW.................................. http://www.locus.com
FTP Address ....ftp://ftp.locus.com/pub

Logal Software, Inc.
125 Cambridge Park Dr.
Cambridge, MA 02140
Main ....(617) 491-4440
WWW................................... http://www.logal.com

Logitech
6505 Kaiser Dr.
Fremont, CA 94555
Main...(510) 795-8500
Customer Svc................................(800) 231-7717
Tech. Support..............................(510) 795-8100
Sales ....(800) 231-7717
Tech. Supp. Fax..........................(510) 505-0978
BBS ....(510) 795-0408
E-Mail ....tech_support@logitech.com
CompuServe ....GO LOGITECH

Lomas Data Products
182 Cedar Hill St
Marlboro, MA 01752
Main...(508) 460-0333

Longshine Technology
2013 N Capitol Ave.
San Jose, CA 95132
Main...(408) 942-1746
BBS ....(408) 942-1745

Lotus Development
55 Cambridge Pky.
Cambridge, MA 02142
Main...(617) 577-8500
Customer Svc................................(800) 345-1043
Tech. Support..............................(800) 223-1662
BBS ....(617) 693-7001
WWW....................http://www.support.lotus.com/
FTP Address................ftp.support.lotus.com/pub

Lotus Word Processing
5600 Glenridge Dr
Atlanta, GA 30342

LSI Logic Corp.
WWW..............................http://www.lsilogic.com/

Lucas Management Systems, Inc.
12701 Fair Lakes Cir, #350
Fairfax, VA 22033
Main...(703) 222-1111
BBS ....(703) 222-8203

Luncity
100 Brickstone Sq
Andover, MA 01810
Main...(800) 526-2489
Tech. Support ....(508) 475-4050
Tech. Supp. Fax ....(508) 475-0550
BBS..(508) 475-0550
E-Mail...lcb@luncity.com

M & T Books
501 Galveston Dr
Redwood City, CA 94063
Main..(800) 628-9658

M-USA Business Systems, Inc.
18111 Preston Rd., #500
Dallas, TX 75252
Main..(800) 421-5355

Mac Avenue
12303 Technology Blvd.
Austin, TX 78727
Main..(512) 331-0446

Macmillan Computer Publishing
201 West 103rd Street
Indianapolis, IN 46290-1094
Main..(317) 581-3500
WWW................................. http://www.mcp.com/

Macmillan New Media
201 W. 103rd St.
Indianapolis, IN 46290
Main..(317) 581-3500
Customer Svc. ....(617) 225-9023
Tech. Support ....(617) 661-2955

Macola Software
333 E Center St, PO Box 485
Marion, OH 43301-0485
Main..(800) 468-0834
Tech. Support ....(614) 382-5999
BBS..(614) 382-0239

Macromedia
600 Townsend St.
San Francisco, CA 94103
Main...(415) 252-2000
Tech. Support...............................(415) 252-9080
Tech. Supp. Fax ....(415) 863-4409
WWW.....................http://www.macromedia.com
FTP Address........................ftp.macromedia.com
CompuServe.........................GO MACROMEDIA
America Online ....macromedia@aol.com

MacroMind, Inc.
600 Townsend St
San Francisco, CA 94103
Main...(800) 248-4477
Tech. Support ....(415) 442-0200

Macronix, Inc.
1348 Riddler Pk Dr
San Jose, CA 95131
Main...(800) 468-4629
BBS...(408) 453-8488
WWW............................http://www.modems.com

Macros Solutions Ltd.
WWW..................................http://www.bittco.com

Macrosft-Whitney
WWW.............................http://www.bancroft.com

Macrosn's New Media
WWW............................http://www.compton.com

Macrosne Software, Inc.
WWW.................................. http://www.chey.com

Macsyma Mathematical Software
WWWhttp://www.digital.com/gnn/meta/internet/mkt/
       macsy

Madge Networks America
2310 North First Street
San Jose, CA 95131-1101
Main .... (408) 955-0700
Customer Svc.................................. (800) 876-2343
Tech. Support................................ (800) 876-2343
Sales .... (408) 955-0700
Tech. Supp. Fax.............................. (408) 955-0970
BBS .... (408) 955-0262
WWW................................. http://www.madge.com

Madison Cable
125 Goddard Memorial Dr
Worcester, MA 01603
Main .... (508) 752-7320
BBS... (508) 752-4230

Mag InnoVision
2801 S. Yale St.
Santa Ana, CA 92704
Main .... (714) 751-2008
Customer Svc................................. (714) 751-2008
Tech. Support................................. (714) 751-2008
Sales .... (714) 751-2008
Tech. Supp. Fax............................ (714) 751-5522
E-Mail .... hr@maginnovision.com
WWW...................http://www.maginnovision.com

Magee Enterprises, Inc.
PO Box 1587
Norcross, GA 30071
Main .... (800) 662-4330
Tech. Support................................. (770) 446-6611
Tech. Supp. Fax............................. (770) 368-0719
BBS .... (404) 368-0719

Magic Software
1200 Main St. Suite B
Irvine, CA 92714
Main .... (800) 345-6244
Tech. Support.............................. (714) 250-1720
Tech. Supp. Fax........................... (714) 250-7404
BBS .... (714) 250-8945
WWW............................ http://www.magic-sw.com
CompuServe ....70521.645@compuserve.com

Magic Solutions
610 Vermeulen Pl
Franklin Lakes, NJ 07417
Main..(201) 587-1515
BBS...(201) 529-1808

Magitronic Technology, Inc.
10 Hub Dr
Melville, NY 11747
Main..(516) 454-8255
Tech. Support...............................(800) 347-5454
BBS...(516) 454-8266

Magix Computer Products
1840 W 220th St, #305
Torrance, CA 90501
Main..(800) 878-6249
Tech. Support...............................(213) 782-3553
BBS...(213) 782-3866

Magnavox/Phillips
1 Philips Dr.
Knoxville, TN 37914
Main..(423) 521-3260
Customer Svc..............................(310) 217-1300
Tech. Support...............................(900) 555-5500
BBS...(310) 532-6436
WWW.........................http://www.magnavox.com

Main Street Computer
1656 Main St
Sarasota, FL 34236
Main..(800) 456-6246
Tech. Support...............................(813) 954-9017

Management Systems Designers
131 Park St NE
Vienna, VA 22180
Main..(703) 281-7440
BBS...(703) 281-7636

Manhattan Electric Cable
203 Progress Dr
Manhattan, CT 06040
Main..(800) 228-6322
Tech. Support...............................(914) 967-8000
Tech. Supp. Fax..........................(860) 643-3556
BBS...(914) 967-1616

Mannesmann Tally Corp.
8301 S 180th St, PO Box 97018
Kent, WA 98064
Main..(800) 843-1347
Tech. Support...............................(206) 251-5524
BBS...(206) 251-5520
WWW...............................http://www.tally.com

Mansfield Software Group
PO Box 532
Storrs, CT 06268
Main..(203) 429-8402
Tech. Supp. Fax..........................(860) 487-1185

MapInfo Corp.
200 Broadway
Troy, NY 12180
Main..(800) 327-8627
Tech. Support...............................(518) 274-8673

Mark of the Unicorn
222 3rd St
Cambridge, MA 02142
Main..(617) 576-2760

MarketSmart
WWW.....................http://www.marketsmart.com

Massachusetts Institute of Technology
One Amherst St
Cambridge, MA 02139
Main..(617) 253-8408

Mastersoft, Inc.
6991 E Camelback Rd., #A-320
Scottsdale, AZ 85251
Main..(800) 624-6107
Tech. Support...............................(602) 277-0900
BBS...(602) 970-0706

Mathematica, Inc.
402 S Kentucky Ave., #210
Lakeland, FL 33801
Main...(800) 852-6284
Customer Svc. ....(800) 852-6284
Tech. Support ....(813) 682-1128
BBS...(813) 686-5969

MathSoft
101 Main Street
Cambridge, MA 02142-1521
Main...(617) 577-1017
Customer Svc. ....(800) 628-4223
Tech. Support ....(617) 577-1778
Sales..(800) 628-4223
Tech. Supp. Fax ....(617) 577-8829
E-Mail...............................support@mathsoft.com
WWW...........................http://www.mathsoft.com/

MathSoft Europe
WWW...........................http://www.mathsoft.com

Mathtype
WWW...........http://www.mathtype.com/mathtype

MathWorks, Inc., The
Cochituate Place, 24 Prime Park Wy
Natick, MA 01760
Main...(508) 647-7000
BBS...(508) 653-2997
WWW.......................http://www.mathworks.com/

MatrixSoft - SWAG
WWW................http://www.interlog.com/~jfanjoy

Matrox Electronic Systems
1025 St. Regis
Dorval, PQ H9P2T4
Canada
Main...(514) 685-2630
Customer Svc. ....(514) 685-2630
Tech. Support ....(514) 685-2630
Sales..(514) 685-2630
Tech. Supp. Fax ....(514) 685-2853
BBS...(514) 685-6008
WWW...........................http://www.matrox.com

Maxell Corp. of America
22-08 Rt 208
Fair Lawn, NJ 07410

Maxim Technology
3930 W 29th S, #35
Wichita, KS 67217
Main .... (316) 941-9797
Tech. Support............................... (316) 941-9797
BBS... (316) 941-9883

Maximum Computer Technologies
WWW............................http://www.maxtech.com/

Maximum Strategy
WWW........................... http://www.maxstrat.com/

Maxis
2121 North California Blvd. Suite 60
Walnut Creek, CA 94596-3572
Main .... (510) 933-5630
Customer Svc............................... (800) 336-2947
Tech. Support............................... (510) 927-3905
Sales .... (800) 336-2947
Tech. Supp. Fax........................... (510) 927-3581
BBS... (510) 254-3869
E-Mail .... support@maxis.com
WWW...................................... http://www.maxis.com
FTP Address ....ftp 199.182.213.85
CompuServe .... GO GAMPUB
America Online...........................maxis@aol.com

Maxpeed Corp.
1120 Chess Dr
Foster City, CA 94404
Main .... (415) 345-5447
BBS... (415) 345-6398

MaxTech
WWW............................http://www.maxtech.com/

Maxtor - California
211 River Oaks Pkwy
Sante Fe, CA 95134
Main..(800) 262-9867
Tech. Support................................(408) 432-1700
BBS ....(408) 433-0457
WWW..............................http://www.maxtor.com/

Maxtor - Colorado
1861 Lefthand Cir
Longmont, CO 80501
Main..(800) 356-5333
Tech. Support................................(800) 262-9867
WWW..............................http://www.maxtor.com/

MBP Software & Systems Technology
1131 Harbor Bay Pkwy, #260
Alameda, CA 94501-6540
Main..(800) 231-6342
Tech. Support................................(415) 769-5333
BBS ....(415) 769-5735

McAfee Associates
2710 Walsh Ave.
Santa Clara, CA 95051
Main..(408) 988-3832
Customer Svc.................................(908) 530-0440
Tech. Support................................(408) 970-9727
Sales ....(408) 988-3832
Tech. Supp. Fax.............................(408) 970-9727
BBS ....(408) 970-9727
E-Mail ....support@mcafee.com
WWW..............................http://www.mcafee.com
FTP Address................................ftp.mcafee.com
CompuServe ....GO MCAFEE
America Online..MCAFEE

MCBA, Inc.
330 N. Brand Blvd.
Glendale, CA91203
Main..(818) 242-9600
Tech. Supp. Fax.............................(818) 500-4805
BBS ....(818) 500-4805

McCarty Associates, Inc.
455 Boston Post Rd.
Old Saybrook, CT 06475-9949
Main ....(203) 388-6994
BBS...(203) 388-6826

McCaw Cellular Communications
WWW..............................http://www.airdata.com/

McData
310 Interlocken Pkwy
Bloomfield, CO 80021
Main..(800) 545-5773
Tech. Support ....(303) 460-9200
BBS...(303) 465-4996

McDonnell Douglas Communication
5299 DTC Blvd.
Englewood, CO 80111
Main..(303) 769-9400

McDonnell Douglas Network Systems
2560 N 1st St, PO Box 49019
San Jose, CA 95161
Main..(408) 432-5254

MCI Communications Corp.
1133 19th St NW
Washington, DC 20036
Main..(202) 872-1600

Measurement & Control Products
415 Madison Ave., 22nd Floor
New York, NY 10164
Main..(212) 662-6012

MECC
6160 Summit Dr. North
Minneapolis, MN 55430-4003
Main..(612) 569-1500
WWW.............................. http://www.mecc.com/

Media Cybernetics, Inc.
8484 Georgia Ave., #200
Silver Spring, MD 20910
Main..(800) 992-4256
Tech. Support ....(301) 495-3305
BBS...(301) 495-5964

Media Factory
1930 Junction
San Jose, CA 95131
Main..(800) 879-9536
Tech. Support ....(800) 879-9536
Tech. Supp. Fax ....(408) 954-8915
BBS...(408) 954-8915
WWWhttp://www.mediafactoryinc.com/index.html

Media Mosaic
WWW...................http://www.media-mosaic.com

Media Source
120 Interstate N Pkwy E, #200
Atlanta, GA 30339
Main..(800) 356-2553
Tech. Support ....(404) 952-2990
BBS...(404) 952-1432

Media Synergy
WWW..........................http://www.mediasyn.com

Media Vision, Inc.
47221 Fremont Blvd.
Fremont, CA 94538
Main..(800) 638-2807
Tech. Support ....(510) 770-9905
BBS...(510) 770-8648
WWW.......................... http://www.mediavis.com

MegaHaus
2201 Pine Dr.
Dickenson, TX 77539
Main..(800) 426-0560
Tech. Support ....(713) 333-1944
BBS...(713) 333-3024

Megahertz
605 North 5600 West
Salt Lake City, UT 84116
Main .... (800) 527-8677
Customer Svc................................ (801) 320-7777
Tech. Support................................ (801) 320-7777
Sales .... (800) 527-8677
Tech. Supp. Fax........................... (801) 320-6020
BBS... (801) 320-8841
E-Mail...............................techsupport@mhz.com
WWW.........................http://www.megahertz.com
FTP Address ....ftp.megahertz.com
CompuServe ....GO MEGAHERTZ
America Online........................GO MEGAHERTZ

Megasource
32100 Telegraph Rd., #220
Birmingham, MN 48010
Main .... (313) 647-5977
BBS... (313) 647-1260

Megatel Computer Corp.
125 Wendell Ave.
Weston, ONT M9N 3K9
Canada
Main .... (416) 245-2953
BBS... (416) 245-6505

MEI/Micro Center
1100 Suiteelwood Rd.
Columbus, OH 43312
Main .... (800) 634-3478
Tech. Support............................... (614) 481-4417
BBS... (614) 486-6417
WWW.................................http://www.meiu.com

Meiko
WWW................................http://www.meiko.com/

Memorex Telex
WWW....................................http://www.mtc.com/

Mendelson Electronics
340 E 1st St
Dayton, OH 45402
Main.................................(800) 422-3525
Tech. Support..........................(513) 461-3525
BBS....................................(513) 461-3391

Meridian Data, Inc.
5615 Scotts Valley Dr
Scotts Valley, CA 95066
Main.................................(408) 438-3100
BBS...................................(408) 438-6816
WWW....................http://www.meridiandata.com

Merisel
200 Continental Blvd.
Segundo, CA 90245
Main.................................(800) 645-7778
Tech. Support..........................(213) 537-7771
Sales..................................(310) 615-3080

Merritt Computer Products, Inc.
5565 Red Bird Center Dr, #150
Dallas, TX 75237
Main.................................(214) 339-0753
BBS...................................(214) 339-1313

Meta Software Corp.
150 Cambridge Park Dr
Cambridge, MA 02140
Main.................................(800) 227-4106
Tech. Support..........................(617) 576-6920

Metagraphics Software Corp.
200 Clock Tower Pl Suite 201E
Carmel, CA 93923
Main.................................(800) 332-1550
Tech. Support..........................(408) 438-1550
Tech. Supp. Fax.......................(408) 622-8945
BBS...................................(408) 438-5379

MetaTools, Inc.
WWW......................http://www.hsc.com/

Methode Electronics
7444 W Wilson Ave.
Chicago, IL 60656
Main.................................(800) 323-6858
Tech. Support..........................(708) 867-9600
BBS...................................(708) 867-9130

Metra Information Systems
4539 N. Port Loop
Fremont, CA 94538
Main.................................(800) 733-9188
Tech. Supp. Fax.......................(510) 226-0231
BBS...................................(408) 730-5933

MetraByte Corp.
440 Myles Standish Blvd.
Tauton, MA 02780
Main.................................(508) 880-3000

Metrics Inc.
WWW......................http://www.metrics.com/

Mextel Corp.
159 Beeline Rd.
Bensenville, IL 60106
Main.................................(800) 888-4146
Tech. Support..........................(312) 595-4146
Tech. Supp. Fax.......................(708) 595-4149

Meyer & Associates, Inc.
231 Market Pl, #185
San Ramon, CA 94583
Main.................................(415) 277-1975

Mibro, Inc.
64 W 36th St
New York, NY 10016
Main.................................(800) 223-0322
BBS...................................(212) 695-0982

Mica Computer Center
10204 Norwalk Blvd.
Santa Fe, CA 90670
Main.................................(800) 872-6422
Tech. Support..........................(213) 944-1850
BBS...................................(213) 941-3958

Micom Communications
4100 Los Angeles Ave.
Semi Valley, CA 93063
Main ....(800) 642-6687
Tech. Support ....(805) 583-8600
Tech. Supp. Fax ....(805) 583-1997

Micom-Interlan, Inc.
155 Swanson Rd.
Boxboro, MA 01719
Main ....(800) 526-8255

Micro Computer Systems Inc.
WWW ....http://www.mcsdallas.com/

Micro Design International
6566 University Blvd.
Winter Park, FL 32792
Main ....(407) 677-8333
BBS ....(407) 677-8365

Micro Dynamics
8555 16th St, #700
Silver Springs, MD 20910
Main ....(301) 589-6300
Tech. Supp. Fax ....(301) 589-3414

Micro Express, Inc.
1811 Kaiser Ave.
Irvine, CA 92714
Main ....(800) 989-9900
Tech. Support ....(714) 852-1400
Tech. Supp. Fax ....(714) 852-1225
BBS ....(714) 852-1225

Micro Integration
1 Science Park
Fastburg, ML 27532
Main ....(800) 832-4526
Sales ....(301) 369-0842
Tech. Supp. Fax ....(301) 689-0808
BBS ....(301) 777-3462

Micro Logic Corp.
89 Leuning St.
S. Hackensack, NJ 07602
Main ....(800) 342-5930
Tech. Support ....(201) 342-2462
Tech. Supp. Fax ....(201) 342-0370
BBS ....(201) 342-0370
WWW ....http://www.miclog.com

Micro Sense
320 Andrew Ave.
Leucadia, CA 92024
Main ....(800) 544-4252
Tech. Support ....(619) 632-8621
Tech. Supp. Fax ....(619) 753-6133
BBS ....(619) 753-6133
WWW ....http://www.microsense.com

Micro Smart, Inc.
200 Homer Ave.
Ashland, MA 01721
Main ....(800) 370-9090
Tech. Support ....(508) 872-9090
Tech. Supp. Fax ....(508) 881-7708
BBS ....(508) 881-1520

Micro Solutions Computer Products
132 W Lincoln Hwy
DeKalb, IL 60115
Main ....(815) 756-3411
BBS ....(815) 756-2928

Micro Sports
Customer Svc ....(800) 937-7737
Tech. Support ....(615) 877-7815
BBS ....(615) 870-5694
E-Mail ....support@microsports.com
WWW ....http://www.microsports.com/

Micro Star
1105 2nd St
Encinitas, CA 92024
Main ....(800) 444-1343
Tech. Support ....(619) 436-0493

Micro Systems
1524 County Line Rd.
York Springs, PA 17372
Main..(800) 548-5182
Tech. Support..............................(717) 528-8802

Micro Technology, Inc.
490 S E. LaPalma
Anaheim, CA 92807
Main..(800) 999-9684
Tech. Support..............................(714) 970-0300
Tech. Supp. Fax...........................(714) 693-2202

Micro World Computers
9090 N Suitemmons Frwy
Dallas, TX 75247
Main..(800) 825-6050
Tech. Support..............................(214) 637-0522
BBS...(214) 631-4817

MicroBiz
300 Corporate Dr.
Mahwah, NJ 07430
Main..(800) 637-8268
Tech. Support..............................(914) 592-2120
Tech. Supp. Fax...........................(201) 512-1919
BBS...(914) 592-2192
WWW..............................http://www.microbiz.com

MicroCal, Inc.
22 Industrial Dr E
Northampton, MA 01060
Main..(800) 969-7720
Tech. Support..............................(413) 586-7720
BBS...(413) 586-0149

Microchip Technology Inc.A1247
2355 West Chandler Blvd.
Chandler, AZ 85224
Main..(508) 480-9990
Sales...(508) 480-9990
WWW.............http://www.ultranet.com/biz/mchip/

Microcom Systems, Inc.
500 River Ridge Dr
Norwood, MA 02062
Main..(800) 822-8224
Tech. Support..............................(617) 551-1999
BBS...(617) 551-1968
WWW..........................http://www.microcom.com

MicroComputer Accessories, Inc.
5405 Jandy Pl, PO Box 66911
Los Angeles, CA 90066-0911
Main..(800) 521-8270
BBS...(213) 306-8739

Microcomputer Concepts
15200 Tranistor Ln
Huntington Beach, CA 92649
Main..(800) 772-3914
Tech. Support..............................(714) 898-3002
Sales...(714) 898-3002

Microdyne / Eagle Technology
3601 Eisenhower Ave.
Suite No 300
Alexandria, VA 22304
Main..(703) 329-3700
Customer Svc...............................(800) 726-5267
Tech. Support..............................(800) 726-5267
Sales...(800) 726-5267
Tech. Supp. Fax...........................(703) 329-3721
BBS...(703) 960-8509
E-Mail.............................techsup@mcdy.com
WWW..............................http://www.mcdy.com
FTP Address.................................ftp.mcdy.com
CompuServe.............................GO MICRODYNE

Microdyne Corp.
207 S Peyton St
Alexanderia, VA 22314
Main..(800) 366-4526
Tech. Support..............................(703) 739-0500
BBS...(703) 683-8924
WWW..............................http://www.mcdy.com

Microfield Graphics, Inc.
9825 SW Sunchine Ct
Beaverton, OR 97005
Main ....(800) 334-4922
Tech. Support ....(503) 626-9393
Tech. Supp. Fax ....(503) 641-9331
BBS..(503) 641-9333

MicroGate Corp.
9501 Capital of Texas Hwy
Austin, TX 78720-3398
Main................................(800) 444-1982
Tech. Support ....(512) 345-7791
Sales..(512) 345-7791

Micrografx
1303 E. Arapaho Rd.
Richardson, TX 75081
Main................................(800) 371-7783
Customer Svc. ....(800) 733-3729
Tech. Support ....(800) 733-3729
BBS................................(214) 234-2694
WWW.........................http://www.micrografx.com

MicroHelp
Main................................(770) 516-0899
Customer Svc. ....(770) 516-0899
Tech. Support ....(770) 516-0899
Sales................................(800) 775-8645
BBS................................(404) 516-1497
WWW.........................http://www.microhelp.com

Microlab, Inc.
22976 Freeway Pk Dr
Farmington Hills, MI 48024
Main................................(810) 474-7711
BBS................................(313) 474-7291

Microline Computers
46757 Fremont Blvd.
Fremont, CA 94538
Main................................(415) 770-1900
Tech. Support ....(415) 770-1903
BBS................................(415) 770-1912

Microlite Corp.
2315 Mill St.
Ali Quippa, PA 15001-2228
Main ....(412) 375-6711
Tech. Support...............................(412) 375-6711
Tech. Supp. Fax...........................(412) 375-6908
BBS.. (127) 717-125
WWW............................. http://www.microlite.com

Microlytics, Inc.
2 Tobey Village Office Pk
Pittsford, NY 14354
Main .... (800) 828-6293
Tech. Support...............................(716) 248-9150

Micron Technology
WWW...............................http://www.micron.com

Micron Technology, Inc.
8000 S. Federal Way (mail stop 407)
Boise, ID 83707
Main .... (208) 368-4400
Tech. Support...............................(800) 642-7661
Tech. Supp. Fax...........................(208) 368-4435
WWW...............................http://www.micron.com

MicroNet Technology
80 Technology
Irvine, CA 92718
Main .... (714) 453-6100
Customer Svc...............................(714) 453-6100
Tech. Support...............................(714) 453-6060
Sales .... (714) 453-6101
Tech. Supp. Fax...........................(714) 453-6101
BBS .... (714) 837-7164
E-Mail...................................tech@micronet.com
WWW........................... http://www.micronet.com

Micronics/Orchard Technology
221 Warren Ave.
Fremont, CA 94539-7085
Main .... (510) 651-2300
Customer Svc...............................(510) 683-0323
Tech. Support...............................(510) 661-3000
Sales .... (510) 683-0323
Tech. Supp. Fax...........................(510) 651-6982
BBS .... (510) 651-6837

Micropolis
21211 Nordhoff St.
Chatsworth, CA 91311
Main..............................(818) 709-3300
Customer Svc.............................(818) 709-3325
Tech. Support....................(818) 709-3325
Tech. Supp. Fax...........................(818) 709-3497
BBS................................(818) 709-3310
WWW.........................http://www.micropolis.com/

MicroPress, Inc.
68-30 Harro St.
Forest Hills, NY 11375
Main...............................(718) 575-1816
Tech. Supp. Fax...........................(718) 575-8038
E-Mail............salessupport@micropress-inc.com
WWW..................http://www.micropress-inc.com

Microprocessors Unlimited, Inc.
24000 S Peoria Ave.
Beggs, OK 74421
Main...............................(918) 267-4961
Tech. Support...............................(918) 267-4966
Tech. Supp. Fax...........................(918) 267-3879
BBS................................(918) 267-3879

MicroProse Software, Inc.
180 Lakefront Dr
Hunt Valley, MD 21030
Main..............................(410) 771-1151
WWW.......................http://www.microprose.com/

Microprose/Spectrum Holobyte
WWW.......................http://www.microprose.com

Microrim, Inc.
15395 SE 30th Pl
Bellevue, WA 98007
Main...............................(800) 248-2001
Tech. Support..............................(206) 649-9500
Tech. Supp. Fax...........................(206) 746-9350
E-Mail..............support@microrim.com

Microsales
7701 NW 56th St
Miami, FL 33166
Main..............................(800) 222-8324
Tech. Support..............................(305) 477-7140
Tech. Supp. Fax...........................(305) 477-7342
BBS................................(305) 599-9586

MicroSim Corp.
20 Fairbanks
Irvine, CA 92718-9905
Main..............................(800) 245-3022
Tech. Support..............................(714) 770-3022

MicroSlate
9625 Ignace St, #D
Brossard, Quebec J4Y 2P3
Canada
Main...............................(514) 444-3680
Tech. Supp. Fax...........................(514) 444-3683
BBS................................(514) 444-3683

Microsoft Corp.
1 Microsoft Way
Redmond, WA 98025-6399
Main..............................(206) 882-8080
Customer Svc. ....(800) 426-9400
Tech. Support..............................(206) 635-3313
BBS................................(206) 936-6735
WWW.........................http://www.microsoft.com/

Microsoft Corp.
1 Microsoft Way
Redmond, WA 98025-6399
WWW.........................http://www.microsoft.com

Microsoft Corp. - Basic
1 Microsoft Way
Redmond, WA 98025-6399
Main..............................(800) 426-9400
WWW.........................http://www.microsoft.com

Microsoft Corp. - Developer Support
1 Microsoft Way
Redmond, WA 98025-6399
Main..............................(800) 426-9400
WWW.........................http://www.microsoft.com

Microsoft Corp. - DOS 5 & 6
1 Microsoft Way
Redmond, WA 98025-6399
Main...(800) 426-9400
Tech. Support ....(206) 646-5104
WWW............................ http://www.microsoft.com

Microsoft Corp. - DOS support
1 Microsoft Way
Redmond, WA 98025-6399
Main...(800) 426-9400
WWW............................ http://www.microsoft.com

Microsoft Corp. - Language Support
1 Microsoft Way
Redmond, WA 98025-6399
Main...(800) 426-9400
WWW............................ http://www.microsoft.com

Microsoft Corp. - MS Word Support
1 Microsoft Way
Redmond, WA 98025-6399
Main...(800) 426-9400
Tech. Support ....(206) 462-9673
WWW............................ http://www.microsoft.com

Microsoft Corp. - OS/2
1 Microsoft Way
Redmond, WA 98025-6399
Main...(800) 426-9400
WWW............................ http://www.microsoft.com

Microsoft Corp. - Sales
1 Microsoft Way
Redmond, WA 98025-6399
Main...(800) 426-9400
Tech. Support ....(206) 637-7098
WWW............................ http://www.microsoft.com

Microsoft Corp. - Windows Technical
1 Microsoft Way
Redmond, WA 98025-6399
Main...(800) 426-9400
WWW............................ http://www.microsoft.com

Microsoft's Advanced Technology
WWW........... http://www.research.microsoft.com/

Microsolutions Computer Products
132 W Lincoln Hwy
DeKalb, IL 60115
Main .... (815) 756-3411

MicroSpeed
5005 Brandin Ct.
Fremont, CA 94538
Main .... (510) 490-1403
Customer Svc.............................. (800) 232-7888
Tech. Support.............................. (800) 232-7888
Sales .... (800) 232-7888
Tech. Supp. Fax........................... (510) 490-1665
BBS .... (510) 490-1664
WWW........................ http://www.microspeed.com
FTP Address .... ftp.mircospeed.com

Microstar Computer Technology
3180 Olympic Blvd.
Santa Monica, CA 90404
Main .... (213) 453-7500

Microstar Lab.
WWW......... http://www.mstarlabs.com/mstarlabs/

Microsystems Software, Inc.
600 Worcester Rd.
Framingham, MA 01701
Main .... (508) 626-8511
Tech. Supp. Fax........................... (508) 626-8515
BBS .... (508) 626-8515
E-Mail.............................. support@microsys.com
WWW............................ http://www.microsys.com

MicroTech
7304 15th Ave. NE
Seattle, WA 98115
Main .... (800) 521-9035
Tech. Support.............................. (206) 526-7989
Tech. Supp. Fax........................... (206) 522-6727
BBS .... (206) 522-6727

Microtek Lab
3715 Doolittle Dr.
Redondo Beach, CA 90278
Main.................................(310) 297-5000
Customer Svc.................(310) 297-5000
Tech. Support..................(310) 297-5000
BBS................................(310) 297-5102
WWW....................http://www.mri.com/

Microtek Lab, Inc.
680 Knox St
Torrance, CA 90502
Main.................................(800) 654-4160

Microtest, Inc.
4747 N. 22nd St.
Phoenix, AZ 85016
Main.................................(800) 526-9675
Tech. Supp. Fax.............(602) 952-6660
BBS................................(602) 971-6963
WWW.........................http://www.microtest.com

MicroUnity
WWW.........................http://www.microunity.com/

MicroVideo Learning Systems
250 Park Ave. S. 10th Floor
New York, NY 10011
Main.................................(800) 231-4021
Tech. Support..................(212) 777-9595
Tech. Supp. Fax.............(212) 777-9597

Microware Distributors - WA
18465 NE 65th St
Redmond, WA 98052
Main.................................(800) 888-6349

Microwave Filter Co, Inc.
6743 Kinne St
East Syracuse, NY 13057
Main.................................(800) 448-1666
Tech. Support..................(315) 437-3953
Tech. Supp. Fax.............(315) 463-1467
BBS................................(315) 463-1467
America Online...............mfc@as.com

Microwave Networks
10795 Rockley Rd.
Houston, TX 77099
Main................................(713) 495-7123
Tech. Supp. Fax.............(713) 495-8728

Microwave Radio Comm
20 Alpha Rd.
Chelmsford, MA 01824-4168
Main................................(508) 250-1110
BBS................................(508) 256-5215

MicroWay, Inc.
PO Box 79
Kingston, MA 02364
Main................................(508) 746-7341
Tech. Supp. Fax.............(508) 746-4678
BBS................................(508) 746-4678

MicroWest Software Systems
10992 San Diego Mission Rd., #110
San Diego, CA 92108
Main................................(800) 826-8231
Tech. Support..................(619) 280-0440
Tech. Supp. Fax.............(619) 280-0467
BBS................................(619) 280-0467

Microwork
47 W St Andrews
Deerfield, IL 60015
Main................................(708) 498-8979
BBS................................(708) 498-9897

Microx
9821 Katy Frwy #260
Houston, TX 77024
Main................................(713) 467-7000

Midern Computer
18005 Cortney Ct
City of Industry, CA 91748
Main................................(800) 669-1624
Tech. Support..................(818) 964-8682
Tech. Supp. Fax.............(818) 964-2381
BBS................................(818) 964-2381

Midisoft
P.O. Box 1000
1605 N.W. Sammamish Rd., Suite 205
Issaquah, WA 98027
Main ....(206) 391-3610
Customer Svc. ....(206) 881-7176
Tech. Support ....(206) 391-3610
Sales...(800) 776-6434
Tech. Supp. Fax ....(206) 391-3422
BBS..(206) 391-7966
E-Mail..............................techsup@midisoft.com
WWW.............................http://www.midisoft.com
FTP Address..............................ftp.midisoft.com
CompuServe................................GO MIDISOFT
America Online .... midisoft@aol.com

Midwest Micro-Peripherals
6910 US Rte 36 E
Fletcher, OH 45326
Main ....(800) 423-8215
Tech. Support ....(800) 243-0313
BBS..(515) 782-4166

Midwestern Diskette
509 W Taylor Hwy 34
Creston, IA 50801
Main..(800) 332-3035
Tech. Support ....(800) 221-6332
Tech. Supp. Fax ....(515) 782-4166
BBS..(515) 782-4166

Miltape Business Products
500 Richardson Rd. S
Hope Hull, AL 36043
Main..(334) 284-8665

MIPS Technologies, Inc.
WWW.................................. http://www.mips.com

Miramar Systems, Inc.
201 N Salsipuedes, #205
Santa Barbara, CA 93103
Main..(805) 966-2432

MIS Computer Systems
45395 N. Port Loop W
Fremont, CA 94538
Main .... (800) 733-9188
Tech. Supp. Fax......................... (510) 226-0230

Mitsubishi Electronics
5665 Plaza Dr.
Cypress, CA 90630
Customer Svc............................. (800) 344-6352
Tech. Support............................. (800) 344-6352
BBS.. (714) 236-6286

Mitsubishi Electronics America
991 Knox St
Torrance, CA 90502
Main .... (800) 843-2515

Mitsubishi Electronics Sales C
8885 Woodbine Ave.
Markham, ONT L3R 5G1
Canada

Mitsubishi International Corp.
520 Madison Ave.
New York, NY 10022
Main .... (212) 605-2339
Tech. Supp. Fax........................... (212) 605-1847
BBS.. (212) 605-1847
E-Mail................................. support@milusa.com

Mitten Software
10709 Wayzata Blvd.
Minnetonka, MN 55305
Main .... (800) 825-5461
Tech. Support............................. (612) 593-5019
Tech. Supp. Fax......................... (612) 593-5028

MKS
35 King St N
Waterloo, ONT N2J 2W9
Canada
Main .... (800) 265-2797
BBS.. (519) 884-8861

Modem Controls
432 N Clark St, #202
Chicago, IL 60610
Tech. Support...............................(312) 321-0018
BBS ....(312) 321-1276

Modgraph
149 Middlesex Tpke
Burlington, MA 01803
Main..(800) 327-9962
Tech. Support...............................(617) 229-4800

Modular Avcom Systems
513 Maude Ct
Sunnyvale, CA 94086
Main..(408) 733-5000
Tech. Supp. Fax..........................(408) 733-5329

Mohawk Wire & Cable
9 Mohawk Dr
Leominster, MA 01543
Main..(800) 422-9961
Tech. Support...............................(508) 537-9961
Tech. Supp. Fax...........................(508) 537-4358

Molex
2222 Wellington Ct
Lisle, IL 60532
Main..(708) 969-4550
Tech. Support...............................(800) 786-6539
Tech. Supp. Fax...........................(708) 968-8356

Momentum Software Corp.
401 S Van Brunt St
Englewood, NJ 07631
Main..(201) 871-0077
Tech. Support...............................(800) 767-1462
Tech. Supp. Fax...........................(201) 871-0807
E-Mail ....comments@momsoft.com
WWW..............................http://www.momsoft.com

Money Smith Cyberport
WWW.........http://www.nmia.com:80/~monsmith/

Monolithic Systems Corp.
7050 Tucson Way
Englewood, CO 80112
Main..(800) 525-7661

Monotype Typography
150 S. Wacker Dr. #2630
Chicago, IL 60606
Main..(312) 855-1440
Customer Svc. ....(800) 666-897
Tech. Support ....(800) 666-6897
Tech. Supp. Fax ....(312) 855-9475

Montrose Products
28 Sword St.
Auburn, MA 01501
Main..(800) 346-6626
Tech. Support ....(508) 791-3161
Tech. Supp. Fax ....(508) 793-9862

Morning Star Techologies
WWW .... http://www.morningstar.com/

Morningstar
53 W Jackson Blvd.
Chicago, IL 60604
Main..(312) 427-1985
BBS...(312) 427-9215

Morris Consulting
1052 Doreen Place #2
Venice, CA 90291
Main..(310) 399-7351
Tech. Support ....(310) 399-7351
Tech. Supp. Fax ....(310) 399-7351
E-Mail.............................. bmorris@ix.netcom.com

Mortice Kern Systems
WWW................................. http://www.mks.com

Morton Management, Inc.
12079 Tech Rd.
Silver Spring, MD 20904
Tech. Support ....(301) 622-5600
BBS..(301) 622-5438

Mosaic Multisoft
WWW...................... http://www.cts.com/~mosaic/

Moses Computers
15466 Los Gatos Blvd.
Los Gatos, CA 95032
Main.................................(408) 358-1550
BBS..................................(408) 356-9049

Motorola, Inc.
10700 N De Anza Blvd.
Cupertino, CA 95014
Tech. Support ....(800) 365-3694
BBS.................................(408) 366-4804
WWW...........................http://www.motorola.com/

Mountain Lake Software
298 Fourth Ave., Suite 401
San Francisco, CA 94118-2468
Main.................................(800) 669-6574
Tech. Support ....(415) 752-6515
Sales.................................(800) 669-6574
Tech. Supp. Fax ....(415) 752-6506
E-Mail...........................techsupport@mtlake.com
WWWhttp://www.woodwind.com/mtlake/index.html

Mountain Network Solutions, Inc.
240 Hacienda Ave.
Campbell, CA 95008-6687
Main.................................(800) 458-0300
Tech. Support ....(408) 439-3216
BBS..................................(408) 438-7697

Mouse Systems Corp.
47505 Seabridge Dr
Fremont, CA 94538
Main.................................(510) 656-1117
BBS..................................(510) 770-1924

Mozart Systems Corp.
1350 Bayshore Hwy, #630
Burlingame, CA 94010
Main.................................(415) 340-1588
BBS..................................(415) 340-1648

MuliWorld Games
54 6th Ave. NW
St Paul, MN 55112

Multi-Industry Tech
16717 Norwalk Blvd.
Cerritos, Ca 90703
Main .... (800) 366-6481
Tech. Support............................ (213) 421-9960
Tech. Supp. Fax.......................... (310) 802-9218
BBS.. (213) 802-9218

Multi-Tech Systems, Inc.
2205 Woodale Dr
Mounds View, MN 55112
Main .... (800) 328-9717
Tech. Support............................. (612) 785-3500
BBS.. (612) 785-9874
WWW...........................http://www.multitech.com/

Multicom Publishing
1100 Olive Way, Suite 1250
Seattle, WA 98101
Main .... (206) 622-5530
WWW...........................http://www.multicom.com

MultiMicro, Inc.
582 Folsom St
San Francisco, CA 94105
Tech. Support.............................. (415) 979-0140

Murata Business Systems
5560 Tennyson Pkwy
Plano, TX 75024
Main .... (800) 543-4636
Tech. Support............................. (214) 403-3300

Mustang Software, Inc.
PO Box 2264
Bakersfield, CA 93303
Main .... (800) 999-9619
Tech. Support............................. (805) 395-0223
BBS .... (805) 395-0713
WWW........................ http://www.mustang.com/

MW Media
WWW......................... http://www.mwmedia.com/

MWI
196 Technology, #1
Irvine, CA 92718
Main..(714) 753-0360
Tech. Support..............................(714) 753-0360
BBS..(714) 753-0363

Mylex
34551 Ardenwood Blvd.
Fremont, CA 94555
Main..(510) 796-6100
Customer Svc...............................(510) 796-6100
Tech. Support..............................(510) 796-6100
Sales..(510) 796-6100
Tech. Supp. Fax...........................(510) 745-7715
BBS..(510) 793-3491

Myoda, Inc.
1057 Shore Rd.
Naperville, IL 60563
Tech. Support..............................(708) 369-5199
Tech. Supp. Fax...........................(708) 369-5935
BBS..(708) 369-6068

Myricom Inc.
WWW.....................................http://www.myri.com/

NAMCO
2531 237th St, #124
Torrance, CA 90505
Main..(213) 539-0701

Nanao USA Corp.
23535 Telo Ave.
Torrance, CA 90505
Main..(800) 800-5202
Tech. Support..............................(310) 325-5202
Tech. Supp. Fax...........................(310) 530-1679
BBS..(310) 530-1679
WWW.................http://www.traveller.com/nanao/

Napersoft, Inc.
WWW...........................http://www.napersoft.com/

National Braille Press, Inc.
88 St Suitephen St
Boston, MA 02115
Main..(617) 266-6160

National Datacomm
2/F 28 Industry E 9 Rd., Science-Bas
Hsin-chu, Taiwan 30077 ROC
Main...((03) 5)7-8396
BBS..((03) 5)7-7799

National Institute of Sci/Tech
5285 Port Royal Rd.
Springfield, VA 22181

National Instruments Corp.
6504 Bridge Point Pkwy
Austin, TX 78730-5039
Main..(800) 433-3488
Tech. Support ....(512) 794-0100
Tech. Supp. Fax ....(512) 794-5794
WWW...............................http://www.natinst.com

National Semiconductor
Personal Systems Div.
2900 Semiconductor Dr.
Santa Clara, CA 95052
Main..(408) 721-5000
Customer Svc. ....(408) 721-1878
Tech. Support ....(800) 272-9959
Sales..(408) 721-8412
Tech. Supp. Fax ....(800) 272-9959
WWW.....................................http://www.nsc.com/

Nationwide Computer Distributor
109 Bowers St
Jersey City, NJ 07307
Tech. Support ....(201) 659-2977
BBS..(201) 659-3345

Navisoft
WWW.............................http://www.navisoft.com/

NCR Corp.
1700 S Patterson Blvd.
Dayton, OH 45479
Main...(513) 445-5000
BBS...(513) 445-4184

NDC Communications
2180 Bering Dr.
San Jose, CA 95131
Main...(408) 428-9108
Customer Svc. ....(800) 362-1118
Tech. Support ....(800) 632-1118
WWW....................................http://www.ndc.com

NEBS Software (One-Write Plus)
20 Industrial Park
Nashua, NH 03062
Customer Svc. ....(603) 880-5100
Sales...(800) 882-5254
Tech. Supp. Fax ....(603) 880-5102
BBS..(800) 937-9951
WWW..................................http://www.nebs.com

NEC America
110 Rio Roblee
San Jose, CA 95134
Main...(800) 222-4632
Tech. Support ....(408) 433-1277
BBS...(408) 433-1241
WWW................................... http://www.nec.com/

NEC Technologies, Inc.
1255 Michael Dr
Wood Dale, IL 60191
Main...(800) 366-0476
Tech. Support ....(708) 860-9500
Tech. Supp. Fax ....(508) 264-8673
WWW................................... http://www.nec.com/

Needham's Electronics
4630 Beloit Dr. #20
Sacramento, CA 95838
Main .... (916) 924-8037
Tech. Support.............................. (916) 924-8037
Tech. Supp. Fax........................... (916) 924-8065
BBS.. (916) 972-9960
E-Mail...............................needhams@quick.com
WWW......... http://www.quiknet.com//~needhams

Net Manage
2340 130th Ave. N.E.
Bellevue, WA 98005-1754
Main .... (206) 869-9600
Tech. Support.............................. (206) 885-0559
Sales .... (206) 885-4272
Tech. Supp. Fax........................... (206) 885-0127
BBS.. (206) 881-0905
E-Mail................. echosupport@netmanage.com
WWW........................http://www.netmanage.com
FTP Address .... ftp.netmanage.com
CompuServe ....GO ECHO

Net-Link
1881 Worcester Rd.
Framingham, MA 01701
Main .... (508) 879-6306
Tech. Support.............................. (508) 370-3641
Tech. Supp. Fax........................... (508) 872-8136
BBS.. (508) 872-8136
E-Mail................................. support@netlink.com

NetFrame Systems, Inc.
1545 Barber Ln
Milpitas, CA 95035
Main .... (408) 944-0600
Tech. Support.............................. (408) 434-4194
Tech. Supp. Fax........................... (408) 474-4228

Netis Technology, Inc.
1544 Century Point Dr 1606
Milpitas, CA 95035
Main .... (408) 263-0368
Tech. Supp. Fax........................... (408) 263-4624

Netlink
1881 Wrecster
Framingham, MA 01701
Main..(919) 878-8612
BBS...(919) 878-2132

Netmagic Systems
2393 Maple Ave.
Peekskill, NY 10566
Main..(914) 739-4579

NetManage, Inc.
10725 N. Deanza
Cupertino, CA 95014
Main..(408) 973-7171
BBS...(408) 257-6405
WWW.......................http://www.netmanage.com/

NeTpower
WWW...........................http://www.netpower.com

NetPro Computing
7975 North Hayden Rd., Suite B200
Scottsdale, AZ 85258
Main..(602) 998-5008
E-Mail..................................... Info@NetPro.com
WWW............................ http://www.netpro.com

Netscape Communications
WWW.......................... http://home.netscape.com

Netwise
2477 55th St
Boulder, CO 80301-9761
Main..(800) 733-7722
Tech. Support...............................(303) 442-8280

Network Access
WWW..............................http://www.nas.com

Network Appliance
WWW............................. http://www.netapp.com

Network Communications Corp.
5501 Green Valley Dr
Bloomington, MN 55437-1003
Main...(800) 333-1896
Tech. Support ....(800) 451-1984
Tech. Supp. Fax ....(612) 844-0487
BBS..(612) 844-0487
WWW................... http://www.netcommcorp.com

Network Design & Annalysis
60 Gough Rd., 2nd Floor
Markham, ONT L3R 8X7
Canada
Main..(800) 387-4234
Tech. Support ....(416) 477-9534
BBS..(416) 477-9572

Network Engineering
12860 Hollocrest Rd., #232
Dallas, TX 75231
Main..(800) 365-4048
BBS..(214) 477-9572

Network Enhancement Tools
20218 Bridgedale Ln
Humble, TX 77338
Main..(713) 446-2154
Tech. Support ....(713) 446-2154
Tech. Supp. Fax ....(713) 540-3048
BBS..(713) 975-7211

Network Equipment Technologies
800 Saginaw Dr
Redwood City, CA 94063
Main..(800) 952-6300
Tech. Support ....(415) 366-4400
Tech. Supp. Fax ....(415) 366-5675

Network General Corp.
4200 Bohannon Dr
Menlo Park, CA 94025
Main..(800) 952-6300
BBS..(415) 321-0855
WWW................................... http://www.ngc.com/

Network Inc.
350 N Bernardo Ave.
Mountain View, CA 94043
Tech. Support ....(415) 694-0650
Tech. Supp. Fax ....(405) 961-7711
BBS...(415) 961-7711
WWW..................................... http://www.ncd.com

Network Interface Corp.
15019 W 95th St
Lenexa, KS 66215
Tech. Support ....(913) 894-8941
BBS...(913) 894-0226

Network Management, Inc.
19 Rector St
New York, NY 10006
Main...(800) 526-8737
Tech. Support ....(212) 797-3800
BBS...(212) 797-3817

Network Peripherals, Inc.
2880 Zanker Rd., #206
San Jose, CA 95134
Main...(408) 954-7300

Network Products Corp.
1440 W Colorado Blvd.
Pasadena, CA 91105
Main...(800) 638-7765
Tech. Support ....(818) 440-1973
Tech. Supp. Fax ....(818) 441-6894
BBS...(818) 441-6894

Network Solutions
505 Huntmar Pk Dr
Herndon, VA 22070
Main...(703) 742-0400
BBS...(703) 742-0846

Network Systems
7600 Boone Ave. N
Minneapolis, MN 55428
Main...(612) 424-4888
BBS...(612) 424-2853

Network Wizards
WWW..................................... http://www.nw.com/

NetWorth, Inc.
8404 Easters Blvd.
Irving, TX 75063
Main .... (800) 544-5255
Tech. Support...............................(214) 929-6984
Tech. Supp. Fax............................(214) 929-1720
BBS ....(214) 929-4882
WWW........................... http://www.networth.com/

NeuralWare, Inc.
202 Parkway Dr.
Pittsburgh, PA 15275
Main .... (412) 787-8222
Tech. Supp. Fax...........................(412) 787-8220
WWW....................... http://www.neuralware.com

Neuron Data, Inc.
444 High St
Palo Alto, CA 94301
Main .... (415) 321-4488
BBS .... (415) 321-9648

New Brunswick Information Tech
WWW........................ http://www.discribe.ca/nbita

New Media
1 Technology, Bldg. A
Irvine, CA 92718
Main .... (714) 453-0100
Customer Svc................................ (714) 453-0100
Tech. Support................................ (714) 453-0314
Sales .... (714) 453-0100
Tech. Supp. Fax............................ (714) 453-0114
BBS .... (714) 453-0214
E-Mail...... nmctechsupport@newmediacorp.com
WWW.................. http://www.newmediacorp.com
FTP Address ...... http://www.newmediacorp.com/
        bbsfiles/index.html
CompuServe ....GO NEWMEDIA

New MMI Corp.
2400 Reach Rd.
Williamsport, PA 17701
Main..(800) 221-4283
Tech. Support................................(800) 221-4283

New Riders
WWW..............................http://www.mcp.com/nrp/

Newbridge Networks
593 Herndon Pkwy
Herndon, VA 22070-5421
Main..(703) 834-3600
Tech. Support................................(703) 834-5360
BBS..(703) 471-7080

Newer Technology
7803 E Osie, #105
Wichita, KS 67207
Main..(800) 678-3726
Tech. Support................................(316) 685-4904
BBS..(316) 685-9368

NewGen
3545 Cadilac Ave.
Suite "A"
Costa Mesa, Ca 92626
Main..(714) 641-8600
Customer Svc................................(714) 641-8600
Tech. Support................................(714) 641-8600
Sales..(800) 756-0556
Tech. Supp. Fax.............................(714) 641-0900
BBS..(714) 641-3869

Newport Systems Solutions, Inc.
4019 Westerly Pl, #103
Newport Beach, CA 92660
Main..(800) 368-6533
Tech. Support................................(800) 505-8324
Sales..(800) 462-4726
BBS..(714) 752-8389

NewTek, Inc.
215 SW 8th St
Topeka, KS 66603
Main..(800) 843-8934
Tech. Support................................(913) 228-8282
BBS..(913) 354-1584
WWW..............................http://www.newtek.com/

NexGen, Inc.
WWW..............................http://www.nexgen.com/

Next Computer
900 Chesapeake Dr
Redwood City, CA 94036
Main..(415) 366-0900

NeXT Computer, Inc.
WWW..................................http://www.next.com/

NHC Communications
165 GrAve.line
St Laurent, Quebec, Canada H4T 1R3
Main..(800) 361-1965
Tech. Support................................(514) 735-2741
BBS..(514) 735-8057

Nico Mak Computing, Inc.
P.O. Box 919
Bristol, CT 06011 USA
WWW....................http://www.winzip.com/winzip/

Nikon Electronic Imaging
101 Cleveland Ave.
Bayshore,NY 11706
Main..(800) 645-6687
Customer Svc................................(800) 645-6678
Tech. Support................................(516) 547-4355
Sales..(800) 526-4566

Nile Computing Services
329 Green Bay Drive
San Jose, CA 95131

Niles and Associates, Inc.
WWW....................................http://www.niles.com

Nintendo
WWW............................http://www.nintendo.com/

Nissho Electronics USA Corp.
18201 Vo Karmen Ave. #350
Irvine, CA 92715
Main...(800) 233-1837
Tech. Supp. Fax ....(714) 261-8819

Niwot Networks
1880 S. Flatiron Crt. #M
Boulder, CO 80301
Main...(303) 444-7765
BBS...(303) 444-7767
E-Mail..niwot@csn.net
WWW..............http://members.aol.com//niwotnet

Nobel Group Ware Division
625 S State
Orem, UT 84058
Main...(801) 226-6000
Customer Svc. ....(800) 792-7170
Tech. Support ....(800) 861-2146
Sales..(800) 395-7135
BBS...(801) 224-0920

Nobel Technologies, Inc.
PO Box 10423
Burke, VA 22009
Main...(800) 932-8009

Nohau Corp.
51 E Campbell Ave.
Campbell, CA 95008
Main...(408) 866-1820
Tech. Supp. Fax ....(408) 378-7869
BBS...(408) 378-7869

Nokia
WWW................................. http://www.nokia.com/

Nolo Press
950 Parker Street
Berkeley, CA 94710
Main .... (510) 549-1976
Customer Svc.................................. (800) 992-6656
Tech. Support................................. (800) 992-6656
Sales .... (800) 992-6656
Tech. Supp. Fax.............................. (510) 548-5902
WWW...................................... http://www.nolo.com
America Online...............................nolo@aol.com

Nonstop Networks
20 Waterside, #6-J
New York, NY 10010
Main .... (212) 481-8488
Tech. Supp. Fax.............................. (212) 779-2956
BBS... (212) 779-2956

NoRad Corp.
1160 E. Sandhill Ave.
Carson, CA 90746
Main .... (800) 262-3260
Tech. Support................................. (800) 262-3260
Tech. Supp. Fax.............................. (310) 605-5051
BBS... (310) 458-6397

Norda Technologies, Inc.
PO Box 645
Andover, NJ 07821
Main .... (201) 786-6878
Tech. Supp. Fax.............................. (201) 786-5868

Norlinvest Ltd./Visionics Corp.
WWW............... http://www.bahnhof.se/~visionics

Northern Telcom
2305 Mission College Blvd.
Santa Clara, CA 95054
Main .... (408) 988-5550
Tech. Support................................. (408) 988-5550
Tech. Supp. Fax.............................. (408) 988-3528

Northgate Computer Systems, Inc.
PO Box 59080
Minneapolis, MN 55459
Tech. Support................................. (800) 446-5037
BBS... (612) 943-8338

Norton-Lambert
5290 Overpass Rd.
P.O. Box 4085
Santa Barbara, CA 93140
Main..(805) 964-6767
Customer Svc..............................(805) 964-6767
Tech. Support..............................(805) 964-6767
Sales ....(805) 964-6767
Tech. Supp. Fax..........................(805) 683-5679
BBS ....(805) 683-2249
CompuServe ....GO CLOSEUP

Novell, Inc.
1555 N. Technology Way
Orem, UT 84057-2399
Main..(800) 453-1267
Customer Svc..............................(801) 429-7000
Tech. Support..............................(800) 638-9273
BBS ....(801) 429-3308
WWW.................................http://www.novel.com/
FTP Address...... ftp://ftp.novell.com/pub/updates/

Now Software
921 S.W. Washington St., Suite 500
Portland, OR 97205
Main..(503) 274-2810
Customer Svc..............................(503) 274-2800
Tech. Support..............................(800) 689-9414
Sales ....(503) 274-2800
Tech. Supp. Fax..........................(503) 274-6390
E-Mail ....support@nowsoft.com
WWW..............................http://www.nowsoft.com
FTP Address...............................ftp.nowsoft.com
America Online...........................allnow@aol.com

Noyes Fiber Systems
PO Box 398, Rt 106
Laconia, NH 03246
Main..(603) 528-7780
Tech. Support..............................(603) 528-7780
Tech. Supp. Fax..........................(603) 528-2025
BBS ....(603) 528-2025

NRI
4401 Connecticut NW
Washington, DC 20008
Main..(202) 244-1600
Tech. Support ....(202) 244-1600
BBS..(202) 244-2047

Ntergaid, Inc.
2490 Black Rock Tpke, #337
Fairfield, CT 06430
Main..(203) 368-0632

NTI Group, The
3265 Kifer Rd.
Santa Clara, CA 95051
Main..(408) 739-4847
BBS..(408) 739-4847

nuLogic, Inc.
945 Great Plains Ave.
Needham, MA 02192
Main..(617) 444-7680

Number Nine Visual Technology
18 Hartwell Ave.
Lexington, MA 02173
Main..(800) 438-6463
Customer Svc. ....(617) 674-0009
Tech. Support ....(617) 674-0009
BBS..(617) 862-7502

Numonics
101 Commerce Dr
Montgomerville, PA 18936
Main..(800) 247-4517
Tech. Supp. Fax ....(215) 361-0167

NVidia Corp.
WWW.................................http://www.nvidia.com

Nynex Information Solutions Group
4 W Red Oak Ln
White Plains, NY 10604
Tech. Support ....(914) 644-7930
BBS..(914) 694-5755

Oak Tree Publications
WWW.................................... http://www.otp.com

Oakland Group, Inc.A1457
959 Concord St.
Farmingham, MA 01701
Main..(800) 233-3733
Tech. Support ....(617) 491-7311
Tech. Supp. Fax ....(508) 626-2211
BBS..(617) 868-4440

Oaz Communications
44920 OGood Rd.
Fremont, CA 94539
Main..(800) 638-3293
Tech. Support ....(510) 226-0171
Tech. Supp. Fax ....(510) 226-7079
BBS..(408) 226-7079

Object Management Group, The
492 Old Connecticut Path
Framingham, MA 01701
Main..(508) 820-4300
Tech. Supp. Fax ....(508) 820-0307

Ocean Information Systems
WWW............. http://www.ocean-usa.com/ocean/

Ocean Interface Co, Inc.
515 Spanish Ln, #C
Walnut, CA 91789
Main..(714) 595-1212
BBS..(714) 595-9683

OCLI Glare/Guard Division
310 Sutton Pl.
Santa Rosa, CA 95407-7397
Main..(707) 545-6440
Customer Svc. ....(800) 545-6254
Tech. Support ....(707) 525-7807
Tech. Supp. Fax ....(707) 525-7595
WWW....................................... http://www.ocli.com

ODS
1101 E Arapahu Rd.
Richardson, TX 75081
Main..(214) 234-6400

Okidata
532 Fellowship Rd.
Mount Laurel, NJ 08054
Tech. Support...............................(609) 235-2600
BBS...(609) 778-4184
WWW..............................http://www.okidata.com/

Olduvai Corp.
9200 S. Dadeland Blvd. ste. #525
Miami, FL 33156
Main .... (800) 822-0772
Tech. Support...............................(305) 665-4665
Tech. Supp. Fax............................(305) 670-1112
E-Mail....................................olduvaigui.aol.com
WWW..................http://www.shadow.net//olduvai

Olicom USA
900 East Park Blvd.
Suite no 250
Plano, TX 75074
Customer Svc..............................(800) 654-2661
Tech. Support...............................(800) 654-2661
Sales ....(800) 625-4266
Tech. Supp. Fax............................(214) 516-0640
BBS ....(214) 422-9835
E-Mail....................................support@olicom.com
WWW.............................. http://www.olicom.com
FTP Address ....ftp.olicom.com
CompuServe ....GO OLICOM

Olivetti Office USA
765 US Hwy 202, PO Box 6945
Somerville, NJ 08807-0945
Main .... (800) 527-2960
Tech. Support...............................(908) 526-8200
BBS ....(908) 526-8405
WWW..............................http://www.olivetti.com/

Omega Engineering, Inc.
1 Omega Dr, Box 4047
Stamford, CT 06907-0047
Main .... (203) 359-1660
Tech. Supp. Fax............................(203) 359-7700

Omen Technology, Inc.
PO Box 4681
Portland, OR 97231
Main..(503) 614-0430
BBS...(503) 621-3735

Omni-Data Communications
906 N Main
Witchita, KS 67203
Tech. Support...............................(316) 264-5589
BBS...(316) 264-7031
E-Mail......................................odcom@aol.com
WWW.........................http://www.omnidata.com

ON Technology
72 Kent St
Brookline, MA 02146
Main..(800) 767-6683
BBS...(617) 734-4160
WWW......................................http://www.on.com

OnLine Products Corp.
20251 Century Blvd.
Germantown, MD 20874
Main..(800) 922-9204
Tech. Support...............................(301) 428-3700
BBS...(301) 428-2903

Ontrack Computer Systems
6321 Bury Dr.
Ontrack Data Recovery Division
Eden Prairie, MN 55346
Customer Svc...............................(800) 752-1333
Tech. Support...............................(612) 937-2121
Sales...(612) 937-2121
Tech. Supp. Fax...........................(612) 937-5815
BBS...(612) 937-0860
E-Mail.....................................tech@ontrack.com
WWW......................... http://www.ontrack.com
FTP Address..........................ftp://ftp.ontrack.com
CompuServe........................GO ONTRACK, GO
DATARECOVERY 72662,33

Onyx
30799 Pinetree Rd., #303
Cleveland, OH 44124
Main..(216) 498-3488
Tech. Support...............................(216) 498-3488
Sales...(216) 498-0615
Tech. Supp. Fax...........................(216) 498-0661

Opcode Interactive
3641 HAve.n Dr, #A
Menlo Park, CA 94025
Customer Svc...............................(415) 812-3274
Tech. Support...............................(415) 812-3274
E-Mail................................support@opcode.com
WWW...............................http://www.opcode.com

Open Network
215 Berkeley Pl
Brooklyn, NY 11217
Main..(800) 542-0938
Tech. Support...............................(718) 398-3838
Tech. Supp. Fax...........................(718) 638-2240
BBS...(718) 638-2240

Open Systems, Inc.
6477 City West Parkway
Eden Prairie, MN 55344
Main..(800) 328-2276
Tech. Support...............................(612) 929-0011
BBS...(612) 829-1493

Optelecom
9300 Gaither Rd.
Gaithersburg, MD 20877
Main..(301) 840-2121
Tech. Supp. Fax...........................(301) 948-6357
BBS...(301) 948-6357
E-Mail...........................optelecm/dgs.dgsy.com
WWWhttp://www.spidermedia.com//optelcem.html

Optical Cable
5290 Concourse Dr.
Roanoke, VA 24019
Main..(800) 622-7711
Tech. Support...............................(703) 265-0690
Tech. Supp. Fax...........................(703) 265-0724
BBS...(703) 289-9846

Optical Data Systems (ODS)
1101 E. Arapaho Rd.
Richardson, TX 75081-9990
Main...(214) 234-6400
Tech. Supp. Fax ....(214) 234-4059
BBS..(214) 234-1467

Optima Technology Corp.
17062 Murphy Ave.
Irvine, CA 92714
Main...(714) 476-0515
Tech. Supp. Fax ....(714) 476-0613
WWW........... http://www.optimatech.com/optima/

Optisys
9250 N. 43rd Ave. #12
Glendale, AZ 85302
Main...(800) 327-1271
Tech. Support ....(602) 997-9699
Tech. Supp. Fax ....(602) 944-4051
E-Mail.......................................supportoptisys.com

Optus Software
PO Box 101
Highlands, NJ 07732
Tech. Support ....(908) 271-9568
BBS..(908) 271-9572

Ora Electronics
9410 Owensmouth
Chatsworth, CA 91311
Main...(818) 772-2700
Customer Svc. ....(818) 772-2700
Tech. Support ....(818) 772-2700
Sales..(818) 772-2700

Oracle Corp.
20 Davis Dr
Belmont, CA 94002
Main...(800) 345-3267
Tech. Support ....(415) 506-7867
BBS..(415) 598-9216
WWW...............................http://www.oracle.com

Orange Micro, Inc.
1400 N Lakeview Ave.
Anaheim, CA 92807
Main .... (714) 779-2772
Tech. Support............................... (714) 779-2772
Tech. Supp. Fax........................... (714) 779-9332
E-Mail....................ed_garcia@orangemicro.com

Orbit Enterprises, Inc.
PO Box 2875
Glen Ellyn, IL 60138
Main .... (800) 767-6724
Tech. Support............................... (708) 469-3405
Tech. Supp. Fax........................... (708) 469-4895

Orchid Technology, Inc.
45365 North Port Lp W
Fremont, CA 94538
Main .... (800) 767-2443
Tech. Support............................... (510) 661-3000
BBS.. (510) 651-6837
WWW................................http://www.orchid.com/

Order Desk, The
Suite 294, Box 3301B
St Petersburg, FL 33733
Main .... (800) 334-4480

Origin Systems, Inc.
WWW.........................http://www.ea.com/osi.html

Ornetix
WWW...............................http://www.ornetix.com/

Osborne/McGraw Hill
2600 10th St
Berkeley, CA 94710
Main .... (800) 227-0900
Tech. Supp. Fax........................... (510) 549-6603
WWW............................. http://www.osborne.com

Oscar International
PO Box 1234
Walnut, CA 91789
Main .... (714) 595-0339
Tech. Support............................... (714) 595-0339
BBS.. (714) 595-7654

Osmos, Inc.
4151 Business Center Dr
Fremont, CA 94538
Main..(415) 623-1000
BBS...(415) 623-1004

OsoSoft
1472 Sixth Street
Los Osos, CA 93402
Main..(805) 528-1759
WWW...............http://ourworld.compuserve.com/
homepages/os

Oswego Software
Box 310
Oswego, IL 60543
Main..(708) 554-3567
BBS...(708) 544-3573

Other Guys, The
PO Box H
Logan, UT 84321
Main..(800) 942-9402
Tech. Supp. Fax.............................(801) 753-7620

Output Enablers
WWW..........................http://www.io.com/user/oe/

Output Technology Corp. (OTC)
2310 N Fancher Rd.
Spokane, WA 99212-1381
Main..(800) 468-8788
Tech. Support................................(509) 536-0468

P.N.Y. Electronics
200 Anderson Ave.
Moonachie, NJ 07074
Main..(201) 438-6300
Customer Svc................................(201) 438-6300
Tech. Support................................(800) 234-4597
Tech. Supp. Fax.............................(201) 896-9414

Pacific Animated Imaging
WWW.........................http://www.pai-imaging.com

Pacific Data Products
9855 Scranton Rd.
San Diego, CA 92121
Main..(619) 552-0880
Customer Svc................................(619) 587-4690
Tech. Support................................(619) 587-4690
Sales...(800) 737-7117
Tech. Supp. Fax.............................(619) 552-0889
BBS...(619) 452-6329
E-Mail.....................................tech@pacdata.com
WWW.............................http://www.pacdata.com
FTP Address...............................ftp.pacdata.com

Pacific Micro Data, Inc.
16751 Millikan Ave.
Irvine, CA 92714
Main..(800) 933-7575
Tech. Support................................(714) 955-9490
BBS...(714) 756-0672

Pacific Microelectronics, Inc.
201 San Antonio Cir, #C-250
Mountain View, CA 94040
Main..(415) 948-6200

Pacific Softwork
4000 Via Pecscador
Camarillo, CA 93012
Main..(800) 541-9508
Tech. Supp. Fax.............................(805) 484-3929
BBS...(805) 485-8204
WWW...........................http://www.pacificsw.com

Packard Bell
WWW................http://www.packardbell.com/gfx/
gfxhome.html

Page Computer
17798 Westwood Blvd.
Los Angeles, CA 90024
Main..(800) 266-0055
Tech. Support................................(213) 444-0055
BBS...(213) 344-9095

Pages Software, Inc.
WWW...............................http://www.pages.com/

Paladin
3543 Old Conejo Rd., #101 & 102
Newbury Park, CA 91320
Main...(800) 272-8665
Tech. Support ....(805) 499-0318
BBS...(805) 499-4006

Palindrome
600 E. Diehl Rd.
Naperville, IL 60563
Main...(708) 505-3300
Customer Svc. ....(708) 505-3300
Tech. Support ....(708) 505-3300
BBS...(708) 505-3336
E-Mail...............................help@palindrome.com
WWW........................http://www.palindrome.com
FTP Address http://www.palindrome.com/ftp/pub/
CompuServe...........................GO PALINDROME

Palisade Corp.
31 Decker Rd.
Newfield, NY 14867
Main...(800) 432-7475
Tech. Support ....(607) 277-8000

Panacea, Inc.
Londonderry Sq, 50 Nashua Rd., #305
Londonderry, NH 03053
Main...(603) 437-5022
Tech. Support ....(508) 937-1760
Tech. Supp. Fax ....(508) 970-0199

Panamax
150 Mitchell Blvd.
San Rafael, CA 94903-2057
Main...(415) 499-3900
Customer Svc. ....(800) 472-5555
Tech. Support ....(800) 472-5555
Sales...(800) 472-5555
Tech. Supp. Fax ....(415) 472-5542
WWW...............http://www.hooked.net/panamax
FTP Address...............................ftp.panamax.com

Panasonic Communications
1707 N. Randall Rd., Suite E10
Elgin, IL 60123-7847
Main ....(708) 468-4600
Customer Svc............................. (800) 854-4536
Tech. Support............................. (800) 854-4536
Tech. Supp. Fax........................... (708) 468-4555
WWW.........................http://www.panasonic.com/

Paperback Software International+A1495
2830 9th St
Berkeley, CA 94710
Main .... (800) 255-3242
Tech. Support............................. (415) 644-2116
BBS... (415) 644-8241

PaperDirect, Inc.
57 Romanelli Ave.
South Hackensack, NJ 07606
Main .... (800) 272-7377
Tech. Support............................. (201) 342-6432

Papyrus Design Group, Inc.
35 Medford Street
Somerville, MA 02143
Main .... (617) 868-5440
E-Mail............................. papyrus@world.std.com
WWW..................................http://www.papy.com/

Para Systems, Inc.
1455 LeMay Dr
Carrollton, TX 75007
Main .... (800) 238-7272
Tech. Support............................. (214) 446-7363
BBS... (214) 446-9011

Paradigm Software
805 S Filbert Ct
Suiterling, VA 22170-4712
Main .... (703) 450-0829
BBS... (703) 450-2683

Paradigm Systems
WWW..............................http://www.sf.psca.com/

Paradise/Western Digital
(Phillips Semiconductor)
1000 Business Center Lane
Mt. Prospect, IL 60056
Main...(800) 444-3617
Tech. Support...............................(800) 978-3079
BBS...(714) 753-1234
E-Mail.............................. support@paradise.com
WWW........................... http://www.paradise.com/
FTP Address................ ftp://ftp.paradise.com/pub

Parallax, Inc.
WWW........................http://www.parallaxinc.com/

Parana Supplies
3625 Del Amo Blvd., Suite 260
Torrance, CA 90503
Main...(310) 793-1325
Customer Svc...................................(800) 472-7262
Tech. Support................................(800) 472-7262

Parkplace / Digitalk
5 Hutton Center Dr.
Santa Ana, CA 92707
Main...(714) 513-3000
Customer Svc...................................(714) 513-3000
Tech. Support................................(714) 513-3000
Sales ....(800) 759-7272
Tech. Supp. Fax...........................(714) 513-3100
E-Mail.................................bugs@parkplace.com
WWW........................... http://www.parkplace.com
FTP Address...........................ftp.parkplace.com
CompuServe .... GO PPFORM

Parsons Technology, Inc.
1 Parsons Dr, PO Box 100
Hiawatha, IA 52233-9904
Main...(800) 223-6925
Tech. Support...............................(319) 395-7314
BBS...(319) 393-1002
E-Mail.....................tsupport@parsonstech.com
WWW........................http://www.parsontech.com/

Parsytee
245 W Roosevelt Rd., Bldg 9 Unit 60-
W. Chicago, IL 60185
Main...(708) 293-9500
Tech. Supp. Fax ....(708) 293-9525
WWW............................... http://www.parsytee.de

Passport Designs
65 Miramontos St
Half Moon Bay, CA 94019
Main...(415) 726-0280
Customer Svc. ....(415) 726-0280
Tech. Support ....(415) 726-0280
WWW.......http://www.mozart.mw3.com/passport

PathLink Technology
WWW............................. http://www.pathlink.com/

Patton Electronics Co.A1509
7622 Rickenbacker Dr.
Gaithersburg, MD 20879-9977
Main...(301) 975-1000
Tech. Support ....(301) 975-1000
Tech. Supp. Fax ....(301) 869-9293
E-Mail......................................sales@patton.com
WWW...............................http://www.patton.com/

Paul Mace Software
WWW...............................http://www.pmace.com/

PC & C Research Corp.
5251 Verdugo Way Suite #J
Camarillo, CA 93012
Tech. Support ....(805) 484-1685
Tech. Supp. Fax ....(805) 987-8088
BBS...(805) 987-8088
E-Mail...........................mintronix@interamp.com

PC - Kwik
3800 SW Cedar Hills Blvd. #260
Beaverton, OR 97005
Main...(800) 365-5945
Tech. Support ....(503) 644-8827
Tech. Supp. Fax ....(503) 646-8267
WWW............http://www.teleport.com//~gnome//
pckwik.htm

PC America
3232 Rio Mirada Dr. Bldg. #3
Bakersfield, CA 93308
Main...(805) 323-0707
Tech. Supp. Fax ....(805) 323-9747
BBS...(805) 323-9747

PC Connection
6 Mill St
Marlow, NH 03456
Main...(800) 243-8088
Tech. Support ....(603) 446-7721
BBS...(603) 446-7791

PC Consultants
11026-B Villa Ridge Ct.
Reston, VA 22091-4841
Tech. Support ....(703) 860-0108
BBS...(703) 860-0108
CompuServe........ 76147.346@compuserve.com

PC Craft, Inc.
640 Puente St
Brea, CA 92621
Main...(800) 733-6666
Tech. Support ....(714) 256-5000

PC Designs
2504 N Hemlock Cir
Broken Arrow, OK 74012
Tech. Support ....(918) 251-5550

PC Docs, Inc.
124 Marriott Dr, #200
Tallahassee, FL 32301
Main...(800) 933-3627
Tech. Support ....(904) 942-3627
BBS...(904) 942-1517
WWW.............................. http://www.pcdocs.com/

PC Dynamics
31332 Via Colinas, #102
Westlake Village, CA 91362
Customer Svc...............................(818) 889-1741
Tech. Support...............................(818) 889-1742
Tech. Supp. Fax...........................(818) 889-1014
E-Mail............................... info@pcdynamics.com
WWW......................http://www.pcdynamics.com/
FTP Address .... ftp://ftp.pcdynamics.com

PC Gardian
1133 Francisco Blvd. E. Suite D
San Rafael, CA 94901
Main ....(415) 459-0190
Tech. Supp. Fax............................(415) 459-1162
BBS...(415) 995-2487

PC House
841 E Artesia Blvd.
Carson, CA 90746
Main ....(213) 324-8621
BBS...(213) 324-8654

PC Power & Cooling, Inc.
5995 Ave.nida Encinas
Carlsbad, CA 92008
Main ....(800) 722-6555
Tech. Support...............................(619) 931-5700
Tech. Supp. Fax............................(619) 931-6988
BBS...(619) 931-6988

PC Repair Corp.
2010 State St
Harrisburg, PA 17103
Tech. Support...............................(717) 232-7272
Tech. Supp. Fax............................(717) 232-7898
BBS...(717) 232-7898

PC Time Data Corp.
43038 Christy St
Fremont, CA 94538
Main ....(800) 878-3868
Tech. Support...............................(415) 623-8864
BBS...(415) 623-8865

PCs, PCs, PCs, Inc.
5503 Town Ave.
Suite 3032
Los Angeles, CA 90302

Peachtree Software
1505 Pavilion Pl
Norcross, GA 30093
Main.................................(770) 564-5800
Customer Svc.............................(800) 554-8900
Tech. Support.............................(800) 822-2821
BBS ....(404) 564-5888
WWW.............................. http://www.peach.com
CompuServe .... GO PEACHTREE
America Online................................ PEACHTREE

PennComp
4031 Villanova St
Houston, TX 77005
Main.................................(800) 326-6145
Tech. Support...............................(713) 669-0965

Penril Datacomm
WWW.............................http://www.penril.com/

Pentax Technologies Corp.
100 Technology Dr
Broomfield, CO 80021
Main.................................(303) 460-1600
Tech. Support...............................(303) 460-1820
Tech. Supp. Fax...........................(303) 460-1628
BBS ....(303) 460-1628

PeopleSoft
1600 S Main St, #280
Walnut Creek, CA 94596
Main.................................(510) 946-9460
WWW........................ http://www.peoplesoft.com/

Perceptive Solutions, Inc. (PSI
2700 Flora St
Dallas, TX 75201
Main.................................(800) 486-3278
Tech. Support...............................(214) 954-1774
Tech. Supp. Fax...........................(214) 953-1774
BBS ....(214) 953-1774

Percision Software
8404 Suiterling St
Irving, TX 75063
Main.................................(800) 562-9909
Tech. Support ....(214) 929-4888

Percon
1720 Willow Creek Circle Suite#530
Eugene, OR 97402
Main.................................(800) 873-7266
Tech. Supp. Fax ....(503) 344-1399
BBS.................................(503) 344-1399

Performance Computing
15050 SW Koll Parkway
Suite 2B
Beaverton, Oregon 97006
Main.................................(503) 641-1221
Tech. Supp. Fax ....(503) 641-3344
WWW............. http://www.teleport.com/~pciwww/

Performance System Software
WWW........................http://www.IntNet.net/PSSI/

Performance Technology
7800 IH 10 W, 800 Lincoln Ctr
San Antonio, TX 78230
Main.................................(800) 825-5267
Tech. Support ....(512) 349-3000
BBS.................................(512) 366-0123

Performix
8521 Leesburg Pike, #330
Vienna, VA 22180
Main.................................(703) 448-6606

Peripheral Repair Corp.
9233 Eton Ave.
Chatsworth, CA 91311
Main.................................(800) 627-3475
Tech. Support ....(818) 700-8482
Tech. Supp. Fax ....(818) 700-0533
BBS.................................(818) 700-0533

Perisol Technology
3350 Scott Blvd., #1201
Santa Clara, CA 95054
Main...(800) 447-8226
Tech. Support ....(408) 988-2232
BBS...(408) 988-4431

Persoft
465 Science Dr.
Madison, WI 53711
Main...(608) 273-6000
Customer Svc. ....(800) 368-5283
Tech. Support ....(608) 273-4357
BBS...(608) 273-6595
E-Mail...............................support@persoft.com
WWW...............................http://www.persoft.com
FTP Address...................................ftp.persoft.com

Personal Bibliographic Software+A1540
WWW..... http://www.argus-inc.com/pbs/pbs.html

Personal Composer
3213 W. Wheeler st. #140
Seattle, WA 98199
Main...(800) 446-8088
Tech. Supp. Fax ....(206) 524-5910

Personal Computer Upgrade Taiwan
NO 80 Hsing Yun St
Nel-Hu Taipei, Taiwan, ROC
Main...(279) 413-20

Personal Tex
12 Madrona St.
Mill Valley, CA 94941
Main...(415) 388-8853
Tech. Supp. Fax ....(415) 388-8865
E-Mail...pti@crl.com
WWW.............................http://www.crl.com/~pt1/

Personal Training Systems
173 Jefferson Dr.
Menlo Park, CA 95025
Main .... (415) 462-2100
Customer Svc.............................. (800) 832-2499
Tech. Support.............................. (800) 832-2499
Sales .... (800) 832-2499
Tech. Supp. Fax.......................... (415) 462-2101
WWW.................................... http://www.ptst.com

Phar Lap Software, Inc.
60 Aberdeen Ave.
Cambridge, MA 02138
Main .... (617) 661-1510
BBS... (617) 876-2972

Philips
WWWhttp://www.semiconductors.philips.com/ps/

Philips Consumer Electronics Corp.
1 Philips Dr
Knoxville, TN 37914-1810
Main .... (615) 521-4499

Philtek Power
4320 Swee Rd. Unit B
Blaine, WA 98230
Main .... (800) 727-4877
Tech. Support............................... (360) 332-7252
Tech. Supp. Fax........................... (360) 332-7253
BBS... (206) 647-1564

Phoenician Faire
3545 Cadiliac Ave.
Costa Mesa, CA 92626
Main .... (800) 999-7713
Tech. Support............................... (714) 549-4669

Phoenix Technologies/Eclipse+A1550
2770 De La Cruz Blvd.
Santa Clara, CA 95050
Main .... (408) 654-9000
Customer Svc.............................. (714) 440-8000
Tech. Support.............................. (714) 440-8000
BBS.. (714) 440-8026
E-Mail................................. sales@firmware.com
WWW............. http://www.ptltd.com/phoenix.html

Photonics Corp.
1515 Center Point Dr.
Milpitas, CA 95035
Main....................................(800) 628-3033
Tech. Support......................(408) 262-7700
Tech. Supp. Fax..................(408) 955-7950
BBS....................................(408) 370-3172

Photoring
2060 Emery Ave., #254
La Habra, CA 90631
Main....................................(213) 691-0698
BBS....................................(213) 691-0698

Physicians Practice Management
350 E New York
Indianapolis, IN 46204
Main....................................(800) 428-3515
Tech. Support......................(317) 262-4515

Pictorius Inc.
WWW...........................http://www.pictorius.com/

Piiceon
1996 Lundy Ave.
San Jose, CA 95131
Main....................................(408) 432-8030
Customer Svc......................(800) 366-2983
Tech. Support......................(408) 432-8030
Sales..................................(800) 366-2983
Tech. Supp. Fax..................(408) 943-1309
BBS....................................(408) 431-8998

Pinnacle Micro
19 Technology
Irvine, CA 92718
Main....................................(800) 553-7070
Customer Svc......................(714) 727-3300
Tech. Support......................(714) 727-3200
Tech. Supp. Fax..................(714) 789-3097
BBS....................................(714) 453-8619
WWW...................http://www.pinnaclemicro.com

Pinnacle Publishing, Inc.
1800 72nd Ave. S, #217
Kent, WA 98032
Main....................................(800) 231-1293
Tech. Support......................(206) 251-1900
BBS....................................(206) 251-5057

Pioneer Computer, Inc.
49066 Milmont Dr
Fremont, CA 94538
Main....................................(415) 623-0808

Pioneer New Media Technologies
Multimedia & Mass Storage
2265 E. 220th St.
Long Beach, CA 90810
Main....................................(800) 444-6784
Customer Svc......................(310) 952-2111
Tech. Support......................(800) 872-4159
Tech. Supp. Fax..................(310) 952-2100

Pirelli Cable
700 Industrial Dr
Lexington, SC 29072
Main....................................(803) 957-4200
BBS....................................(803) 957-4628

Pivar Computing Services, Inc.
165 Arlington Heights Rd.
Buffalo Grove, IL 60089
Main....................................(800) 266-8378
Tech. Support......................(847) 459-6010
Tech. Supp. Fax..................(847) 459-6095

PKWare, Inc.
9025 N Deerwood Dr
Brown Deer, WI 53226
Main....................................(414) 354-8699
BBS....................................(414) 354-8559

Platinum Software Corp.
195 Technology West
Irvine, CA 92718
Main...(800) 453-4000
Customer Svc................................(800) 453-4000
Tech. Support.............................(800) 333-5242
Sales...(800) 453-4000
Tech. Supp. Fax.........................(714) 453-4091
BBS...(714) 727-1255

Platinum Software International+A1583
17 Thornburn Rd.
North Potomac, MD 20878
Main...(301) 309-9169

Platium Tech Santa Barbara Lab
340 S Kellogg Ave.
Goleta, CA 93117
Main...(805) 683-5777
WWW............................... http://www.softool.com

PlexCom
2255 Agate Court
Semi Valley, CA 93065
Main...(805) 522-3333
Tech. Supp. Fax...........................(805) 583-4764
BBS...(805) 583-4764

Plextor
4255 Burton Dr.
Santa Clara, CA 95054
Main...(408) 980-1838
Customer Svc...............................(408) 980-1838
Tech. Support.............................(408) 980-1838
BBS...(408) 986-1569
WWW............................... http://www.plexor.com

Plotworks, Inc.
16440 Eagles Crest Rd.
Ramona, CA 92065
Main...(619) 457-5090
Tech. Supp. Fax...........................(619) 789-4923
BBS...(619) 789-4923

Polaris Software
1928 DonLee Place
Escondido, CA 92029
Main .... (619) 735-2300
Customer Svc.............................. (800) 338-5943
Tech. Support............................. (619) 735-2300
Sales .... (800) 722-5728
Tech. Supp. Fax.......................... (619) 738-0113
BBS.. (619) 738-8640

Polygon
1350 Baur Blvd.
St Louis, MO 63132
Main .... (314) 432-4142
Tech. Supp. Fax.......................... (314) 997-9696
BBS.. (314) 997-9696
E-Mail .... info@polygon.com
WWW.............................http://www.polygon.com
CompuServe .... 723.2201@compuserve.com

Polywell Computers, Inc.
1461-1 San Mateo Ave.
South San Francisco, CA 94080
Main .... (800) 999-1278
Tech. Support............................. (415) 583-7222
Tech. Supp. Fax.......................... (415) 583-1974
BBS.. (415) 583-1974
E-Mail .... polywell@lx.netcom.com
WWW.............................http://www.polywell.com

Popkin Software & Systems, Inc.
11 Park Pl, 19th Floor
New York, NY 10007
Main .... (212) 571-3434

Portrait Display Labs
WWW....................http://www.sirius.com/~inform/

Positive Software Co.
1318 Main Street
Dartmouth, NS B2Z 1B2
Canada
Main .... (902) 434-6444
WWW........................http://www.pointofsale.com/

Power Computing Corp.
WWW.........................http://www.powercc.com/

Power Express
WWWhttp://www.baynet.com/powerexpress.html

Power-Plus
4100 Caren Rd.
Austin, TX 78744
Main..(800) 878-5530
Tech. Support.................................(514) 443-3372
Tech. Supp. Fax............................(512) 443-3518
BBS ....(214) 631-8697
FTP Address................................... ftp@10.com

Power-Up Software Corp.
2929 Campus Dr
San Mateo, CA 94403
Main..(800) 851-2917
Tech. Support.................................(415) 345-5900
BBS ....(415) 345-5575

Powersoft
561 Virginia Rd.
Concord, MA 01742
Main..(508) 287-1500
Customer Svc.................................(508) 287-1500
Tech. Support.................................(508) 287-1500
WWW.......................... http://www.powersoft.com
FTP Address.............. ftp://ftp.powersoft.com/pub/

PR Newswire
WWW........................http://www.prnewswire.com

Practical Peripherals, Inc.
31245 La Baya Dr
Westlake Village, CA 91362
Main..(800) 442-4774
Customer Svc...............................(770) 840-9966
Tech. Support...............................(770) 840-9966

Praegitzer Industries
WWW...................................... http://www.pii.com/

Precision Data Products
PO Box 8367
Grand Rapids, MI 49518
Main..(800) 968-0888
Tech. Support.................................(616) 698-2242
BBS ....(616) 698-9047

Prescience Corp.
814 Castro St, #111
San Francisco, CA 94114
Main..(415) 282-5864

Price Waterhouse
6500 Rock Spring Dr.
6th Floor
Bethesda, MD 20817
Main..(601) 365-7963

Prima International
3350 Scott Blvd., Bldg 7
Santa Clara, CA 95054
Main..(408) 727-2600
Tech. Supp. Fax ....(408) 727-2435

Primavera Systems, Inc.
2 Bala Plaza
Bala Cynwyd, PA 19004
Main..(800) 423-0245
Tech. Support ....(215) 667-8600
BBS...(215) 667-7894
WWW........................ http://www.primavera.com/

Prime Portable Manufacturer
1431 Potrero Ave., #E
South El Monte, CA 91733
Main..(800) 966-7237
Tech. Support ....(818) 444-7606
Tech. Supp. Fax ....(818) 444-1027
BBS...(818) 444-1027

Princeton Review Publishing
2315 Broadway
New York, NY 10024-4332
Main..(212) 874-8282
WWW.............................. http://www.review.com/

Printer Connection
9865 Mesa Rim Rd.
Lorton, VA 22079
Main..(800) 622-7060
Customer Svc. ....(800) 479-6092
Tech. Supp. Fax ....(619) 587-9001

Printer Ribbon Supply
PO Box 920145
Norcross, GA 30092
Main ....(800) 438-7745
Tech. Support ....(770) 446-1547

Printer Works, The
3481 Arden Rd.
Hayward, CA 94545
Main ....(800) 225-6116
Tech. Support ....(415) 887-6116
Tech. Supp. Fax ....(510) 786-0589
BBS...(415) 786-0589
E-Mail........................support@printerworks.com

Printers Plus
PO Box 499
Grover, MO 63040
Customer Svc. ....(314) 532-6977
Tech. Support ....(314) 532-6977
Sales..(314) 532-6977
Tech. Supp. Fax ....(314) 458-0606
BBS...(314) 532-2285

Pro CD, Inc.
222 Rosewood Dr.
Danvers, MA 01923
Main ....(508) 750-0000
Customer Svc. ....(508) 750-0055
Tech. Support ....(508) 777-7766
Tech. Supp. Fax ....(508) 750-0070
E-Mail....................technical.support@procd.com
WWW................................http://www.procd.com

Process Software
959 Concord St
Framingham, MA 01701
Main ....(800) 722-7770
Tech. Support ....(508) 879-6994
Tech. Supp. Fax ....(508) 879-0042
WWW.............................http://www.process.com

Procom Technology, Inc.
200 McCormick Ave.
Costa Mesa, CA 92626
Main .... (800) 800-8600
Tech. Support................................ (714) 549-9949
BBS... (714) 549-0527
WWW.............................. http://www.procom.com/

Procomp USA, Inc.
6777 Engle Rd.
Cleveland, OH 44130
Main .... (216) 234-6387
Tech. Support................................ (216) 234-6387
BBS... (216) 234-2233

Prodigy Services Co.
445 Hamilton Ave.
White Plains, NY 10601
Main .... (914) 448-8000
WWW...............................http://www.prodigy.com/

Professor Jones
1940 W State St
Boise, ID 83702
Main .... (800) 553-2256
Tech. Support................................ (208) 342-6948
BBS... (208) 342-6948

Programmer's Paradise
1163 Shrewsbury Ave.
Shrewsbury, NJ 07702
Main .... (800) 445-7899
Tech. Support............................. (201) 389-9228
BBS... (201) 389-9227

Programmer's Shop
5 Bond Park Rd.
Hingham, MA 02043
Main .... (800) 421-8006
Tech. Support................................ (617) 740-3846
BBS... (617) 749-2018

Progress Software Corp.
5 Oak Park
Bedford, MA 01730-9960
Main...(800) 327-8445
Tech. Support..............................(617) 275-4500
BBS...(617) 275-4595
WWW.............................http://www.progress.com

Project Software & Development
20 University Rd.
Cambridge, MA 02138
Main...(617) 661-1444
Tech. Supp. Fax...........................(617) 661-1642

Prometheus Products
9440 Tualatin-Sherwood Rd.
Tualatin, OR 97062
Main...(503) 692-9600
Customer Svc................................(800) 477-3473
Tech. Support..............................(503) 692-9601
Sales ....(800) 477-3473
Tech. Supp. Fax...........................(503) 639-3946
BBS..(503) 691-5199
E-Mail.............................promeths@teleport.com
CompuServe 76004.527
America Online.................prometheus@aol.com

Promptus Communications, Inc.
207 High Point Ave.
Portsmouth, RI 02817
Main...(401) 683-6100
BBS..(401) 683-6105

Proteon, Inc.
2 Technology Dr
Westborough, MA 01581
Customer Svc................................(508) 898-3100
Tech. Support..............................(508) 898-3100
BBS..(508) 366-7827
WWW.............................http://www.proteon.com/

Proto View Development Corp.
162 Kingdom Ave.
New York, NY 10312
Main...(718) 948-5195

ProWorks
2371 NW Maser Dr.
Corvalis, OR 97330
Main...(503) 752-9885
Tech. Supp. Fax...........................(503) 567-8820
BBS..(503) 567-8820
WWW.............................http://www.proworks.com

Proxim, Inc.
295 N Bernardo Ave.
Mountain View, CA 94043
Main...(415) 960-1630
BBS..(415) 964-5181

Proxima
The Desktop Projection Co.
9440 Carroll Park Dr.
San Diego, CA 92121
Main...(800) 447-7694
Customer Svc................................(800) 447-7694
Sales...(800) 447-7692
Tech. Supp. Fax...........................(619) 677-5680
WWW.............................http://www.proxima.com/

Proxima Corp.
9440 Carroll Park Dr.
San Diego, CA 92121
Main...(800) 582-2580
Tech. Support..............................(619) 457-5500

PseudoCorp+A1625
2597 Potter St.
Eugene, OR 97405
Main...(541) 683-9173
Tech. Supp. Fax...........................(541) 683-9183
BBS..(804) 873-2154
E-Mail.............................rhowdem@teleport.com
WWW.......http://www.teleport.com/tildarhowdem

PSI Integration, Inc.
851 E Hamilton Ave., #200
Campbell, CA 95008
Main...(800) 622-1722
Customer Svc................................(800) 622-1722
Tech. Support..............................(408) 559-8544
BBS..(408) 559-8548

PT Diagnostic Software
WWW.http://www.enet.net/eg/egnet/paintac.html

Public Brand Software
PO Box 51315
Indianapolis, IN 46251
Main ....(617) 252-5260
Tech. Support ....(317) 856-7571

Publishing Perfection
PO Box 307
Menomonee Falls, WI 53051
Main ....(800) 782-5974
Tech. Support ....(414) 252-5000
Tech. Supp. Fax ....(414) 252-9120
BBS...(414) 255-2071

Pure Data Ltd.
180 West Beaver Creek Rd.
Richmond Hill, ONT A4B1B4
Main ....(905) 731-6444
Customer Svc. ....(905) 731-6444
Tech. Support ....(905) 731-6444
Sales ....(905) 731-6444
Tech. Supp. Fax ....(905) 731-7017
BBS...(905) 731-4679
WWW .... http://www.puredata.com/

Pyramid
WWW.............................http://www.pyramid.com/

Q/Car
1 Meca Way
Norcross, GA 30093
Main ....(770) 923-6666

QL Systems, Inc.
275 Sparks St, #901
Ottawa, Ontario K1R 7X9
Canada
Main ....(613) 238-3499

QLogic Corp. / Emulex
28832 Hedgerow
Mission Viejo, CA 92692
Main .... (714) 888-9625
Customer Svc. .... (800) 854-7112
Tech. Support .... (800) 854-7112
Tech. Supp. Fax .... (714) 662-1445
BBS .... (714) 662-1445
E-Mail .... tech_support@emulex.com
WWW............................... http://www.emulex.com/
FTP Address .... ftp.emulex.com

QMS, Inc.
1 Magnum Pass
Mobile, AL 36618
Main .... (800) 523-2696
Tech. Support .... (334) 639-4447
BBS .... (334) 633-0013
WWW.................................... http://www.qms.com

Qplus, Inc.
2020 Beechwood Blvd.
Pittsburgh, PA 15217
Main .... (412) 521-9525

Quadralay Corp.
WWW.......................... http://www.quadralay.com/

Quadram
1 Quad Way
Norcross, GA 30093
Main .... (770) 923-6666
BBS .... (770) 564-5528

Qualcomm Inc.orp.orated
WWW........................ http://www.qualcomm.com/

Qualitas
Tech. Support .... (301) 907-7400
Tech. Supp. Fax .... (301) 907-7400
BBS .... (301) 718-6061
E-Mail .... tech@qualitas.com
WWW.............................. http://www.qualitas.com
FTP Address .... ftp://ftp.qualitas.com/pub/
CompuServe .... PCVENA
America Online.................................... QUALITAS

Quality America, Inc.
WWW..................... http://www.qa-inc.com/qa-inc

Quality Software Products
5711 W Slauson Ave., #240
Culver City, CA 90230
Main.. (800) 628-3999
Tech. Support............................... (213) 410-0303
BBS .... (213) 410-0124

Qualix Group
1900 S Norfolk St, #224
San Mateo, CA 94403-1151
Main.. (415) 572-0200
Tech. Supp. Fax........................... (415) 572-1300
BBS .... (415) 572-1300
WWW............................... http://www.qualix.com/

Qualstar Corp.
6709 Independence Ave.
Canoga, CA 91303
Main.. (818) 592-0061
Tech. Support............................... (818) 592-0061
Tech. Supp. Fax........................... (818) 592-0116
BBS .... (818) 592-0116

Quantex Micro Systems Inc.
400 B. Pierce St.
Somerset, NJ 08873
Main.. (800) 950-6660
Tech. Supp. Fax........................... (908) 563-0407
BBS .... (201) 563-4999

Quantum Corp.
500 McCarthy Blvd.
Milpitas, CA 95035
Main.. (408) 894-4000
BBS .... (408) 894-3218
WWW............................ http://www.quantum.com

Quantum Effect Design
WWW.......... http://www.qedinc.com/qed/qed.html

Quantum Software Systems, Ltd.
175 Terrence Matthews Crescent
Kanata, ONT K2M 1W8
Canada
Main.. (613) 591-0931
BBS .... (613) 591-3579

Quark
1800 Grant Street
Denver, CO 80203
Main.. (303) 894-8888
Customer Svc. .... (303) 894-8888
Tech. Support .... (303) 894-8899
Sales.. (800) 788-7835
Tech. Supp. Fax .... (303) 894-3399
E-Mail.................................... wintech@quark.com
WWW............................... http://www.quark.com/
CompuServe...... 70414.2101@compuserve.com
America Online .... WINQUARK@aol.com

Quarterdeck
13160 Mindanao Way
Floor 3
Marina Del Rey, CA 90292-9705
Main.. (310) 309-3700
Customer Svc. .... (800) 354-3222
Tech. Support .... (310) 392-9701
Sales.. (310) 309-3700
BBS .... (310) 314-3227
E-Mail........................... support@qdeck.com
WWW............................... http://www.qdeck.com
FTP Address................................. ftp.qdeck.com

Quest Tech
1324 Vendels Circle
Suite No 101
Paso Robles, CA 93446
Main.. (805) 237-6262
Customer Svc. .... (800) 448-1184
Tech. Support .... (800) 448-1184
Sales.. (800) 448-1184
Tech. Supp. Fax .... (805) 461-6267
BBS .... (805) 237-6266
E-Mail.................................... info@questtech.com
WWW......................... http://www.questtech.com/

Questron
1011 Commerce Ct.
Buffalo Grove, IL 60089-2362
Main...(312) 763-0763
Tech. Supp. Fax ....(847) 465-3770
BBS..(312) 763-8330

Quick Electronics, Inc.
10800 76th Ct N
Largo, FL 34647
Main...(800) 800-5500
Tech. Support ....(813) 546-0311
Tech. Supp. Fax ....(813) 544-5500
BBS..(813) 544-5500

QuickLogic
WWW.........................http://www.quicklogic.com/

Quill Corp.
100 Schelter Rd.
Lincolnshire, IL 60069-3621
Main...(708) 634-6650
Tech. Support ....(708) 634-6650
BBS..(708) 634-5699

Quingen Systems
530 Causeway Dr
Wrightsville Beach, NC 28480
Main...(919) 256-9119

Quinn-Curtis
35 Highland Cir
Needham, MA 02194
Main...(617) 449-6155
Tech. Supp. Fax ....(617) 449-6109
BBS..(617) 449-6109
WWW......... http://www.quinn-curtis.com/~quinn/

Quintus Computer Systems, Inc.
1310 Villa St
Mountain View, CA 94041
Main...(800) 542-1283
Tech. Support ....(415) 965-7700
BBS..(415) 965-0551

R & L Electronics
609 S Key Ave.
Lampasa, TX 76550
Main ....(800) 533-8676
Tech. Support...............................(512) 556-8228
BBS ....(512) 556-2041

R A D Data Communications
900 Corporate Dr
Mahwah, NJ 07430
Main ....(201) 529-1100
BBS ....(201) 529-5777

Rabbit Software, Inc.
7 Great Valley Pkwy
Malvern, PA 19355
Main ....(800) 245-7253
Tech. Support...............................(215) 647-0440
BBS ....(215) 640-1379

Racal-Datacom, Inc.
1601 North Harrison Parkway
P.O. Box 407044
Fort Lauderdale, FL 33340-7044
Main ....(305) 846-1601
Customer Svc..............................(800) 526-8255
Tech. Support...............................(508) 263-9929
Tech. Supp. Fax...........................(508) 635-9140
BBS ....(508) 264-4345
E-Mail.............. cust_service@rimail.interlan.com
WWW..................................http://www.racal.com/
FTP Address ....ftp://ftpserv.interlan.com/ftpserve/

Racal-Milgo
1601 N Harrison Pkwy
PO Box 407044
Ft Lauderdale, FL 33340-9926
Main ....(800) 722-2555
Tech. Support...............................(305) 846-4811
Tech. Supp. Fax...........................(305) 846-4942
BBS ....(305) 846-4942
WWW...................................http://www.racal.com

Racore Computer Products
170 Knowlws Dr, #206
Los Gatos, CA 95030
Main..(800) 635-1274
Tech. Support...............................(408) 374-8290
BBS ....(408) 374-6653

RAD Technologies
WWW...................................... http://www.rad.com

Radiant Communications
PO Box 867, 5001 Hadley Rd.
South Plainfield, NJ 07080
Main..(800) 969-3427
Tech. Support...............................(908) 757-7444
BBS ....(908) 757-8666

Radius / E-Machines
215 Moffett Park Dr.
Sunnyvale, CA 94089
Main..(408) 541-5700
Customer Svc...............................(408) 541-5750
Tech. Support...............................(408) 541-6100
Sales ....(408) 541-2900
Tech. Supp. Fax...........................(408) 541-5094
BBS ....(408) 541-6190
E-Mail..................................infornet@radius.com
WWW.............................http://www.radius.com
FTP Address.................................ftp.radius.com
CompuServe 76004,2155
America Online.........................radius@aol.com

Raima Corp.
PO BOX 795
Issaquah, WA 98027
Main..(800) 327-2462
Tech. Support...............................(206) 747-5570
Tech. Supp. Fax...........................(206) 557-5200
BBS ....(206) 557-5200
WWW...............................http://www.raima.com

Rainbow Technology
50 Technology Dr.
Irvine, CA 92718
Main..(800) 843-0413
Tech. Supp. Fax ....(714) 450-7450
BBS...(704) 523-7651
E-Mail..............................techsupport@rnbo.com
WWW...................................http://www.rnbo.com

Rand McNally Media Services
WWW ....http://www.randmedia.ie/rand/

RasterOps
2500 Walsh Ave.
Santa Clara, CA 95051
Main...(408) 562-4200
Tech. Support ....(800) 729-2656
Sales...(800) 729-2656
Tech. Supp. Fax ....(317) 576-7770
BBS...(317) 577-8777
WWW ....http://www.truevision.com
FTP Address.............................ftp.truevision.com
CompuServe...........................GO TRUEVISION
America Online .... Keyword Truevision

RB Software
1109 Arnette Ave.
Durham, NC 27707

ReadySoft Inc.A1660
3375 14th Ave., Units 7 & 8
Markham, ONT L3R 0H2
Canada
Main...(905) 475-4801
WWW...........................http://www.readysoft.com

Real Time Devices, Inc.
200 Innovation Blvd.
State College, PA 16803
Main...(814) 234-8087
Tech. Supp. Fax ....(814) 234-5218
BBS...(814) 234-6864

Real World Corp.
282 Loudon Rd., PO Box 2051
Concord, NH 03302-2051
Main...(800) 678-6336
Tech. Support ....(603) 224-2200
BBS...(603) 224-1955

RealAudio
WWW..........................http://www.realaudio.com/

Reality Online, Inc.
WWW..........................http://www.moneynet.com

Reasonable Solutions
2101 W Main St
Medford, OR 97501
Main...(800) 876-3475
Tech. Support ....(503) 776-5777
BBS...(503) 773-7803

Reasoning Systems
WWW..........................http://www.reasoning.com/

Recital Corp., Inc.
85 Constitution Ln
Danvers, MA 01923
Main...(508) 750-1066

Recreational Software Advisory
WWW..............http://www.rsac.org/users/rsacinfo

Red-Hawk
1405 S Milpitas
Milpitas, CA 95035
Main...(408) 945-1800
BBS...(408) 945-1396

ReefNet Software
WWW...............http://www.interlog.com/~reefnet

Reflection Technology
240 Bear Hill Rd.
Waltham, MA 02154
Main...(617) 890-5905

Reliable Communications
PO BOX 816
Angelscamp, CA 95222
Main .... (800) 222-0042
Tech. Support............................ (408) 996-0230
Tech. Supp. Fax........................ (209) 736-0425
BBS... (408) 996-3367
E-Mail...........................rcisystem@goldrush.com

Reliable Electric
11333 Addison St
Franklin Park, IL 60131
Main .... (708) 455-8010
BBS... (708) 451-5516

Remee Products
186 N Main St
Florida, NY 10921
Main .... (800) 431-3864
Tech. Support............................. (914) 651-4431
Tech. Supp. Fax.......................... (914) 651-4160
BBS... (914) 651-4160

Renaissance GRX, Inc.
2265 116th Ave. NE
Bellevue, WA 98004
Main .... (206) 454-8086

Repco
2421 N Orange Blossom Trl
Orlando, FL 32804
Main .... (800) 950-5633
Tech. Support............................. (407) 843-8484
BBS... (407) 841-0331

Reply Corp.
4435 Fortran Dr
San Jose, CA 95134
Main .... (408) 942-4804
BBS... (408) 942-4897

Resource Concepts Computer Out
15203 Midway Rd.
Addison, TX 75244
Main .... (800) 962-7795
Tech. Support............................. (214) 386-5515
BBS... (214) 386-5642

Resource Planning Associates+A1679

95 Brown Rd.
Langmuir Bldg, #231
Ithaca, NY 14850
Main...(800) 432-7721
Tech. Support...............................(607) 257-4305
BBS ....(607) 257-2820

Responsive Software

WWW..............http://www.holonet.net/responsive

Retix

2401 Colorado Ave.
Santa Monica, CA 90404-3563
Main...(800) 255-2333
Tech. Support...............................(310) 828-3400
BBS ....(310) 828-2255

Reveal

WWW..............................http://www.reveal.com/

Revelation Technologies

181 Habor Dr.
Stanford, CT 06902
Main...(800) 262-4747
Tech. Support...............................(212) 689-1000
WWW.........................http://www.revelation.com/

RG Software Systems, Inc.

6900 E Camelback Rd., #630
Scottsdale, AZ 85251
Main...(602) 423-8000
BBS ....(602) 423-8389

Ricoh Corp.

5 Dedrick Pl
West Caldwell, NJ 07006
Main...(201) 882-2000

Riser Bond Instruments

1207 M St. PO BOX 188
Aurora, NB 68818
Main...(402) 694-5201
BBS ....(402) 694-2386

Riverbend Group

1491 Chain Bridge Rd.
McLean, VA 22101
Main...(703) 883-0616

Robec Distributors

425 Privet Rd.
Horsham, PA 19044
Main...(215) 675-9300

Rockwell International

WWW..............................http://www.rockwell.com

Rockwell Network Systems

7402 Hollister Ave.
Santa Barbara, CA 93117
Main...(800) 262-8023
Tech. Support ....(805) 968-4262
BBS...(805) 968-6478
E-Mail... support@rns.com
WWW...................................... http://www.rns.com

Rodime, Inc.

901 Broken Sound Pkwy
Boca Raton, FL 33487
Main...(407) 994-6200
Tech. Support ....(800) 765-9292
BBS...(407) 997-6135

Roland Corp. U.S.

Desktop Media Production
7200 Dominion Cir.
Los Angeles, CA 90040
Main...(213) 685-5141
Customer Svc. ....(213) 685-5141
Tech. Support ....(213) 685-5141
Sales...(213) 685-5141

Roland Digital Group

15271 Barranca Pkwy
Irvine, CA 92718
Main...(714) 727-2100
Tech. Supp. Fax ....(714) 727-2112
BBS...(714) 975-0569

Ron Teck
1450 Boot Rood
Buildling 400A
West Chester, PA 19380
Main ....(610) 429-3701
Customer Svc. ....(800) 321-7259
Tech. Support ....(800) 321-7259
Tech. Supp. Fax ....(610) 429-3810

Rose Electronics
10850 Wilcrest, #900
PO Box 742571
Houston, TX 77274
Main..(800) 333-9343
Tech. Support ....(713) 933-7673
BBS...(713) 933-0044

Rosetta Technologies
9417 Princess Palm Ave.
Tampa, FL 33619
Main..(800) 937-4224
Tech. Support ....(813) 620-1107

ROSS Technology
WWW.................................. http://www.ross.com/

Rupp Corp.
7285 Franklin Ave.
Los Angeles, CA 90046
Main..(213) 850-5394
Tech. Supp. Fax ....(213) 874-5646

Rupp Technology Corp.
3228 East Indian School Rd.
Phoenix, AZ 85018
Main..(602) 224-9922
Customer Svc. ....(602) 224-9922
Tech. Support ....(602) 224-9922
Sales..(800) 844-7755
Tech. Supp. Fax ....(602) 224-0898
WWW...................................... http://www.rupp.com
FTP Address.....................................ftp.rupp.com
CompuServe...GO RUPP
America Online ....dpa@aol.com

RYBS Electronics, Inc.
351 W. Arapahoe
Boulder, CO 80302
Main ....(303) 444-6073
Tech. Support................................(303) 444-7927
Tech. Supp. Fax...........................(303) 449-9259
BBS..(303) 449-9259
E-Mail...sales@bybs.com

Sabina International
675 Brea Canyon Rd., #5
Walnut, CA 91789
Tech. Support............................... (714) 594-6336
BBS.. (714) 595-4008

Safe Power Systems
528 W 21st St
Tempe, AZ 85282
Main .... (602) 894-6864
Sales... (800) 325-5848

Safeware, The Insurance Agency
2929 N High St.
PO Box 02211
Columbus, OH 43202-9990
Main .... (800) 848-3469
Tech. Support................................ (614) 262-0559
BBS... (614) 262-1714
CompuServe .... GO SAFE

Sager Computer
18005 Cortney Ct
City of Industry, CA 91748
Main .... (800) 669-1624
Tech. Support............................... (818) 964-4849
BBS... (818) 964-2381

Sageware
1282 Garner Ave.
Schenectady, NY 12309
Main .... (518) 377-1052

SAI Systems Laboratories, Inc.
911 Bridge Port Ave.
Shelton, CT 06484
Main...(800) 331-0488
Tech. Support..............................(203) 929-4959
Tech. Supp. Fax..........................(203) 929-6948
BBS ....(203) 929-6948

Saint Croix Computers
6640 Shady Oak Rd.
Eden Prairie, MN 55344
Main...(800) 950-0174
Tech. Support..............................(612) 943-8618
BBS ....(612) 943-3854

Sales Partner Systems, Inc.
770 West Granada Blvd.
Suite 116
Ormond Beach, FL 32174
Main...(904) 672-8434
WWW..........................http://www.spsi.com:8080

Samsonite
11200 East 45th Ave.
Denver, CO 80239
Main...(303) 373-2000
Customer Svc...............................(800) 223-7627
Tech. Support..............................(303) 373-6666
Sales ....(800) 223-7627
Tech. Supp. Fax..........................(303) 373-6300

Samsung
Information Systems Div.
105 Challenger Rd.
Ridgefield Park, NJ 07660
Main...(201) 229-4000
Customer Svc...............................(800) 446-0262
Tech. Support..............................(800) 446-0262
BBS ....(201) 691-6238
WWW.. http://www.samsung.co.kr/samsung.html

Samsung Information Systems America
3655 N 1st St
San Jose, CA 95134-1708
Main...(800) 446-0262
Tech. Support..............................(800) 446-0262

Samtron
A Division of Samsung Electronics America
18600 Broadwick St.
Rancho Dominguez, CA 90220
Main ....(310) 537-7000
Customer Svc. ....(714) 522-1282
Tech. Support ....(714) 522-1282

Sandy Corp.
1500 W Big Beaver Rd.
Troy, MI 48084
Main..(810) 649-0800

Santa Cruz Operation
400 Encinal St.
P.O. Box 1900
Santa Cruz, CA 95061-1900
Main..(408) 425-7222
Customer Svc. ....(800) 347-4381
Tech. Support ....(408) 425-7222
Tech. Supp. Fax ....(408) 458-4227
BBS...(408) 426-9495
E-Mail...support@sco.com
WWW .... http://www.sco.com/index.html
CompuServe.............................GO SCOFORUM

Santorini Consulting & Design
2147 Union St
San Francisco, CA 94123
Main ....(415) 563-6398
Tech. Supp. Fax ....(415) 563-0332
E-Mail...................santorini@applelink.apple.com

Sanyo/Icon
764 E Timpanogos Pkwy
Orem, UT 84057-6212
Main ....(800) 877-2696
Tech. Support ....(801) 225-6888
BBS...(801) 226-0651

Saratoga Group, The
12930 Saratoga Ave., #12980
Suite #E
Saratoga, CA 95070-9902
Main..(408) 446-9115
BBS...(408) 446-9134
WWW .... http://www.cyberwise.com

Saros
10900 NE 8th St.
1515 Plaza Ctr
Bellevue, WA 98004
Main...(206) 646-1066
WWW................................. http://www.saros.com

SAS Industries
3091 N Bay Dr
North Bend, OR 97459
Main...(800) 245-4657
Tech. Support ....(503) 756-2508
Tech. Supp. Fax ....(503) 756-7728
BBS...(503) 756-7728
WWW....................................http://www.sas.com/

SBT Corp.
1 Harbor Dr
Sausalito, CA 94965
Main...(415) 444-9900
BBS...(415) 331-1951

Scantron
WWW...........................http://www.scantron.com/

Sceptre
WWW.............. http://www.gus.com/emp/sceptre/
sceptre.html

Scholastic
WWW..........................http://scholastic.com:2005

Scientific Endeavors Corp.
508 N Kentucky St
Kingston, TN 37763
Main...(615) 376-4146
BBS...(615) 376-1571

SciTech Software
WWW..........................http://www.scitechsoft.com/

Scitex
WWW.......................http://www.pink2.scitex.com/

Scitor Corp.
333 Middlefield Rd. 2nd Floor
2nd Floor
Mewlo Park, CA 94025
Main .... (415) 570-7700

SCO
WWW.................................... http://www.sco.com/

SCorp.ion Systems
175 5th Ave., #2624
New York, NY 10010
Main .... (415) 864-2956

SCS Compute
3633 136th Pl SE
Suite 300
Bellevue, WA 98006
Main .... (206) 643-2050
Customer Svc.............................. (800) 877-8297
Tech. Support.............................. (800) 877-8297
Sales .... (800) 326-1040
Tech. Supp. Fax........................... (206) 562-1783
BBS.. (800) 729-1040

Seagate Technology
920 Disc Dr.
Scotts Valley, CA 95066
Main .... (408) 438-6550
Customer Svc.............................. (408) 438-6550
Tech. Support.............................. (408) 438-8222
Sales .... (408) 438-8111
Tech. Supp. Fax........................... (408) 438-8137
BBS.. (408) 438-8771
WWW............................. http://www.seagate.com
CompuServe ....GO SEAGATE
America Online........................ seagate@aol.com

Seagull Scientific Systems
15127 NE 24th, #333
Redmond, WA 98052
Main .... (206) 451-8966

Secure-It, Inc.
18 Maple Ct
East Longeadow, MA 01028
Main...(800) 451-7592
Tech. Support................................(413) 525-7039
WWW....http://www.owls.com/secureit/index.html

Security APL
WWWhttp://www.secapl.com/secapl/Welcome.html

SEEQ Technology
WWW..................................http://www.seeq.com/

Sega
WWW.............................. http://www.segaoa.com/

Segue Software, Inc.
WWW............................... http://www.segue.com

Seiko Instruments (USA), Inc.
1144 Ringwood Ct
San Jose, CA 95131
Main...(800) 888-0817
Tech. Support................................(408) 922-5800

Selfware, Inc.
6734 Curran St
McLean, Va 22101
Main...(703) 506-0400

Selos
1324 Vendels Cir
Paso Robles, CA 93446
Main...(800) 448-1184
Tech. Support................................(805) 237-6262
Tech. Supp. Fax...........................(805) 237-6271
WWW...http://www.slownet.org~/hright/felos.html

SemWare
4343 Shallowford Rd., #C-3
Marietta, GA 30062-6213
Main...(770) 641-9002
BBS ....(770) 640-6213
WWW............................. http://www.semware.com

Sequent Computer Systems
Beaverton, OR
Main...(800) 327-5545
WWW.............................http://www.sequent.com/

Serif, Inc.
WWW................................... http://www.serif.com/

Server Technology
1288 Hammerwood Ave.
Sunnyvale, CA 94089
Main...(408) 745-0300
Customer Svc. ....(800) 835-1515
Tech. Support ....(800) 835-1515
Sales..(800) 835-1515
Tech. Supp. Fax ....(408) 745-0392
WWW..........................http://www.severtech.com
FTP Address...........................ftp.servertech.com
CompuServe................................... GO SERVER

1776
8632 South Sepulveda Blvd.
Suite 203
Los Angeles, CA 90045
Main...(310) 215-1776
Tech. Supp. Fax ....(310) 216-1107

7th Level
1110 East Collins Blvd.
Suite 122
Richardson, TX 75081
Main...(214) 437-4858
Customer Svc. ....(214) 437-4858
Tech. Support ....(214) 437-4858
Sales..(214) 437-4858
Tech. Supp. Fax ....(214) 437-2717
E-Mail................................. support@7thlevel.com
WWW............................... http://www.7thlevel.com
FTP Address...............................ftp.7thlevel.com
CompuServe................................... GO SEVEN
America Online .... Keyword SEVEN

Shaffstall Corp.
7901 E 88th St
Indianapolis, IN 46256
Main..(800) 248-3475
Tech. Support ....(317) 842-2077
BBS..(317) 842-9294

Shamrock Computer
828 Via Alondra
Camarillo, CA 93010
Main..(800) 729-2898
Tech. Support ....(805) 388-9045

Shany, Inc.
PO Box 34016
Los Angeles, CA 90034
Main..(310) 204-0111
BBS..(310) 204-0110

Shape Electronics, Inc.
2105 Corporate Dr
Addison, IL 60101
Main..(800) 367-5811
Tech. Supp. Fax ....(708) 620-0784

Sharp Electronics
Sharp Plaza
Mahwah, NJ 07430
Main..(201) 529-8200
Customer Svc. ....(800) 237-4277
Tech. Support ....(800) 447-4700

Sharp's, Inc.
PO Box 326
Menchincsville, VA 23111
Main..(804) 730-9697
Tech. Support ....(804) 730-9697
BBS..(804) 746-1978

Shecom Computers
3981 E. Mira Loma
Anaheim, CA 92806
Main..(800) 366-4433
Tech. Support ....(714) 634-4800
BBS..(714) 637-6293

Ship Star Associates
36 Woodhill Dr
Newark, DE 19711
Main ....(302) 738-7782
BBS..(302) 738-0855

Shiva Corp.
North West Park
63 Third Ave.
Burlington, MA 01803
Main ....(617) 270-8300
Customer Svc.................................(617) 252-6300
Tech. Support................................(617) 270-8400
BBS..(617) 273-0023
WWW.................................. http://www.shiva.com
FTP Address ....ftp.shiva.com

Shopping Planet
WWW.................. http://www.shoppingplanet.com/

ShowCase
WWW............http://www.millcomm.com/wwwmill/
showcase/millcomm.

Shreve Systems
2421 Malcolm St
Shreveport, LA 71108
Main ....(800) 227-3971
Tech. Support................................(318) 635-1121
BBS..(318) 865-2006

Shugaart Corp.
9292 Jeronimo Rd.
Irvine, CA 92718
Main ....(714) 770-1100
Tech. Support................................(714) 770-1100
BBS..(714) 859-4960

Siecor Electro-Optic Products
800 17th St. NW
Hickory, NC 28601
Main ....(800) 634-9064
Tech. Support................................(704) 327-5000
BBS..(704) 327-5488

Siemans-Nixdorf
WWW....................................... http://www.sni.com

Siemens Componets, Inc.
2191 Laurelwood Rd.
Santa Clara, CA 95054-1514
Main..(800) 456-9229

Siemens Nixdorf Information Sytem
200 Wheeler Rd.
Burlington, MA 01803
Main..(617) 273-0480

Siemens Nixdorf Printing System
5600 Broken Sound Blvd.
Boca Raton, FL 33487
Main..(407) 997-3100

Siemon Co.
76 Westbury Park Rd.
Watertown, CT 06795
Main..(203) 274-2523
BBS ....(203) 274-0940

Sierra On-Line
3380-146th Place SE
Suite 300
Bellevue, WA 98007
Main..(206) 649-9800
Tech. Support...............................(209) 868-3898
WWW.................................http://www.sierra.com/

Sigma Data
PO Box 1790
New London, NH 03257-9949
Main..(800) 446-4525
Tech. Support...............................(603) 526-6909
BBS ....(603) 526-6915

Sigma Designs
46501 Landing Parkway
Fremont, CA 94538
Main..(510) 770-0100
Customer Svc...............................(303) 339-7120
Tech. Support...............................(303) 339-7120
Sales ....(510) 770-0100
Tech. Supp. Fax...........................(510) 770-2640
BBS ....(510) 770-0111
WWW...........................http://www.realmagic.com
FTP Address.........................ftp.REALmagic.com

Silicon Graphics
WWW.....................................http://www.sgi.com/

Silicon Graphics, Inc.
2011 N Shoreline Blvd.
Mountain View, CA 94043-7311
Main..(415) 960-1980
Tech. Supp. Fax ....(415) 961-0595
BBS..(415) 968-3579
WWW.....................................http://www.sgi.com

SilverPlatter
WWW.......................http://www.silverplatter.com/

SIMBA Information Inc.
WWW............................http://www.simbanet.com

SimmSaver Technology, Inc.
WWW.............http://www.elysian.net/simmsaver/

Simpact Associates, Inc.
9210 Sky Park Ct
San Diego, CA 92123
Main..(619) 565-1865

Simple Technology
3001 Daimler St.
Santa Ana, CA 92705
Main..(714) 476-1180
Customer Svc. ....(714) 475-1180
Tech. Support ....(714) 476-1180
BBS..(714) 476-9034

Sinper Corp.
31 Mountain Blvd., Bldg N
Warren, NJ 07060
Main..(800) 822-1596
Tech. Support ....(201) 755-9880
BBS..(201) 755-9230

Sirius Publishing
7320 E. Butherus Dr., Suite 100
Scottsdale, AZ 85260
Main...(602) 951-3288
Customer Svc. ....(602) 951-3288
Tech. Support ....(602) 951-8405
Sales...(800) 247-0307
Tech. Supp. Fax ....(602) 951-3884
WWW ....http://www.siriusnet.com
FTP Address...............................ftp.siriusnet.com

Sitka Corp.
950 Marina Village Pkwy
Alameda, CA 94501
Main..(800) 445-8677
Tech. Support ....(415) 769-8711
BBS..(415) 769-8771

Sizzleware Shareware Library
PO Box 6429
Lake Charles, LA 70606
Main...(800) 356-2697
Tech. Support ....(318) 474-1548

Skillsbank Corp.
WWW...........................http://www.skillsbank.com

Sky Computers, Inc.
27 Industrial Ave.
Chelmsford, MA 01824
Main...(508) 250-1920
Tech. Supp. Fax ....(508) 250-0036
WWW....................................http://www.sky.com

Small Computer Co., The
41 Saw Mill River Rd.
Hawthorne, NY 10532
Main...(914) 769-3160
BBS..(914) 769-3653

Smart Software, Inc.
392 Concord Ave.
Belmont, MA 02178
Main...(617) 489-2743

Smith, Samuel H.A1782
5119 N 11th Ave., #332
Phoenix, AZ 85013

Socket Communications
WWW........................http://www.socketcom.com/

Soft Hard Systems
6301 Desoto Ave. #C
Woodland Hills, CA 91367
Main .... (818) 999-9531
Tech. Support............................. (818) 999-9531
BBS.. (818) 999-9683

Soft Shell Systems
1163 Triton Dr.
Foster City, CA 94404
Main .... (800) 322-7638
Tech. Support............................. (415) 571-9000

Softbridge Group, The
125 Cambridge Park Dr.
Cambridge, MA 02140
Main .... (800) 955-9190
Tech. Support............................. (617) 576-2257
Tech. Supp. Fax......................... (617) 864-7747
BBS.. (617) 864-7747

SoftCop International, Inc.
935 Sheldon Court
Burlington, ONT L7L 5K6
Canada
Main .... (905) 681-3269
WWW..............................http://www.softcop.com

Softdisk Publishing
606 Common St.
Shreveport, LA 71101
Main .... (318) 221-8718
WWW.............................. http://www.softdisk.com

SoftInfo
WWW........................http://www.icp.com/softinfo/

Softkey International
450 Franklin Rd.
Suite 100
Marietta, GA 30067
Main..............................(770) 514-6300
Customer Svc..............(770) 428-0008
Tech. Support...............(770) 428-0008
Sales ....(800) 227-5609
Tech. Supp. Fax...........(770) 427-1150
BBS.............................(770) 514-6332

SoftKlone
327 Office Plaza Dr, #100
Tallahassee, FL 32301
Main..............................(800) 634-8670
Tech. Support...............(904) 878-8564
Tech. Supp. Fax...........(904) 877-9763
BBS.............................(904) 877-9763
WWW...........................http://www.softklone.com

SoftMail Direct
WWW..............................http://www.softmail.com

SoftQuad, Inc.
56 Aberfoyle Crescent, 5th Floor
Toronto, ONT M8X 2W4
Canada
Main..............................(416) 239-4801
Tech. Supp. Fax...........(416) 239-7105
E-Mail...........................support@sq.com
WWW...........................http://www.sq.com/

Softronics
5085 List Dr.
Colorado Springs, CO 80919
Main..............................(800) 225-8590
Tech. Support...............(719) 593-9540
Tech. Supp. Fax...........(719) 548-1878
BBS.............................(719) 548-1878
WWW...........................http://www.softronics.com

SoftSource
301 W Holly St.
Bellingham, WA 98225
Main..............................(360) 676-0999
BBS.............................(360) 671-1131

Software AG
WWW.........................http://www.sofwareag.com/

Software Architects, Inc.
19102 N Creek Pkwy, #101
Bothell, WA 98011
Main..............................(206) 487-0122
Tech. Supp. Fax...........(206) 487-0467
BBS.............................(206) 487-0467

Software Creations, Inc.
8402 Laurel Fair Circle
Suite # 207
Tampa, FL 33610
Main..............................(800) 767-3279
Tech. Support ....(813) 684-8291
Tech. Supp. Fax ....(813) 622-7046
BBS.............................(813) 622-7046

Software Development Systems,
815 Commerce Dr.
Suite 250
Oak Brook, IL 60521
Main..............................(800) 448-7733
Tech. Support ....(708) 971-8170
Tech. Supp. Fax ....(708) 971-8513
BBS.............................(708) 971-8513
E-Mail..........................Support@sdi.com

Software Directions, Inc.
1572 Sussex Turnpike
Randolph, NJ 07869
Main..............................(800) 346-7638
Tech. Support ....(201) 584-8466
BBS.............................(201) 584-7771

Software Environments
PO Box 2129
Mission Viejo, CA 92690
Main..............................(800) 927-1481

Software Innovations
WWW................................http://www.innov.com/

Software Interphase, Inc.
82 Cucumber Hill Rd., #140
Foster, RI 02825
Main...(800) 542-2742
Tech. Supp. Fax ....(401) 397-6814
BBS...(401) 397-6814
WWW.......................http://www.sinterphase.com

Software Marketing Group, Inc.
1101 Walnut St. Suite 350
Des Moines, IA 50309
Main...(800) 395-0209
Tech. Support ....(515) 284-0209
Tech. Supp. Fax ....(515) 284-5147
BBS...(515) 284-5147
E-Mail... opis@netins.net

Software Metrics
WWW.............................. http://www.metrics.com/

Software Packaging Associates
WWW............................. http://www.softpack.com

Software Partners, Inc.
999 Commercial St
Palto, CA 94303
Main...(415) 857-1110

Software Productivity Centre
WWW........ http://www.spc.ca/spc/Welcome.html

Software Products International
9920 Pacific Heights Blvd.
San Diego, CA 92121-4330
Main...(800) 937-4774
Tech. Support ....(619) 450-1526
BBS...(619) 450-1921

Software Publishing Corp.
8404 Suiterling St
Irving, TX 75063
Main...(800) 562-9909
Tech. Support ....(214) 929-4888
BBS...(214) 929-1655

Software Publishing Corp.
111 N. Market St.
San Jose, CA 95113
Main .... (408) 537-3000
Customer Svc.................................. (800) 234-2500
Tech. Support.................................. (408) 988-4005
Sales .... (800) 336-8360
Tech. Supp. Fax........................... (408) 537-3512
BBS .... (408) 537-3512

Software Science, Inc.
168 S. Park
San Francisco, CA 94017
Main .... (800) 468-9273
Tech. Support.................................. (415) 467-6840
Tech. Supp. Fax........................... (415) 479-2563
E-Mail .... ssi@well.com
WWW.......................http://www.well.com/user/ssi

Software Spectrum
2140 Merritt Dr.
Garland, Texas 75041
Main .... (800) 624-0503
Tech. Supp. Fax........................... (800) 864-7878
WWW.......................http://www.swspectrum.com

Software Support
300 International Parkway
Suite No 320
Heathrow, FL 32746
Main .... (407) 333-4433
Customer Svc.................................. (800) 756-4463
Tech. Support.................................. (800) 873-4357
Sales .... (800) 756-4463
Tech. Supp. Fax........................... (407) 333-9080

Software Ventures
2907 Claremont Ave.
Berkeley, CA 94705
Main .... (510) 644-3232
Customer Svc.................................. (510) 644-3232
Tech. Support.................................. (510) 644-1325
Sales .... (510) 644-3232
Tech. Supp. Fax........................... (510) 848-0885
BBS .... (510) 849-1912
WWW............................ http://www.svcdudes.com
FTP Address ....ftp.svcdudes.com

Software.Net
WWW...http://software.net

Softwave Technologies, Inc.
WWW....................http://www.gate.net/~softwave

Solbourne Computer, Inc.
1790 38th St. Suite #300
Boulder, CO 80301
Main...(800) 752-9721
Tech. Support...............................(303) 772-3400
Tech. Supp. Fax............................(303) 417-2820
BBS...(303) 417-2820

Solectek Accessories
6370 Nancy Ridge Dr., Suite 109
San Diego, CA 92121
Main...(619) 450-1220
Customer Svc................................(619) 450-1220
Tech. Support...............................(619) 450-1220
Sales ....(619) 450-1220
Tech. Supp. Fax............................(619) 457-2681
BBS ....(619) 450-6537
WWW...................http://www.solecteck@cts.com
FTP Address.....................ftp.solecteck@cts.com

Solomon Software
200 E. Hardin St.
Findlay, OH 45840
Main...(800) 879-0444
Tech. Support...............................(419) 424-0422
Tech. Supp. Fax............................(419) 424-3000
BBS ....(419) 424-3400
WWW............................http://www.solomon.com

Solutions Engineering
2409 Linden Ln
Silver Spring, MD 20910
Main...(800) 635-6533
Tech. Support...............................(301) 652-2738
Tech. Supp. Fax............................(301) 608-3015

Sonic Systems
575 North Castoria Ave.
Sunnyvale, CA 94086
Main..(408) 736-1900
Customer Svc. ....(408) 736-1900
Tech. Support ....(408) 736-1900
Sales..(408) 736-1900
Tech. Supp. Fax............................(408) 736-7228
BBS...(408) 736-7228
E-Mail.................................. tech@sonicsys.com
WWW............................http://www.sonicsys.com
FTP Address...............................ftp.sonicsys.com

SONY Electronics
WWW................................. http://www.sony.com/

Sound Quest
West 13th Ave. Suite #2131
Vancouver, BC VS41V8
Canada
Main..(800) 667-3998
Tech. Supp. Fax ....(604) 874-8971
BBS...(604) 874-8971
CompuServe......76702.2205@compuserve.com

Sound Source Unlimited
2985 East Hillcrest Dr.
Unit "A"
Westlake Village, CA 91362
Main..(805) 494-9996
Customer Svc. ....(805) 494-9996
Tech. Support ....(805) 494-9996
Sales..(800) 877-4778
Tech. Supp. Fax ....(805) 495-0016
BBS...(805) 373-8589
WWW..........................http://www.chris.com/~ssi/
FTP Address....................................ftp.chris.com
CompuServe.......................................75361,1544
America Online ....ssi@aol.com

SourceMate Information Systems
20 Sunnyside Ave. Suite #E
Mill Valley, CA 94941
Main..(800) 877-8896
Tech. Support ....(415) 381-1011
Tech. Supp. Fax ....(415) 381-6902
BBS...(415) 381-6902
WWW...................... http://www.sourcemate.com

South Hills Electronics
760 Beechnut Dr.
Pittsburgh, PA 15205-9925
Main ....(800) 245-6215

Southern Computer Systems
2732 7th Ave. S
Birmingham, AL 35146
Main ....(800) 533-6879
Tech. Supp. Fax ....(205) 322-4851
BBS..(205) 322-4851
WWW.................................http://www.scsinc.om

Soyo USA, Inc.
1209 John Reed Ct.
City of Industry, CA 91745
Main ....(818) 330-1712
Tech. Supp. Fax ....(818) 968-4161
BBS..(818) 968-4161

SPARC
WWW................................http://www.sparc.com/

Spectragraphics Corp.
9707 Waples St.
San Diego, CA 92121
Main ....(619) 450-0611
Tech. Supp. Fax ....(619) 450-0218
WWW.............................http://www.spectra.com/

Spectrum
1021 S Wolfe Rd.
Sunnyvale, CA 94086
Main..(408) 738-4387
Tech. Supp. Fax ....(408) 738-4702
BBS..(408) 738-4702

Spectrum Human Resource System
1625 Broadway #2800
Denver, CO 80202
Main..(800) 334-5660
Tech. Support ....(303) 534-8813
Tech. Supp. Fax ....(303) 595-9970
BBS..(303) 595-9970

Specurity Industries (1989), L
8 Abba Hillel St.
Ramat Gran, Israel
BBS...(972) 375-1230

Speedware
WWW.......................http://www.speedware.com/

Spinnaker Software Corp.
1 Athenaeum St.
Cambridge, MA 02142
Main .... (800) 323-8088
Customer Svc.............................. (800) 227-5609
Tech. Support.............................. (617) 494-1200
Tech. Supp. Fax.......................... (617) 494-1219
BBS.. (617) 494-1219

Spiral Software
16 Auburn Pl.
Brookline, MA 02146
Tech. Support.............................. (617) 739-1511
Tech. Supp. Fax.......................... (617) 739-4836
E-Mail.............................easyplot@spiralsw.com

Spirit of Performance
73 Westcott Rd.
Harvard, MA 01451
Main .... (508) 456-3889

SPRY, Inc.
1319 Dexter Ave. N
Seattle, WA 98109
Main .... (206) 286-1412
BBS .... (206) 286-1722
WWW.................................http://www.spry.com/

SPSS, Inc.
444 N Michigan Ave.
Chicago, IL 60611
Main .... (800) 543-5837
Tech. Support.............................. (312) 329-2400
BBS .... (312) 329-3668
WWW.................................http://www.spss.com/

Spyglass, Inc.
PO BOX 6388
Champaign, IL 61826
Main...(217) 355-6000
Tech. Supp. Fax...........................(217) 355-8925
BBS ....(217) 355-8925
WWW...........................http://www.spyglass.com/

Stac Electronics
12636 High Bluff Dr.
San Diego, CA 92130-2093
Main..(619) 794-4300
Customer Svc..............................(800) 522-7822
Tech. Support...............................(619) 794-3700
Sales ....(800) 522-7822
Tech. Supp. Fax...........................(619) 794-3715
BBS ....(619) 794-3711
E-Mail.......................software.support@stac.com
WWW...............................http://www.stac.com
FTP Address.....................................ftp.stac.com

Stallion Technologies, Inc.
2880 Research Pk Dr.
Suite 160
Soquel, CA 95073
Main..(800) 347-7979
Tech. Support..............................(408) 395-5775
Tech. Supp. Fax...........................(408) 395-6396
BBS ....(408) 395-6396
WWW..............................http://www.stallion.com

Standard Microsystems Corp.
Component Products Division
80 Arkay Dr.
Hauppauge, NY 11788
Main..(516) 435-6000
Customer Svc..............................(516) 273-3100
Tech. Support..............................(800) 638-5323
Sales ....(516) 435-6000
BBS ....(714) 707-2481

Star Gate Technologies, Inc.
29300 Aurora Rd.
Solon, OH 44139
Main..(800) 782-7428
Tech. Support..............................(216) 349-1860
BBS ....(216) 349-2056

Starfish Software
Main...(408) 461-5800
WWW.............................http://www.simplify.com/

StarPress, Inc.
425 Market St.
5th Floor
San Francisco, CA 94105
WWW..........http://www.starpress.com/starpress

Startek, Inc.
71 Lyman St
Northboro, MA 01532
Main..(800) 225-8528
Tech. Support ....(508) 393-9393
BBS..(508) 393-8528

State of the Art
56 Technology W.
Irvine, CA 92718
Main..(800) 854-3415
Sales...(714) 753-0374

StatSoft
2300 E. 14th St.
Tulsa, OK 74104
Main..(918) 749-1119
Tech. Supp. Fax ....(918) 749-2217
BBS..(918) 749-2217
WWW..........................http://www.statsoftinc.com

STB Systems
1651 N. Glenville Dr.
Suite 210
Richardson, TX 75081
Main..(214) 234-8750
Customer Svc. ....(214) 234-8750
Tech. Support ....(214) 234-8750
BBS..(214) 437-9615

Steinberg/Jones
1312 Bering Ave.
Chatsworth, CA 91311
Main..(818) 993-4091
Tech. Supp. Fax ....(818) 701-7452
BBS..(818) 701-7453
America Online ....steinberg@aol.com

Sterling Software, Inc.
200 W Lowe
Fairfield, IA 52556
Main...(515) 472-7077
Tech. Supp. Fax ....(515) 472-7198
BBS...(515) 472-7198

Stirling Group, The
1100 Woodfield Rd.
Roselle, IL 60172
Main...(708) 307-9197
Tech. Support ....(708) 240-0041
Sales..(708) 240-9110
Tech. Supp. Fax ....(708) 240-9120
BBS...(708) 240-9137
CompuServe......76702.1607@compuserve.com

Stony Brook Software
187 E Wilbur Rd. Suite #4
Thousand Oaks, CA 91360
Main...(800) 624-7487
Tech. Support ....(805) 496-5837
Tech. Supp. Fax ....(805) 496-7429
BBS...(805) 496-7429

Storage Computer Corp.
11 Riverside Street
Nashua, NH 03062-1373
Main...(603) 880-3005
Tech. Supp. Fax ....(603) 889-7232
WWW.............................http://www.storage.com/

Storage Dimensions
1656 McCarthy Blvd.
Milpitas, CA 95035
Main...(408) 954-0710
Customer Svc. ....(408) 894-1349
Tech. Support ....(408) 894-1325
Sales..(408) 954-0710
Tech. Supp. Fax ....(408) 944-1203
BBS...(408) 944-1221
E-Mail....................................support@xstor.com
WWW....................http://www.galahad.xstor.com
FTP Address........................ftp.glahad.xstor.com

Storage Technology
2270 South 88th Street
Louisville, CO 80028-4393
Main ....(303) 673-2658
Tech. Supp. Fax...........................(303) 673-2869
WWW...............................http://www.stortek.com/

Storm Software, Inc.
1861 Landings Dr.
Mountain View, CA 94043
Main ....(415) 691-6600
WWW...............http://www.stormsoft.com/storm/

Strata, Inc.
2 W. St. George Blvd.
St. George, UT 84770
Main ....(801) 628-5218
Customer Svc...............................(800) 678-7282
Tech. Support...............................(801) 628-9751

Stratus Computer
55 Fairbanks Blvd.
Marlboro, MA 01752
Main ....(508) 460-2000
Tech. Supp. Fax...........................(508) 481-8945

Stream International, Inc.
105 Rosemont Rd.
Westwood, MA 02090
Main ....(617) 751-1000
Tech. Supp. Fax...........................(617) 751-7751
WWW...............http://www.stream.com/intro.html

Strider Technology
1019-C 16th St NE
Hickory, NC 28601
Main ....(704) 324-1498

Structured Software
4031 West Plano Parkway
Suite No 205
Plano, TX 75093
Main ....(214) 985-9901
Customer Svc...............................(800) 235-9901
Tech. Support...............................(800) 235-9901
Tech. Supp. Fax...........................(214) 612-2035

SubLOGIC
501 Kenyon
Chanmpaign, IL 61820
Main...(217) 359-8482
Customer Svc.................................(217) 359-8482
Tech. Support.................................(217) 359-8482
Sales ....(217) 359-8482
Tech. Supp. Fax.............................(217) 352-1472

Summit Micro Design
149 Kifer Ct.
Sunnyvale, CA 94086
Main...(408) 739-6348
Tech. Support.................................(408) 739-6348
Tech. Supp. Fax.............................(408) 739-4643

Sun Microsystems
2550 Garcia Ave.
Mountain View, CA 94043
Main...(415) 960-1300
Customer Svc.................................(800) 643-8300
Tech. Support.................................(800) 872-4786
Sales ....(415) 960-1300
BBS ....(415) 969-9131
E-Mail ....support-request-@sun.com
WWW...............................http://www.sun.com
FTP Address......................................ftp.sun.com

Sun Moon Star
1941 Ringwood Ave.
San Jose, CA 95134
Tech. Support.................................(408) 452-7811
BBS ....(408) 452-1411

Sun Service / SunSoft
1494 California Circle
Building 2
Milpitas, CA 95035
Main...(800) 872-4786
Customer Svc.................................(415) 960-3200
Tech. Support.................................(800) 872-4786
Sales ....(800) 872-4786
Tech. Supp. Fax.............................(408) 956-8430
WWW........................ http://www.sunsoft/sun.com

Suncom Technologies
6400 W Gross Point Rd.
Niles, IL 60648
Main...(708) 647-4040

SunConnect
2550 Garcia Ave.
Mountain View, CA 94043
Main...(800) 786-7638

SunPics
2550 Garcia Ave.
Mountainview, CA 94043
Main...(800) 872-4786
Tech. Support.................................(415) 960-1300

SunStar Interactive
WWW...............................http://www.sunstar.com

Super Computer
5980 Lakeshore Dr.
Cypress, CA 90630
Main...(714) 826-9680
Tech. Supp. Fax ....(714) 826-9681
BBS..(714) 826-9681

SuperMac Technology
485 Potrero Ave.
Sunnyvale, CA 94086
Main...(408) 245-2202

Support Group, Inc.
PO Box 130
McHenry, MD 21541
Main...(800) 872-4768
Tech. Supp. Fax ....(301) 387-7322

Supra
312 S.E. Stonemill Dr., Suite 150
Vancouver, WA 98684
Main..(360) 604-1481
Customer Svc. ....(800) 774-4965
Tech. Support ....(541) 967-2490
Sales..(800) 727-8772
Tech. Supp. Fax ....(541) 967-2401
BBS..(541) 967-2444
E-Mail................................... pctech@supra.com
WWW..............................http://www.supra.com
FTP Address..................................ftp.supra.com
CompuServe.......................................GO SUPRA
America Online ....SupraCorp@aol.com

Sur Prob
1478 N Tech Blvd., #101
Gilbert, AZ 85234
Tech. Support ....(602) 497-4200
Tech. Supp. Fax ....(602) 497-4242
BBS..(602) 497-4242

Sutrasoft
10506 Permian Dr
Sugarland, TX 77478
Main...(713) 491-2088
Tech. Supp. Fax ....(713) 240-6883
BBS..(713) 240-6883

Sutton Designs
The De Witt Bldg
215 N Cayuga St.
Ithaca, NY 14850
Main...(800) 326-8119
Tech. Support ....(607) 277-4301
BBS..(607) 277-6983

Swan Technologies
3075 Research Dr
State College, PA 16801
Main...(800) 468-9044
Tech. Support ....(814) 234-2236
BBS..(814) 237-4450

Swanson Analysis Systems, Inc.
PO Box 65
Houston, PA 15342
Main ....(412) 746-3304

Swfte+A1843 International, Ltd.
Stone Mill Office Park
724 Yorklyn R
Hockessin, DE 19707
Main ....(800) 237-9383
Tech. Support................................(302) 234-1740
BBS..(302) 234-1760
WWW...............................http://www.swfte.com/
CompuServe ..... 76004.3520@compuserve.com

Swiss Telecom, NA
2001 L St NW, #902
Washington, DC 20036
Main ....(800) 966-1145

Sybase, Inc.
6475 Christie Ave.
Emeryville, CA 94608
Main ....(800) 879-2273
Tech. Support................................(415) 596-3500
BBS..(415) 596-4508
WWW...............................http://www.sybase.com/

Sydex
PO Box 5700
Eugene, OR 97405
Main ....(541) 683-6033
Tech. Supp. Fax............................(541) 683-1622
WWW...............................http://www.sydex.com

SyDOS (Division of SyQuest)
47071 Bayside Pky.
Fremont, CA 94538
Main ....(510) 226-4137
Customer Svc................................(800) 437-9367
Tech. Support...............................(800) 249-2440
Sales ....(800) 245-2278

Symantec Corp.
10201 Torre Ave.
Cupertino, CA 95014
Main..(408) 253-9600
Customer Svc...............................(800) 441-7234
Tech. Support................................(800) 441-7234
BBS ....(541) 484-6699
WWW..........................http://www.symantec.com/
CompuServe ....GO SYMANTEC
America Online................................ SYMANTEC

Synctronics
980 Buenos Ave., Sutie C2
San Diego, CA 92110
Main..(800) 444-5397
Tech. Support.................................(619) 275-3525
Tech. Supp. Fax............................(619) 275-3520

Synergis Technologies, Inc.
593 Skippack Pike
Blue Bell, PA 19422
Main..(800) 836-5440
Tech. Support..................................(215) 643-9050

Synergystex International
3065 Nationwide Pkwy.
Brunswick, OH 44212
Main..(216) 225-3112

Synernetics, Inc.
85 Rangeway Rd.
North Billerica, MA 01862
Main..(508) 670-9009
BBS ....(508) 670-9015

Synex Systems Corp.
1176 W Georgia St, #800
Vancouver, British Columbia, Canada
Main..(604) 688-8271

Synopsys
700 East Middlefield Rd.
Mountain View, CA 94043
Main..(415) 962-5000
Customer Svc...............................(415) 541-7737
Tech. Support.................................(415) 245-8005
WWW..........................http://www.synopsys.com/

Syntrex
2621 Van Baren Ave.
Valley Forge, PA 19484-3027
Main...(800) 526-2829
Tech. Support ....(201) 542-1500
BBS..(201) 542-3957

Syquest
47923 Warm Springs Blvd.
Fremont, CA 94539
Main...(800) 245-2278
Tech. Support ....(415) 490-7511
BBS...(415) 651-3338

Sysper Technologies
1590 Old Oakland Rd., #B-113
San Jose, CA 95131
Main...(800) 441-5484
Tech. Support ....(408) 441-6604
BBS...(408) 441-6609

System Avenue, Inc.
14946 Shoemaker Ave.
Santa Fe Spring,CA 90670
Main...(213) 926-9849
BBS...(213) 926-4472

System Connection
1123 S Orem Blvd.
Orem, UT 84058
Main ....(800) 825-1985
Tech. Support ....(801) 224-3330
BBS...(801) 224-3334

System Powerhouse, Inc.
911 Bunker Hill, #180
Houston, TX 77024
Main...(800) 999-3918
Tech. Support ....(713) 827-1600
BBS...(713) 827-7162

Systems & Computer Technology
4 Country View Rd.
Wayne, PA 19355
Main ....(610) 647-5930
WWW.............................http://www.sctcorp.com/

Systems Compatibility Corp.
401 N Wabash, #600
Chicago, IL 60611
Main................................(800) 333-1395
Tech. Support ....(312) 329-0700
Tech. Supp. Fax ....(312) 670-0820
BBS................................(312) 670-0820

Systems Manufacturing Technoloy
PO Box 1320
San Marcos, CA 92079-1320
Main................................(800) 648-6262

Systems Plus, Inc.
500 Clyde Ave.
Mountain View, CA 94043
Main................................(415) 969-7047
Tech. Supp. Fax ....(415) 969-0118

Systems Strategies
225 W 34th St.
New York, NY 10001
Main................................(212) 279-8400
BBS................................(212) 967-8368

T.H.E. Journal
150 El Camino Real
Suite 112
Tustin, CA 92680-3670
Main................................(714) 730-4011
WWW.........................http://www.thejournal.com/

Ta Engineering
1605 School St
PO Box 186
Moraga, CA 94556
Main................................(415) 376-8500

Tadiran - CA
2975 Bowers Ave.
Santa Clara, CA 95051
Main................................(408) 354-5473
BBS................................(408) 727-0560

Tadiran - NY
20 Seaview Blvd.
Port Washington, NY 11050
Main................................(516) 621-4980
Tech. Supp. Fax..........................(516) 621-4517
BBS................................(516) 621-4517

Tadpole Technology Inc.
12012 Technology Blvd.
Austin, Texas 78727
Main................................(512) 219-2200
Sales................................(800) 232-6656
Tech. Supp. Fax..........................(512) 219-2222
E-Mail................................support@tadpole.com
WWW................................http://www.tadpole.com/

Taesung Industries, Inc.
2001 Westside Pkwy, #240
Alpharetta, GA 30201
Main................................(800) 874-3160
Tech. Support................................(404) 664-8944
BBS................................(404) 664-5252

Talaris Systems
6059 Cornerstone Ct W.
PO Box 26158
San Diego, CA 92196
Main................................(619) 587-0787

Talton/Louley Engineering
9550 RidgehAve.n Ct
San Diego, CA 92123
Main................................(619) 631-8205

Tandberg Data
2685-A Park Center Dr.
Simi Valley, CA 93065
Main................................(805) 579-1000
Customer Svc................................(805) 579-1000
Tech. Support................................(805) 579-1000
Tech. Supp. Fax................................(805) 579-2555

Tandem Computers
19333 Vallco Pkwy
Cupertino, CA 95014
Main................................(408) 285-6000
WWW................................http://www.tandem.com/

Tandon Corp.
405 Science Dr
Moorpark, CA 93021
Main...(800) 800-8850
Tech. Support................................(805) 523-0324
BBS...(805) 529-8408

Tandy Corp.
1800 One Tandy Ctr
Ft Worth, TX 76102
Main...(817) 390-3011
BBS...(817) 390-2774

Tangent Computer, Inc.
197 Airport Blvd.
Burlingame, CA 94010
Main...(800) 223-6677
Tech. Support................................(415) 342-9388
BBS...(415) 342-9380

Tangram Systems
118 Mackenan Dr, #100
Cary, NC 27511
Main...(919) 481-4444
BBS...(919) 460-0003

Targus
6180 Valleyview
Buena Park, CA 90620
Main...(714) 523-5429
Customer Svc..................................(714) 523-5429
Tech. Support................................(714) 523-5429
Sales ....(714) 523-5429
Tech. Supp. Fax.............................(714) 523-0153

Tatung
2850 El Presidio St.
Long Beach, CA 90810
Main...(213) 979-7055
Tech. Supp. Fax.............................(310) 637-8484
WWW................................ http://www.tatung.com/

Tatung Co. of America
2850 El Presidio St.
Long Beach, CA 90810
Main...(800) 827-2850
Tech. Support ....(213) 979-7055
Tech. Supp. Fax ....(310) 637-8484
BBS..(213) 637-8484

Tatung Science & Technology
2060 Ringwood Ave.
San Jose, CA 95131
Main...(408) 435-0140

TEAC America
Data Storage Products Division
7733 Telegraph Rd.
Montebello, CA 90640
Main...(213) 726-0303

Teac America, Inc.
7733 Telegraph Rd.
Monebello, CA 90640
Main...(213) 726-0303
Tech. Support ....(213) 726-0303
BBS...(213) 727-7650

Tech Data Corp.
5350 Tech Data Dr.
Clearwater, FL 34620
Main...(800) 553-7976

Tech Hackers, Inc.
50 Broad St.
New York, NY 10004
Main...(212) 344-9500

Technical Aesthetics Operation
501 W 5th St.
Rolla, MO 65401
Main...(800) 264-1121
Tech. Support ....(573) 364-4925
BBS...(573) 364-5631
CompuServe....102677.1563@compuserve.com

Technical Challenge
601 Oakwood Square
East Aurora, NY 14052
Main..(800) 344-2370
Tech. Support ....(716) 655-0400
BBS..(716) 655-2373

Technicallt Elite
1686 Del Ave.
Campbell, CA 95008
Main..(800) 543-8887
Tech. Support ....(408) 370-4300
Tech. Supp. Fax ....(408) 370-4222
BBS..(408) 370-4222
WWW...............................http://www.tecelite.com

Technologic Systems
18277 Timber Trails
Marysville, OH 43040
Main..(213) 644-2230
Tech. Support ....(513) 644-2230

Technology Applications, Inc.
1350 Elbridge Payne Rd.
Suite 207
Chesterfield, MO, 63017
Main..(314) 530-1981
Tech. Supp. Fax ....(314) 530-1788
WWW............................http://www.techapp.com/

Technology Squared, Inc.
5198 West 76th St.
Edina, MN 55439
Main..(612) 832-9144
Customer Svc. ....(800) 685-7809
Tech. Support ....(800) 685-7809
Sales..(800) 762-3531
Tech. Supp. Fax ....(612) 831-7770

Technology USA
Lock Dr.
Leomister, MA 01453
Main..(508) 534-1434
BBS..(508) 537-6761

Tekelec
26580 W Agoura Rd.
Calabasas, CA 91302
Main ....(800) 835-3532
Tech. Support................................(818) 880-5656
BBS..(818) 880-6993

TekNow!
2606 S 40th St
Tempe, AZ 85034
Main ....(800) 899-7262
Tech. Support..............................(602) 437-8070
BBS..(602) 437-2211

Teknowledge Corp.
1810 Embarcadero Rd.
Palo Alto, CA 94303
Main ....(415) 424-0500
Tech. Supp. Fax............................(415) 493-2645
WWW....................http://www.teknowledge.com/

Tektronix Corp.
P.O. Box 1000
Wilsonville, OR 97070-1000
Main ....(503) 682-3411
WWW.................................http://www.tek.com/

Telco Systems, Inc.
45550 Northport Loop E.
Fremont, CA 94538
Main ....(800) 776-8832
BBS..(415) 656-3031

Tele-Tech
PO Box 757
McAfee, NJ 07428
Main ....(800) 433-6181

Telebit Corp.
1315 Chesapeake Tererace
Sunnyvale, CA 94089
Main ....(800) 835-3248
Tech. Support................................(408) 734-5200
BBS..(408) 734-3333
WWW................................http://www.telebit.com/

Telebyte Technology, Inc.
270E Pulaski Rd.
Greenlawn, NY 11740
Main...(800) 835-3298
Tech. Support..............................(516) 423-3232
BBS ....(516) 385-8184

Teleconferencing Communication
219 N Aldine
Park Ridge, IL 60068
Main...(708) 318-6896

Telect
PO Box 665
Liberty Lake, WA 99019
Main...(509) 926-6000
BBS ....(509) 926-8915
WWW................................http://www.telect.com

Teledyne Kinetics
PO Box 939012
San Diego, CA 92193-9012
Main...(800) 344-4334
Tech. Support..............................(619) 755-6163
Tech. Supp. Fax...........................(619) 576-0607
BBS ....(619) 755-6163

Teleglobe Communications, Inc.
40 High St
North Andover, MA 01845
Main...(508) 681-0600

Telemart
8804 N 23rd Ave.
Phoenix, AZ 85021
Main...(800) 537-4735
Tech. Support..............................(602) 944-0402
BBS ....(602) 944-1510

Telematics Calabasas
1201 Cypress Rd.
Ft Lauderdale,FL 33309
Main...(800) 327-7944
Tech. Support..............................(305) 772-3070
BBS ....(395) 776-4127

Telenex
7401 Boston Blvd.
Springfield, VA 22153
Main...(800) 368-3261
Tech. Support ....(703) 644-9000
BBS ....(703) 644-9011

TeleProcessing Products
4565 E Industrial St.
Bldg 7-K
Simi Valley, CA 93063
Main...(805) 522-8147
BBS ....(805) 581-6019

Telescan
10550 Richmond, #250
Houston, TX 77042
Main...(800) 324-8353

Telescape Communications
WWW.........................http://www.telescape.com/

Telesystems, Inc.
7501 Suzi Ln
Westminster, CA 92683
Main...(714) 898-2124

Teletek
4600 Pell Dr
Sacramento, CA 95838
Main...(800) 545-6256
Tech. Support ....(916) 920-4600
BBS ....(916) 927-7684

TeleVideo Systems, Inc.
550 E Brokaw Rd.
San Jose, CA 95161-9048
Main...(800) 835-3228
Tech. Support ....(800) 835-3228
BBS ....(408) 954-0623

Teleware, Inc.
300 Roundhill Dr
Rockaway, NJ 07866
Main...(800) 322-6962
Tech. Support ....(201) 334-1154

Ten X Technology, Inc.
4807 Spicewood Springs Rd.
Bldg 3
Austin, TX 78759
Main..(512) 346-8360

Tenex
56800 Magnetic Dr
Mishawaka, IN 46545-7481
Main..(800) 776-6781
BBS...(219) 255-1778

Tera Computer Co.
2815 Eastlake East
Seattle, WA 98102
Main..(206) 325-0800
Tech. Supp. Fax ....(206) 325-2433
WWW....................................http://www.tera.com/

Teradyne, Inc.
321 Harrison Ave.
Boston, MA 02118
Main..(617) 482-2700
Tech. Supp. Fax ....(617) 422-2910
WWW....................http://www.teradyne.com/

TeraTech
100 Park Ave. Suite 360
Rockville, MD 20850
Main..(800) 447-9120
Tech. Support ....(301) 330-6764
Tech. Supp. Fax ....(301) 762-8185
BBS...(301) 963-0436

Terisa Systems
WWW...........................http://www.rsa.com/rsa/pr/
Terisa_Systems.html

Texas Instruments
P.O. Box 650311
M/S 3914
Dallas, TX 75265
Main..(214) 917-6278
Customer Svc. ....(800) 336-5236
Tech. Support ....(800) 848-3927
BBS...(817) 774-6809
WWW...http://www.ti.com/

Texas Microsystems, Inc.
10618 Rockley Rd.
Houston, TX 77099
Main ....(800) 627-8700
Tech. Support ....(713) 933-8050
BBS... (713) 933-1029

TGV, Inc.
603 Mission St
Santa Cruz, CA 95060
Main .... (800) 848-3440
Tech. Support ....(408) 427-4366
Tech. Supp. Fax ....(408) 457-5205
BBS... (408) 427-4365
WWW.............................. http://www.tgv.com/

The Linksys Group, Inc.
17401 Armstrong
Irvine, CA 92714
Main .... (714) 261-1288
Customer Svc.............................. (714) 261-1288
Tech. Support ....(714) 261-1288
Sales .... (714) 261-1288
Tech. Supp. Fax............................ (714) 261-8868
BBS... (714) 222-5111

The McKinley Group
WWW............................ http://www.mckinley.com

The MetaTools Digital Theatre
6303 Carpinteria Ave.
Carpinteria, CA 93013
Main .... (805) 566-6200
Customer Svc.............................. (805) 566-6200
Tech. Support ....(805) 566-6200
WWW...........................http://www.metatools.com

The Nerve Internet Services
WWW......................http://www.he.net/~thenerve/

The Plant Software, Inc.
102 - 930 West 1st. Street
North Vancouver
British Columbia V7P 3N4 Canada
Main................................(604) 682-8424
Tech. Supp. Fax...........................(604) 682-8425
E-Mail .... support@theplant.com
WWW............................. http://www.theplant.com

The Prairie Group
P.O. 65820
West Des Moines, IA 50265-5820
Main................................(515) 225-3720
Customer Svc..............................(515) 225-3720
Tech. Support......................(515) 225-4122
Sales .... (800) 346-5392
Tech. Supp. Fax...........................(515) 225-2422

The Software Toolworks
Mindscape
88 Rowland Way
Novato, CA 94945
Main................................(415) 897-9900
Customer Svc............................(415) 883-3000
Tech. Support.............................(415) 898-5157
WWW........................ http://www.mindscape.com/

The Wollongong Group
1129 San Antonio Rd.
Palo Alto, CA 94303
Main................................(800) 872-8649
Tech. Supp. Fax...........................(415) 962-0286
E-Mail .... support@twg.com
WWW.................................... http://www.twg.com/

Thinking Machines Corp.
14 Crosby Dr.
Bedford, MA 01730
Main...............................(617) 276-0400
Tech. Support..............................(617) 276-0444
WWW................................. http://www.think.com/

Third Planet Publishing
WWW......................... http://www.planeteers.com/

Thomas Conrad
12301 Technology Blvd.
Austin, Texas 78727
Main..................................(512) 433-6000
Tech. Support ....(512) 433-6822
Sales..(800) 332-8683
Tech. Supp. Fax ....(512) 433-6153
BBS...(512) 433-6156
E-Mail.............................support@klaven.tci.com
WWW .... http://www.tci.com/
FTP Address.........................ftp://ftp.tci.com/pub/

Thomas-Conrad - Compaq
Division of Compaq
12301 Technology Boulevard
Austin, TX 78727
Main..................................(512) 433-6000
Customer Svc. ....(800) 332-8683
Tech. Support ....(800) 334-4112
Sales ....(800) 332-6868
Tech. Supp. Fax ....(512) 433-6153
BBS...(512) 433-6156
WWW .... http://www.pci.com
FTP Address............................... ftp.pci.com
CompuServe...............................GO PCFORUM

3Com Corp.
5400 Bayfront Plaza
PO Box 58145
Santa Clara, CA 95052-8145
Main................................(408) 764-5000
Customer Svc. ....(800) 876-3266
Tech. Support ....(800) 876-3266
Sales..(310) 348-8110
Tech. Supp. Fax ....(408) 764-5001
BBS...(408) 980-8204
E-Mail..............................info@3com.com
WWW http://www.3com.com
FTP Address...................................ftp.3com.com
CompuServe..................... GO ASKTHREECOM

3M Private Network Products
6801 Riverplace Blvd.
Austin, TX 78769
Main................................(512) 984-3400
Customer Svc. ....(800) 426-8688
Tech. Supp. Fax ....(800) 626-0329
BBS...(512) 984-6628

Thumper Technologies
PO Box 471012
Tulsa, OK 74147

Tidalwave Technologies, Inc.
WWW............................http://www.tidalwave.com

Tidewater Information Group
1572 Holland Rd.
Suffolk, VA 23434

TigerSoftware
800 Douglas Entrance
Executive Tower
Corel Cables, FL 33134
Main...(800) 888-4437
BBS...(305) 444-5010

Timberline Software
9405 SW Gemini
Beaverton, OR 97005
Main...(503) 644-6001

Time Warner Electronic Publishing
1271 Ave. of the Americas
New York, NY 10020
Main..(212) 522-1212
E-Mail...................72662,670@compuserve.com
WWW...........................http://pathfinder.com/twep

Timeline
23605 Telo Ave.
Torrance, CA 90505
Main...(800) 223-9977
Tech. Support...............................(310) 784-5488
Tech. Supp. Fax ....(310) 784-7590
BBS...(213) 532-6304

Timeplex Corp.
400 Chestnut Ridge Rd.
Woodcliff Lake, NJ 07675
Main..(800) 669-2298

Timeslips
17950 Preston Rd.
Suite 800
Dallas, TX 75252
Main .... (800) 285-0999
Customer Svc.............................. (800) 285-0999
Tech. Support............................... (508) 768-7490
BBS .... (508) 768-7581
WWW............................ http://www.timeslips.com/

Tippecanoe Systems
5674 Stoneridge Dr.
Pleasanton, CA 94588
Main .... (415) 416-8510
Tech. Supp. Fax.......................... (415) 416-8516
E-Mail........................... support@tippecanoe.com
WWW....................... http://www.tippecanoe.com/

TKi
PO Box 2049
Roswell, GA 30077
Main .... (770) 640-1515

Toner Etc
124 Heritage Ave.
Portsmith, NH 03801
Main .... (800) 835-9264
Tech. Support............................... (508) 459-5000
Tech. Supp. Fax.......................... (603) 431-0705

Toner Etc
124 Heritage Ave.
Portsmouth, NH 03801
Main .... (800) 370-8663
Tech. Support............................... (603) 431-3624
Tech. Supp. Fax.......................... (603) 431-0705
BBS .... (603) 431-0705

Tool & Techniques, Inc.
2201 Northland Dr.
Austin, TX 78756
Main .... (800) 444-1945
Tech. Support............................. (512) 449-1308
Tech. Supp. Fax.......................... (512) 459-1309
BBS .... (512) 482-0976
WWW...................http://www.moontower.com/tnt

TOPS Microsystems Corp.
950 Marina Village Pkwy
Alameda, CA 94501
Main...................................(800) 445-8677
Tech. Support.....................(415) 769-9669

Toshiba America - Disk
9740 Irvine Blvd.
PO Box 19724
Irvine, CA 92713-9724
Tech. Support.............................(714) 455-0407
BBS ....(714) 583-3113

Toshiba America - FAX
9740 Irvine Blvd.
PO Box 19724
Irvine, CA 92713-9724
Main..(800) 950-4373

Toshiba America Consumer Products
9740 Irvine Blvd.
Irvine, CA 92718
Main...............................(800) 631-3811
Customer Svc....................(800) 999-4273
Tech. Support.............................(800) 999-4273
BBS ....(714) 837-4408
WWW............................http://www.toshiba.com/

Toshiba International Corp.
13131 W Little York Rd.
Houston, TX 77041
Main...............................(800) 231-1412
Tech. Support.............................(713) 466-0277
Tech. Supp. Fax.........................(713) 466-8773
BBS ....(713) 466-8773

Tosoh USA, Inc.
373 Vintage Pk. Dr. #E
Foster City, CA 94404
Main...............................(415) 286-2385
Tech. Support.............................(415) 286-2385
Tech. Supp. Fax..........................(415) 286-2392
BBS ....(415) 588-2800

Tote-a-lap
1450 Koll Circle #107
San Jose, CA 95112
Main ....(408) 437-1122
Tech. Support ....(408) 437-1186
Tech. Supp. Fax ....(408) 437-1278
BBS...(415) 578-1914

Touchbase Systems, Inc.
160 Laurel Ave.
Northport, NY 11768
Main..(800) 541-0345
BBS..(516) 754-3491

TouchStone Software
2124 Main St.
Huntington Beach, CA 92648
Main.......................................(800) 531-0450
Customer Svc. ....(714) 969-7746
BBS..(714) 969-0688

TPS Electronics
2495 Old Middlefield Way
Mountainview, CA 94043
Main.......................................(800) 526-5920
Customer Svc. ....(405) 988-0141
Tech. Support ....(415) 856-6833
Tech. Supp. Fax ....(415) 988-0289
BBS...(415) 856-3843

Trans International
2120 Howell Ave., #412
Anaheim, CA 92806
Main.......................................(800) 783-2120
Tech. Support ....(714) 634-1583
Tech. Supp. Fax ....(714) 634-0409
BBS...(714) 634-0409

TransEra Corp.
345 E. 800 S
Orem, UT 84058
Main.......................................(801) 224-6550
Tech. Supp. Fax ....(801) 224-0355
BBS...(801) 224-0355

Transition Engineering, Inc.
6475 City W. Pkwy
Eden Prarie, MN 55344
Main...(800) 325-2725
Tech. Support ....(612) 941-7600
Tech. Supp. Fax ....(612) 941-2322
BBS...(612) 941-2322

Transitional Technology, Inc.
5401 E La Palma Ave.
Anaheim, CA 92807
Main...(714) 693-1133
Tech. Supp. Fax ....(714) 693-0225
BBS...(714) 693-0225

Traveling Software
18702 N. Creek Pkwy.
Bothell, WA 98011
Main...(206) 483-8088
Customer Svc. ....(800) 343-8080
Tech. Support ....(206) 483-8088
Sales...(800) 343-8080
Tech. Supp. Fax ....(206) 487-1284
BBS...(206) 485-1736
WWW........................... http://www.travsoft.com
CompuServe...............................GO TRAVSOFT

Trax Softworks, Inc.
5840 Uplander Way
Culver City, CA 90230-6620
Main...(800) 367-8729
Tech. Support ....(213) 649-5800
Tech. Supp. Fax ....(310) 649-6200
BBS...(213) 649-6200
E-Mail...info@traxsoft.com
WWW...............http://www.traxsoft.com/~traxsoft

Trend Micro Devices, Inc.
2421 W 205th St, #D-100
Torrance, CA 90501
Main...(800) 228-5651
Tech. Support ....(310) 782-8190
BBS...(310) 328-5892

Tri-State Computer
650 6th Ave.
New York, NY 10011
Main .... (800) 433-5199
Tech. Support................................ (212) 633-6807
BBS... (212) 962-4635

Tribe
WWW.................................http://www.tribe.com/

Tricord Systems, Inc.
2800 NW Blvd.
Plymouth, MN 55441
Main .... (612) 557-9005
Tech. Support............................ (800) TRI-CORD
BBS... (612) 557-1788

Trident Microsystems, Inc.
189 N. Bernardo
Mountain View, CA 94043
Main .... (415) 691-9211
Tech. Support................................ (415) 691-9211
Tech. Supp. Fax............................ (415) 691-9260
BBS... (415) 691-9260

Trident Software
1001 Bridgeway, #104
Sausalito, CA 94965-9949
Main .... (415) 332-0188
Tech. Supp. Fax............................ (415) 332-0189
WWW...........................http://www.tridentsoft.com

Tripp Lite
500 N Orleans
Chicago, IL 60610-4188
Main .... (312) 329-1601
Tech. Support................................ (312) 329-1602
Tech. Supp. Fax............................ (312) 644-6505
BBS... (312) 644-6505
WWW............................... http://www.tripplite.com

TriSoft
1825 E 38-1/2
Austin, TX 78722
Main.................................(800) 531-5170
Tech. Support.....................(512) 472-0744
Tech. Supp. Fax..................(512) 473-2122
BBS ....(512) 473-2122
E-Mail ....trisoft@bga.com

Trisystems
74 Northeastern Blvd.
Nashua, NH 03062
Main.................................(603) 883-0558
BBS.................................(603) 883-0965

Triticom
PO Box 11536
St Paul, MN 55111
Main.................................(612) 937-0772

Triton Technologies
200 Middlesex Tpk.
Iselin, NJ 08830
Main.................................(908) 855-9440
Customer Svc.....................(908) 855-9440
Tech. Support.....................(908) 855-9440
BBS ....(908) 855-9609

TRM Computers
2106 Arborview
Ann Arbor, MI 48106
Main.................................(313) 994-6289

Trompeter Electronics
31186 La Baya Dr
Westlake Village, CA 91362
Main.................................(818) 707-2020
Tech. Supp. Fax..................(818) 706-1040
BBS ....(818) 706-1040

True Data Products
PO Box 347
Uxbridge, MA 01569
Main.................................(800) 635-0300
Tech. Support.....................(508) 278-6556
Tech. Supp. Fax..................(508) 228-6748

Truevision
2500 Walsh Ave.
Santa Clara, Calif. 95051
Main.................................(408) 562-4200
Sales................................(800) 729-2656
Tech. Supp. Fax ....(408) 562-4065
E-Mail......................support@truevision.com
WWW.http://www.truevision.com/Truevision.html
FTP Address...........................ftp.truevision.com
CompuServe...............................GO Truevision
America Online ....Keyword Truevision

Trusted Information Systems
3060 Washington Rd. (Rt. 97)
Glenwood, MD 21738
Main.................................(301) 854-6889
Tech. Supp. Fax ....(301) 854-5363
E-Mail......................................tis@tis.com
WWW....................................http://www.tis.com/

TRW Information Networks Division
23800 Hawthorne Blvd.
Torrance, CA 90505
Main.................................(714) 852-1313

TSR Systems, Ltd.
116 Oakland Ave.
Port Jefferson, NY 11777
Main.................................(516) 331-6336
BBS.................................(516) 331-6377

Tulin Corp.
2156-H O'Toole Ave.
San Jose, CA 95131
Main.................................(408) 432-9025
Tech. Supp. Fax ....(408) 943-0782
BBS.................................(408) 943-0782
CompuServe......74264.3710@compuserve.com

Turtle Beach Systems
52 Grumbacher Rd.
York, PA 17403
Main.................................(510) 624-6200
Sales................................(800) 884-0190
Tech. Supp. Fax ....(510) 624-6291
BBS.................................(717) 767-5934

Tut Systems
2495 Estand Way
Pleasant Hill, CA 94523
Main..(510) 682-6510
Customer Svc. ....(800) 998-4888
Tech. Support ....(800) 998-4888
Sales...(800) 998-4888
Tech. Supp. Fax ....(510) 682-4125
WWW...............................http://www.tutsys.com/

TVM Professional Monitor Co.
1109 W 9th St.
Upland, CA 91786
Main...(714) 985-4788

Twinhead Corp.
1537 Centre Pointe Dr.
Milpitas, CA 95035
Main..(800) 545-8946
Tech. Support ....(408) 945-0808
Tech. Supp. Fax ....(408) 945-1080
BBS...(408) 945-1080

Tyan Computer
1645 South Main St.
Milpitas, CA 95035
Main..(408) 956-8000
Sales...(408) 956-8000
Tech. Supp. Fax ....(408) 956-8044
BBS...(408) 956-8171
E-Mail................................. support@tyan.com
WWW .... http://www.tyan.com/
FTP Address....................................ftp.tyan.com

Typhoon Media
10029 Orville Rd.
Irvine, CA 92718

TYREX Manufacturing Group
WWW ....http://www.btsweb.com/cable/tyrex/

U-Lead Systems
970 West 190th St.
Suite 520
Torrance, CA 90502
Main..(310) 523-9393
WWW ....http://www.seed.net.tw/~ulead

U-Tron Technologies, Inc.
47448 Fremont Blvd.
Fremont, CA 94538
Main ....(800) 933-7775
Tech. Support...............................(510) 656-3600
Tech. Supp. Fax............................(510) 650-1688
BBS ....(415) 656-1688

U.B. Network
3900 Freedom Cir
Santa Clara, CA 95052
Main ....(800) 777-4526
Customer Svc...............................(800) 873-6381
Tech. Support...............................(408) 562-5620
Tech. Supp. Fax............................(408) 970-7337
BBS ....(408) 970-7383
WWW...............................http://www.ub.com

U.S. Robotics
8100 North McCormick Blvd.
Skokie, IL 60076-2920
Main ....(708) 982-5010
Customer Svc...............................(800) 342-5877
Tech. Support...............................(708) 982-5151
Tech. Supp. Fax............................(708) 933-5800
BBS ....(708) 982-5092
E-Mail.................................support@usr.com
WWW...............................http://www.usr.com

Ubique
WWW...............................http://www.ubique.com/

UMAX Technologies, Inc.
UMAX Data Systems, Inc.
3353 Gateway Boulevard
Fremont, CA 94538
Main ....(510) 651-4000
Customer Svc...............................(800) 562-0311
Tech. Support...............................(800) 562-0311
Sales ....(800) 560-0311
Tech. Supp. Fax............................(510) 651-3710
E-Mail.................................support@umax.com
WWW.................................http://www.umax.com
FTP Address ....ftp.umax.com
CompuServe ....GO UMAX
America Online............................umax@aol.com

Unicom Electric
11980 Telegraph Rd., #103
Santa Fe Springs, CA 90670
Main..(800) 346-6668
Tech. Support...............................(213) 946-9650
Tech. Supp. Fax...........................(213) 946-9167
BBS...(213) 946-7473

Unidata
WWW.......................http://www.unidata.ucar.edu/

Uniface Corp.
1420 Harbor Bay Pkwy, #140
Alameda, CA 94501
Main..(415) 748-6145

Uniplex Business Software
9400 N Central Expy, #1309
Dallas, TX 75231
Main..(800) 356-8063
Tech. Support...............................(800) 338-9940
BBS...(214) 987-0303

UniPress Software, Inc.
2025 Lincoln Hwy, #209
Edison, NJ 08817
Main..(800) 222-0550
Tech. Support...............................(201) 985-8000
BBS...(201) 287-4929
WWW............................http://www.unipress.com/

Unisys
2700 N 1st St.
PO Box 6685
San Jose, CA 95150-6685
Main..(408) 434-2848
Tech. Supp. Fax...........................(408) 434-2131
WWW................................http://www.unisys.com/

Unisys Corp.
PO Box 500
Blue Bell, PA 19424
Main..(800) 448-1424
Tech. Support...............................(215) 986-4011
BBS...(215) 986-2312
WWW...............................http://www.unisys.com/

United Innovations
120 Whiting Farms Rd.
Holyoke, MA 01040
Main..(800) 323-3283
Tech. Supp. Fax...........................(413) 533-7755

Universal Data Systems (UDS)
5000 Bradford Dr.
Huntsville, AL 3505-1993
Main..(205) 430-8000
Tech. Support...............................(800) 221-4380
BBS...(205) 430-8926

Universal Fiber Optics
PO Box 1909
Salem, VA 24153
Main..(703) 389-9844
BBS...(703) 389-4408

Universal Interactive Systems
WWW.........http://www.PrimeNet.Com:80/~vladi/

Universal Technical Systems, Inc.
1220 Rock St.
Rockford, IL 61101
Main..(800) 435-7887
Tech. Support...............................(815) 963-2220
Tech. Supp. Fax...........................(815) 963-8884

Up Software
722 Lombard St.
Suite 204
San Francisco, CA 94133-2300
Main..(415) 921-4691
WWW.......................http://www.dnai.com/~upsoft

Upsonic
1 Park Plaza, #600
Irvine, CA 92714
Main..(800) 877-6642
Tech. Support...............................(714) 833-7161
BBS...(714) 833-7164

US Sprint
12490 Sunrise Valley Dr.
Reston, VA 22096
Main ....(800) 877-1918
Customer Svc. ....(800) 726-0201
Tech. Support ....(703) 689-6000

USA Flex
135 N Brandon Dr.
Glen Ellyn, IL 60139
Main...(800) 872-3539
Tech. Support ....(708) 351-7172
BBS...(708) 351-7204

USA Micro
2888 Bluff St, #257
Boulder, CO 80301
Tech. Support ....(800) 537-8596

User Group Connection
2840 Research Park Dr.
Suite 100
Soquel, CA 95073
Main..(408) 461-5700
Tech. Supp. Fax ....(408) 461-5701
WWW......................http://www.ugconnection.org/

USPC
2019 Ford Rd.
Sheffield, AL 35660
Main...(800) 437-8772
Tech. Support ....(800) 437-8772
BBS...(205) 386-8207

UTI Computers
3640 Westchase Dr.
Houston, TX 77042
Tech. Support ....(713) 789-1466
BBS...(713) 780-7664

UUNET Communications Service
3110 Fairview Pk Dr, #570
Falls Church, VA 22042
Main...(703) 876-5050
BBS...(703) 876-5059

UUNET Technologies
3060 Williams Dr.
Fairfax, Virginia 22031-4648
Main .... (703) 206-5600
Customer Svc................................ (800) 488-6383
Tech. Supp. Fax........................... (703) 206-5601
E-Mail...info@uu.net
WWW...http://www.uu.net/

Valitek, Inc.
100 University Dr.
Amherst, MA 01002
Main .... (800) 825-4835
Tech. Support............................... (413) 586-7408
Tech. Supp. Fax........................... (413) 549-2900
BBS.. (413) 586-6718

ValueStor
1609 Regatta Lane
Suite No "B"
San Jose, CA 95112-1116
Main .... (408) 437-2300
Customer Svc............................... (800) 873-8258
Tech. Support............................... (408) 437-2310
Sales .... (800) 873-8258
Tech. Supp. Fax........................... (408) 437-9333
BBS.. (408) 437-1616
CompuServe .... ourworld.compuserve.com

Vance Systems
3901-V Centerview Dr.
Chantilly, VA 22021
Main .... (703) 471-9402
BBS.. (703) 471-7057

Variant Microsystems
46520 Fremont Blvd.
Fremont, CA 94538
Main .... (800) 666-4227
Tech. Support............................... (408) 980-1880
Tech. Supp. Fax........................... (510) 440-2873
BBS.. (415) 623-1372

Velocity Development
4 Embarcadero Center
Suite No 3100
San Francsico, CA 94111-4106
Main....................................(415) 776-8000
Customer Svc.............................(415) 274-8840
Tech. Support...........................(415) 392-4357
Sales...................................(415) 776-8000
Tech. Supp. Fax.........................(415) 776-8099
E-Mail......................................info@velo.com
WWW....................http://www.velocitygames.com
FTP Address......................ftp.velocitygames.com
CompuServe.......................................76660,2202
America Online..................velocitydev@aol.com

Ven-Tel, Inc.
2121 Zanker Rd.
San Jose, CA 95131-2177
Main....................................(408) 436-7400
BBS.....................................(408) 436-7451

VenturCom, Inc.
215 1st St.
Cambridge, MA 02142
Main....................................(617) 661-1230

Verbatim
1200 W.T. Harris Blvd.
Charlotte, NC 28262
Main....................................(704) 547-6500
Customer Svc.............................(800) 538-8589
Tech. Support...........................(800) 538-8589
Tech. Supp. Fax.........................(704) 547-6565

Verilink
145 Baytech Dr.
San Jose, CA 95134
Main....................................(408) 945-1199
BBS.....................................(408) 262-6260

Verity, Inc.
1550 Plymouth
Mountain View, CA 94043
Main....................................(415) 960-7600
BBS.....................................(415) 960-7698

Vermont Creative Software
Pinnacle Meadows
Richford, VT 05476
Main....................................(800) 848-1248
Tech. Support...........................(802) 848-7731
BBS.....................................(802) 848-3502

Vermont Microsystems, Inc.
11 Tigan St.
Winooski, VT 05404
Main....................................(800) 354-0055

Versant
1380 Willow Rd.
Menlo Park, CA 94025
Main....................................(415) 329-7500
BBS.....................................(415) 325-2380

Versitron
27 McCullough Dr.
New Castle, DE 19720
Main....................................(800) 537-2296
Tech. Support...........................(301) 497-8600
Tech. Supp. Fax.........................(302) 323-8645

Vertex Computer Cable
61 Executive Blvd.
Farmingdale, NY 11735
Main....................................(800) 284-6436
Tech. Support...........................(516) 293-1610
BBS.....................................(516) 293-9650

Vertisoft Systems, Inc.
100 California St, #1400
San Francisco, CA 94111
Main....................................(800) 548-8115

Very Vivid, Inc.
PO Box 127, Station B
Toronto, ONT M5T 2T3
Canada
Main....................................(416) 686-7850

VIA Information Systems
101 Carnegie Center, #209
Princeton, NJ 08450
Main...(609) 243-0433
BBS...(609) 243-0202

Viasyn/CompuPro
26538 Danti Ct.
Hayward, CA 94545

Vicon Computer Corp.
271 Mt Pleasant Ave.
West Orange, NJ 07052
Main...(800) 284-8426
Tech. Support ....(201) 325-0121
BBS...(201) 325-2571

Victory Enterprises
223 W. Anderson Ln.
Austin, TX 78751-1728
Main...(800) 421-0103
Tech. Support ....(512) 450-0801
Tech. Supp. Fax ....(512) 450-0869

Video Telecom Corp.
1908 Kramer Ln.
Austin, TX 78758
Main...(800) 284-8871
Tech. Support ....(512) 834-2700
BBS...(512) 834-0692

Video Textbook Training
200 Lakeside Dr, Bldg A-4
Morgantown, WV 26505
Main...(304) 292-0917
BBS...(304) 296-4032

VideoLogic, Inc.
245 1st St
Cambridge, MA 02142
Main...(415) 875-0606
Tech. Support ....(415) 875-6862
Sales...(800) 578-5644
Tech. Supp. Fax ....(800) 203-8587
BBS...(415) 875-7748

Videx, Inc.
1105 NE Cir Blvd.
Corvallis, OR 97330-4285
Main ....(541) 758-0521
BBS...(541) 752-5285
E-Mail..sales@videx.com
WWW..................................... http://www.videx.com

ViewSonic
20480 Business Pky.
Walnut, CA 91789
Main ....(909) 869-7976
Customer Svc...............................(909) 869-7976
Tech. Support...............................(909) 869-7976
Sales ....(909) 869-7976
Tech. Supp. Fax...........................(909) 468-3756
BBS...(909) 468-1241
WWW..........................http://www.viewsonic.com/

Viking Software Services
6804 S. Canton Ave.
Suite 900
Tulsa, OK 74136
Main ....(918) 491-6144
Tech. Supp. Fax...........................(918) 494-2701
BBS ....(918) 494-2701
CompuServe ....71411.212@compuserve.com

Viman Software/Central Design
223 River St. Suite #C
Santa Cruz, CA 95060
Main ....(408) 459-0678
Sales ....(408) 327-9800
Tech. Supp. Fax...........................(408) 458-2862
E-Mail...info@viman.com
WWW...............................http://www.viman.com/

Virgin Games
18061 Fitch Ave.
Irvine, CA 92714
Customer Svc...............................(714) 833-8710
Tech. Support...............................(714) 833-1999
Tech. Supp. Fax...........................(714) 833-2001
BBS ....(714) 833-3305
E-Mail..............................tech_support@vie.com
WWW................................. http://www.virgin.com

Visible
1750 Wallace Ave.
St Charles, IL 60174
Main.................................(800) 323-0628
Customer Svc........................(800) 323-0628
Tech. Support......................(800) 323-0628
Tech. Supp. Fax....................(800) 233-2016

Visio Corp.
520 Pike Street
Suite No 1800
Seattle, WA 98101-4001
Main.................................(206) 521-4600
Customer Svc........................(800) 248-4746
Tech. Support......................(206) 521-4600
Sales ....(800) 446-3335
Tech. Supp. Fax....................(206) 521-4601
WWW.........................http://www.visio.com/
CompuServe ....GO VISIO

Visioneer, Inc.
2860 West Bayshore Rd.
Palo Alto, CA 94303
Main.................................(415) 812-6400
Customer Svc........................(800) 787-7007
Tech. Support......................(415) 884-5548
Sales ....(800) 787-7007
Tech. Supp. Fax....................(503) 884-8474
E-Mail ....tech_support@visioneer.com
WWW......................http://www.visioneer.com/
CompuServe ....GO VISIONEER
America Online...........................Visioneer

Visual Numeric
6230 Lookout Rd.
Boulder, CO 80301
Main.................................(303) 530-9000
Tech. Supp. Fax....................(303) 530-9329
WWW..............................http://www.vni.com

Visual Numerics
9990 Richmond Ave.
Suite 400
Houston, Texas 77042-4548
Main.................................(800) 222-4675
Sales ....(713) 784-3131
Tech. Supp. Fax....................(713) 781-9260
WWW.............................http://www.vni.com/

Visual Solutions, Inc.
487 Groton Rd.
Westford, MA 01886
Main.................................(508) 692-5499
BBS................................(508) 692-3102
WWW.................http://www.alternet.com/vizsim

Visual Technology, Inc.
120 Flandrs Rd.
Westboro, MA 01581
Main.................................(800) 847-8252
Tech. Support ....(508) 836-4400
BBS................................(508) 366-4337

Vitalink Communications Corp.
6607 Kaiser Dr
Fremont, CA 94555
Main.................................(800) 443-5740
Tech. Support ....(415) 794-1100
BBS................................(415) 797-8935

Vitek Systems Distribution
2052 Corte Del Nogal
Carlsbad, CA 92009
Main.................................(800) 366-6655
Tech. Support ....(619) 431-2505
Tech. Supp. Fax ....(619) 431-4751

VMark Software Corp.
5 Strathmore Rd.
Natick, MA 01760
Main.................................(508) 655-3700
BBS................................(508) 655-8395

VMI Lan
5172-B Indian Trail Industrial Pkwy
Norcross, GA 30071
Main.................................(800) 637-8179
Tech. Support ....(404) 263-9055
BBS................................(404) 840-8657

VNP Software
180 Franklin St.
Cambridge, MA 02139
Main ....(802) 496-7799
Tech. Support ....(617) 661-4292
Sales...(802) 496-7799
Tech. Supp. Fax ....(617) 864-6768
WWW..................................... http://www.vnp.com/
FTP Address.......................................ftp.vnp.com

VocalTec
157 Veterans Dr.
Northvale, NJ 07647
Main...(201) 768-9400
Tech. Supp. Fax ....(201) 768-8893
E-Mail...................................... info@vocaltec.com
WWW.............................http://www.vocaltec.com/

Voyetra Technologies
333 5th Ave.
Pelham, NY 10803
Main...(800) 233-9377
Tech. Support ....(914) 966-0600
Tech. Supp. Fax ....(914) 966-1102
BBS..(914) 966-1216

Vu/Text
325 Chestnut St, #1300
Philadelphia, PA 19106
Main...(800) 258-8080
Tech. Support ....(215) 574-4421

Wacom Technology
501 Southeast Columbia Shores Blvd.
Suite No 300
Vancouver, WA 98661
Main...(360) 750-8882
Customer Svc. ....(800) 922-6613
Tech. Support ....(360) 750-8882
Sales...(800) 922-6613
Tech. Supp. Fax ....(360) 570-8924
BBS..(360) 570-0638
WWW............................... http://www.wacom.com
FTP Address................................ftp.wacom.com
CompuServe....................................GO WACOM
America Online ....wacom@aol.com

Waggener Group, The
6915 SW Macadam Ave., #300
Portland, OR 97219
Main .... (503) 245-0905
Tech. Supp. Fax.......................... (503) 244-7261

WAIS, Inc.
690 Fifth Street
San Francisco, CA 94107
Main .... (415) 525-2553
E-Mail....................................frontdesk@wais.com
WWW................................. http://www.wais.com/

Walker, Richer and Quinn, Inc.
1500 Dexter Ave. North
Seattle, WA 98109 USA
Main .... (206) 217-7500
Sales .... (800) 872-2829
Tech. Supp. Fax.......................... (206) 217-0293
WWW......................................http://www.wrq.com

Wall Data Inc.
11332 N.E. 122nd Way
Kirkland, WA 98034-6931
Tech. Support............................... (800) 927-8622
Sales .... (800) 487-8622
Tech. Supp. Fax.......................... (206) 814-4305
BBS .... (206) 814-4361
WWW........................... http://www.walldata.com/
CompuServe .... GO WALLDATA

Wall Street Direct
WWW.................... http://www.cts.com:80/~wallst/

Walnut Creek
WWW............................... http://www.cdrom.com/

Wandel & Goltermann Technologies
1030 Swabia Ct
Research Triangle Park, NC 27709
Main .... (919) 941-5730
BBS .... (919) 941-5751

Ward Systems Group, Inc.
Executive Park West
5 Hillcrest Dr.
Frederick, MD 21703
Main...(301) 662-7950
Tech. Supp. Fax...........................(301) 662-5660
BBS...(301) 663-6656

Watcom Products, Inc.
415 Phillip St
Waterloo, ONT N2L 3X2
Canada
Main...(800) 265-4555
Tech. Support..............................(519) 884-0702
Tech. Supp. Fax...........................(519) 747-4971
BBS...(519) 747-4971
WWW..................................http://www.watcom.com/
FTP Address.................ftp.watcom.com/pub/bbs/

Waterfall Software International
35-46 Regan Center Dr.
Ottawa, ONT K2E 7W5
Canada

Waterloo Maple Software
450 Phillip St.
Waterloo, ONT N2L5J2
Canada
Main...(519) 747-2373
Tech. Supp. Fax...........................(519) 747-5284

Waterloo Microsystems
295 Phillip St
Waterloo, ONT N2L 3W8
Canada
Main...(519) 746-5000
BBS...(519) 884-8590

Wave Systems Corp.
540 Madison Ave.
New York, NY 10022
Main...(212) 755-3282
WWW...........................http://www.wavesys.com

Wavetek RF Products
5808 Churchman Bypass
Indianapolis, IN 46203
Main...(317) 788-9351
Tech. Supp. Fax...........................(317) 782-4607

Way Point Technologies
WWW..http://www.awa.com/waypoint/index.html

Waytek, Inc.
PO Box 690
Chanhassen, MN 55317-9905
Main...(800) 328-2724
Tech. Support..............................(612) 949-0765
Tech. Supp. Fax...........................(612) 949-0965
BBS...(612) 949-0965

Weaver Graphics
5165 S Hwy A1A
Melbourne Beach, FL 32951
Main...(407) 728-4000
Tech. Supp. Fax...........................(407) 728-5978
BBS...(407) 728-5978

Webcom Communications
10555 East Dartmouth
Suite 330
Aurora, CO 80014
Main...(303) 745-5711
WWW..................http://www.infowebcom.com/

Wedge Technology, Inc.
1587 McCandless Dr
Milpitas, CA 95035
Main...(408) 263-9888
Tech. Support..............................(408) 263-0225
BBS...(408) 263-9886

Welcom Software Technology
15995 N Barkers Landing, #275
Houston, TX 77079
Main...(713) 558-0514
Tech. Supp. Fax...........................(713) 584-7928
BBS...(713) 584-7828
E-Mail.......................................support@wst.com
WWW..................http://www.wst.com/index.html
FTP Address..ftp.wst.com

Western Digital
8105 Irvine Center Dr.
Costa Mesa, CA 92718
Main ....(714) 932-5000
Customer Svc. ....(800) 832-4778
Tech. Support ....(800) 832-4778
BBS..................................(714) 753-1234

Western Digital Imaging
800 E Middlefield Rd.
Mountain View CA 94043
Main..................................(800) 832-4778

Western Telematic, Inc.
5 Suiterling
Irvine, CA 92718-9934
Main..................................(800) 854-7226
Tech. Support ....(714) 586-9950
BBS..................................(714) 583-9514

Westlake Data Corp.
PO Box 1711
Austin, TX 78767
Main..................................(512) 328-1041

Westwood Studios
5333 S. Arville
Suite 104
Las Vegas, NV. 89118-2226
Tech. Supp. Fax ....(702) 368-0677
E-Mail.......................... support@westwood.com
WWW........................ http://www.westwood.com/

WexTech Systems
310 Madison Ave.
New York, NY 10117
Main..................................(212) 949-9595
Tech. Supp. Fax ....(212) 949-4007
CompuServe..............................GO WEXTECH

White Pine Software
40 Simon St. Suite #201
Nashua, NH 03060-3043
Main..................................(603) 886-9050
BBS..................................(603) 886-9051
WWW.......................... http://www.whitepine.com

Whitepine Software
1485 Saratoga Ave.
San Jose, CA 95129-4934
Main .... (800) 426-2230
Tech. Support.............................. (408) 446-1919
Tech. Supp. Fax.......................... (408) 446-0666

Whitewater Group, The
1800 Ridge Ave.
Evanston, IL 60201
Main .... (708) 328-3800

Wilcom Products
PO Box 508
Laconia, NH 03247
Main .... (800) 222-1898
Tech. Supp. Fax.......................... (603) 524-3735
BBS.. (603) 528-3804

Wind River Systems, Inc.
1010 Atlantic Ave.
Alameda, CA 94501
Sales.. (800) 545-9463
Tech. Supp. Fax.......................... (510) 814-2010
WWW.............................. http://www.wrs.com/

WINGate Technologies
High Street Court
Suite 303
Morristown, NJ 07960
Main .... (201) 539-2727
Tech. Supp. Fax.......................... (201) 539-2838
BBS.. (201) 539-6782
E-Mail......................................csk@wingate.com
WWW.............................http://www.wingate.com/
FTP Addressftp://ftp.digex.net/pub/access/wingate

Wintek Corp.
1801 South St.
Lafayette, IN 47904-2993
Main .... (800) 742-6809
Tech. Support.............................. (317) 742-8428
WWW................................ http://www.wintek.com

Wintronics
1316 Motor Pkwy.
Hauppauge, NY 11784
Main...(516) 234-8040
BBS...(516) 234-8321

WLT Systems, Inc.
1005 Pawtucket Blvd.
Lowell, MA 01854
Main...(800) 272-9771
Tech. Support...............................(508) 937-7507
BBS...(508) 656-8540

Wolfram Research, Inc.
100 Trade Center Dr.
Champaign, IL 61820-7237
Main...(217) 398-0700
Tech. Support...............................(217) 398-6500
Tech. Supp. Fax...........................(217) 398-0747
BBS...(217) 398-0747
WWW.......................................http://www.wri.com/

WordPerfect Corp.
1555 N Technology Way
Orem, UT 84057
Main...(800) 321-5096
Tech. Support...............................(800) 321-3248
BBS...(801) 225-4414
WWW.......................http://www.wordperfect.com/

WordPerfect/Novell
1555 N. Technology Way
Orem, UT 84057-2339
Main...(801) 429-7000
WWW.................................http://www.novell.com

Working Software
PO Box 1844
Santa Cruz, CA 95061
Main...(408) 423-5696

Worldata
5200 Town Center Circle
Boca Raton, FL 33486
Main...(800) 331-8102
Tech. Supp. Fax...........................(407) 368-8345
E-Mail......................................mail@worldata.com
WWW............................http://www.worldata.com/

Worthington Data Solutions
3004 Mission St.
Suite 220
Santa Cruz, CA 95060
Main...(800) 345-4220
Tech. Support...............................(408) 458-9938
WWW.......................http://www.cruzio.com/~was

Wyse
3471 North First St.
San Jose, CA 95134-1803
Main...(800) 438-9973
Customer Svc................................(800) 370-9973
Tech. Support...............................(800) 800-9973
Sales...(408) 473-1600
Tech. Supp. Fax...........................(408) 922-4390
BBS...(408) 922-4400
WWW.......................http://www.wyse@wyse.com

WYSIWYG Corp.
300 Corporate Pointe, #410
Culver City, CA 90230
Main...(213) 215-9645
BBS...(213) 215-9668

Xcellenet, Inc.
Concorts Pkwy Suite 850
Atlanta, GA 30328
Main...(770) 804-8100
BBS...(770) 804-8102

Xecom, Inc.
374 Turquoise St
Milpitas, CA 95035
Main...(408) 945-6640
BBS...(408) 942-1346

Xerox Palo Alto Research Center
3333 Coyote Hill Rd.
Palo Alto, CA 94304
Main ....(415) 494-4000

Xicor
1344 Main Sreet
Waltham, MA 02154
Main ....(617) 899-5510
Tech. Supp. Fax ....(617) 899-6808
WWW ....http://www.xicor.com/

Xilinx
2100 Logic Dr.
San Jose, CA, 95124
Main ....(800) 255-7778
BBS..(408) 559-9327
E-Mail......................................hotline@xilinx.com
WWW .... http://www.xilinx.com/
FTP Address......................... ftp://www.xilinx.com

Xinet
2560 Ninth Street, Suite 312
Berkeley, CA 94710
Main..(510) 845-0555
Tech. Supp. Fax ....(510) 644-2680
E-Mail...www@xinet.com
WWW ....http://www.xinet.com/

Xinetron
3022 Scott Blvd.
Santa Clara, CA 95054
Main..(800) 345-4415
Tech. Support ....(408) 727-5509
BBS..(408) 727-6499

Xing Technology
BBS..(805) 473-2680
E-Mail............................... support@xingtech.com
WWW .... http://www.xingtech.com/
CompuServe........................ GO XINGSUPPORT

Xircom
2300 Corporate Center Dr.
Thousand Oaks, CA 91320
Main .... (805) 376-9300
Customer Svc............................. (805) 376-9200
Tech. Support............................. (805) 376-9200
Sales .... (800) 438-4526
Tech. Supp. Fax.......................... (805) 376-9100
BBS .... (805) 376-9130
E-Mail..cs@xircom.com
WWW..............................http://www.xircom.com/
CompuServe ....GO XIRCOM

Xpoint Corp.
Norcross, GA 30071
Main .... (404) 446-2764

Xtree Co
4330 Santa Fe Rd.
San Luis Obispo, CA 93401
Main .... (800) 634-5545
Tech. Support............................... (805) 541-0604
BBS.. (805) 541-8053

XVT Software, Inc.
4900 Pearl East Circle
PO Box 18750
Boulder, CO 80308
Main .... (303) 443-4223
BBS.. (303) 443-0969
WWW........................... http://www.csn.net:80/xvt/

Xxera Technologies
9665 E Las Tunas Dr.
Temple City, CA 91780
Main .... (818) 286-5569
Tech. Support............................... (818) 286-5569
BBS.. (818) 286-5228

Xydex
330 Codman Hill Rd.
Boxborough, MA 01719
Main .... (800) 338-5316
Tech. Support............................... (508) 264-9900
BBS.. (508) 264-9930

Xylogics
53 Third Ave.
Burlington, MA 01803
Main..............................(800) 225-3317
Tech. Support.....................(617) 272-8686
Tech. Supp. Fax...........................(617) 273-5392
BBS ....(617) 273-1499
E-Mail ....support@xylogics.com
WWW.......................http://www.xylogics.com/
FTP Address..............................ftp.xylogics.com

Xyplex
295 Foster Street
Littleton, MA 01460
Main..............................(508) 952-4700
Tech. Supp. Fax...........................(508) 952-4702
E-Mail ....support@xyplex.com
WWW.......................http://www.xyplex.com/

Xyplex, Inc.
330 Codman Hill Rd.
Boxborough, MA 01719
Main..............................(800) 338-5316
Tech. Support.....................(508) 264-9900

Xyvision
101 Edgewater Dr.
Wakefield, MA 01880-1291
Main..............................(617) 245-4100
Tech. Supp. Fax...........................(617) 246-6209
WWW.......................http://www.xyvision.com/

Yamaha Corp. of America
CBX Group
6600 Orangethorpe Ave.
Buena Park, CA 90620
Main..............................(714) 522-9011
Customer Svc.............................(714) 522-9011
Tech. Support.....................(714) 522-9011
WWW.......................http://www.yamaha.com/

Yamatech Connectivity Solution
1255 Laialg Dr.
Montreal, Canada H3P2T1
Main..............................(514) 737-5434
BBS ....(514) 737-5495
CompuServe .... 75170.706@compuserve.com

YSC Tech
Willowdale, ONT M2K 2W5
Canada
Main..............................(416) 733-0228

Z-RAM
22 Morgan
Irvine, CA 92718-2022
Main..............................(714) 454-1500
Customer Svc.............................(714) 454-1500
Tech. Support ....(714) 454-1500
Sales..............................(714) 454-7500
Tech. Supp. Fax ....(714) 830-4726

Zanthe Information/Sterling Solution
500-36 Antares Dr.
Ottawa, ONT K2E 7W5
Canada
Main..............................(800) 267-9972
Tech. Support ....(613) 727-1397
Tech. Supp. Fax ....(613) 727-9868
BBS..............................(613) 727-6940

Zaphod Industries
PO Box 442
Northwood, NH 03261
Main..............................(603) 942-5077
Tech. Supp. Fax ....(603) 942-7466

Zenith Data Systems
1501 Feehanville Dr.
Prospect, IL 60056
Main..............................(800) 523-9393
Tech. Support ....(708) 699-4800

Zenith Electronics
1000 Milwaukee Ave., #288
Glenview, IL 60025-2493
Main..............................(708) 391-8000
BBS..............................(708) 391-8919

Zenographics
34 Executive Park
Suite 150
Irvine, CA 92714
Main......................................(714) 851-6352
Sales.....................................(714) 851-6352
Tech. Supp. Fax ....(714) 851-1314
BBS.......................................(714) 851-3860
E-Mail................................ support@zeno.com
WWW............................... http://www.zeno.com
CompuServe...... 76702.1351@compuserve.com

Zeos International, Ltd.
530 5th Ave. NW
St Paul, MN 55112
Main.....................................(800) 423-5891
Tech. Support ....(612) 633-5877
BBS.......................................(612) 633-1325

Zephyr Development Corp.
11 Greenway Plaza, #520
Houston, TX 77046-1104
Main.....................................(800) 966-3270
Tech. Support ....(713) 623-0089
Tech. Supp. Fax ....(713) 623-0091
BBS.......................................(713) 623-0091

Zeus Phonstuff
1000 Holcomb Woods Pkwy, #410-C
Roswell, GA 30076
Main.....................................(404) 587-1541
BBS.......................................(404) 587-1609

ZFC
WWW................ http://www.nl.net/~zfc/index.html

Zilog
210 East Hacienda Ave.
Campbell, CA 95008-6600
Main.....................................(408) 370-8000
Tech. Supp. Fax ....(408) 370-8056
E-Mail....................................support@zilog.com
WWW.........http://www.zilog.com/zilog/index.html

Zinc Software
405 South 100 East
Second Floor
Pleasant Grove, Utah 84062
Main .... (801) 785-8900
Tech. Supp. Fax.......................... (801) 785-8996
E-Mail.....................................tech@zinc.com
WWW................................. http://www.zinc.com/

Zoom Telephonics
207 South Street
Boston, MA 02111
Main .... (617) 423-1072
Customer Svc............................. (617) 423-1072
Tech. Support............................ (617) 423-1076
Sales .... (800) 666-6191
Tech. Supp. Fax.......................... (617) 423-5536
BBS .... (617) 423-3733
WWW.............................http://www.zoomtel.com
FTP Address .... ftp.zoomtel.com
America Online........................... zoomt@aol.com

Zsoft Corp.
450 Franklin Rd., #100
Marietta, GA 30067
Main .... (770) 428-0008
Tech. Support............................ (770) 428-0008
BBS .... (770) 427-1150

Zylab Corp.
100 Lexington Dr, #201
Buffalo Grove, IL 60089
Main .... (800) 544-6339
Tech. Support............................ (708) 459-8000
BBS .... (708) 632-1129

ZyXEL Communications
4920 East La Palma Ave.
Anaheim, CA 92807
Main .... (714) 693-0808
Tech. Support............................ (714) 693-0808
Tech. Supp. Fax.......................... (714) 693-8811
BBS .... (714) 693-0762
E-Mail....................................tech@zyxel.com
WWW................................. http://www.zyxel.com/
CompuServe ..... 71333.2734@compuserve.com